Assessment Guide

Grade K

INCLUDES:

- Prerequisite Skills Inventory
- Beginning-of-Year, Middle-of-Year, and End-of-Year Benchmark Tests
- Chapter Tests in Common Core Assessment Formats
- Critical Area and Chapter Performance Assessments and Student Work Samples
- Getting Ready for Grade 1 Tests
- Individual and Class Record Forms
- Correlation to Standards

Printed in the U.S.A.

ISBN 978-0-544-21289-3

2 3 4 5 6 7 8 9 10 0868 22 21 20 19 18 17 16 15 14 13

4500431265 A B C D E F G

Contents

Tests and Record Forms

Overview of *California Go Math!* Assessment

How Assessment Can Help Individualize Instruction

The *Assessment Guide* contains several types of assessment for use throughout the school year. Assessment pacing can also be found in the *California Go Math! Teacher Edition*. The following pages will explain how these assessments can be utilized to diagnose children's understanding of the Common Core State Standards and to guide instructional choices, improve children's performance, and to help facilitate their mastery of this year's objectives.

Diagnostic Assessment

Prerequisite Skills Inventory in the *Assessment Guide* should be given at the beginning of the year or when a new child arrives. This multiple-choice test yields insight regarding understanding of prerequisite skills. Test results provide information about the review or intervention that children may need in order to be successful in the coming year. The Prerequisite Skills Activities are provided as intervention for this inventory.

Beginning-of-Year Test in the *Assessment Guide*, is multiple-choice format and should be utilized early in the year to establish on-grade level skills that children may already understand. This benchmark test will allow customization of instructional content to optimize the time spent teaching specific objectives. Suggestions for intervention are provided for this test.

Show What You Know in the *Student Edition* is provided for each chapter. It assesses prior knowledge from previous grades as well as content taught earlier in the current grade. Teachers can customize instructional content using the intervention options provided. The assessment should be scheduled at the beginning of each chapter to determine if children have the prerequisite skills.

Diagnostic Interview Assessment in the *Teacher Edition* is designed to provide an optional instrument to evaluate each child's level of accomplishment for the chapter's prerequisite skills on the **Show What You Know**. The interview task items test children at the concrete or pictorial level where appropriate.

Formative Assessment

Lesson Quick Check in every lesson of the *Teacher Edition* monitors children's understanding of the skills and concepts being presented.

Lesson Practice for every lesson in the *Standard Practice Book* helps children achieve fluency, speed, and confidence with grade level skills and concepts.

Mid-Chapter Checkpoint in the *Student Edition* provides monitoring of children's progress to permit instructional adjustments, and when required, to facilitate children's mastery of the objectives.

Middle-of-Year Test in the *Assessment Guide* assesses the same standards as the Beginning-of-Year Test, allowing children's progress to be tracked and providing opportunity for instructional adjustments, when required.

Portfolios encourage children to collect work samples throughout the chapter as a reinforcement of their progress and achievements.

Summative Assessment

Chapter Review/Tests in the *Student Edition* indicate whether additional instruction or practice is necessary for children to master the concepts and skills taught in the chapter. These tests include items presented in a variety of Common Core assessment formats.

Chapter Tests in the *Assessment Guide* evaluate children's mastery of concepts and skills taught in the chapter. These tests assess the mastery of the Common Core standards taught in a chapter. Item types on these tests are similar to ones a child would encounter on a test to assess Common Core standards.

Performance Assessment Tasks in the *Assessment Guide* are provided for each Chapter and Critical Area. Each assessment contains several tasks to assess children's ability to use what they have learned and provides an opportunity for children to display their thinking strategies. Each set of tasks is accompanied by teacher support pages, a rubric for scoring, and examples of student work for the task.

End-of-Year Tests in the *Assessment Guide* assess the same standards as the Beginning- and Middle-of-Year Tests. It is the final benchmark test for the grade level. When children's performance on the End-of-Year Test is compared to performance on the Beginning- and Middle-of-Year Tests, teachers are able to document children's growth.

Getting Ready Tests in the *Assessment Guide* evaluate the children's understanding of concepts and skills taught as readiness for the next grade level. These tests are available in a mixed-response format comprised of multiple choice and short answer.

Assessment Technology

The **Personal Math Trainer** offers online homework, assessment, and intervention. There are pre-built tests that lead to intervention and a personal study plan. Algorithmically generated technology-enhanced items have wrong answer feedback and learning aids.

Data-Driven Decision Making

California Go Math! allows for quick and accurate data-driven decision making so you can spend more instructional time tailoring to children's needs. The **Data-Driven Decision Making** chart with Diagnostic, Formative, and Summative Assessments provides prescribed interventions so children have a greater opportunity for success with the Common Core standards.

Intervention and Review Resources

For skills that children have not yet mastered, the *Reteach Book*, Tier 1 and Tier 2 RtI Activities in the *Teacher Edition*, or *The Personal Math Trainer* provide additional instruction and practice on concepts and skills in the chapter.

Using Individual Record Forms

The *Assessment Guide* includes Individual Record Forms (IRF) for all tests. On these forms, each test item is correlated to the standard it assesses. There are intervention resources correlated to each item as well. A common error explains why a child may have missed the item. These forms can be used to:

- Follow progress throughout the year.
- Identify strengths, weaknesses, and provide follow-up instruction.
- Make assignments based on the intervention options provided.

Performance Assessment

Performance Assessment, together with other types of assessment, can supply the missing information not provided by other testing formats. Performance Assessments, in particular, help reveal the thinking strategies children use to work through a problem. Performance Assessments with multiple tasks for each chapter and Critical Area are provided in the *Assessment Guide*.

Performance Assessment is provided in many places in *California Go Math!*

Each of these assessments has several tasks that target specific math concepts, skills, and strategies. These tasks can help assess children's ability to use what they have learned to solve everyday problems. Each assessment focuses on a theme. Teachers can plan for children to complete one task at a time or use an extended amount of time to complete the entire assessment.

Teacher support pages introduce each Performance Assessment. These are followed by the tasks for the children. A task-specific rubric helps teachers evaluate children's work. Papers to illustrate actual children's work are also provided to aid in scoring.

Portfolio Assessment

A portfolio is a collection of each child's work gathered over an extended period of time.

A portfolio illustrates the growth, talents, achievements, and reflections of the learner and provides a means for you and the child to assess performance and progress.

Building a Portfolio

There are many opportunities to collect children's work throughout the year as you use *California Go Math!* Give children the opportunity to select some work samples to be included in the portfolio.

- Provide a folder for each child with the child's name clearly marked.
- Explain to children that throughout the year they will save some of their work in the folder. Sometimes it will be their individual work; sometimes it will be group reports and projects or completed checklists.

Evaluating a Portfolio

The following points made with regular portfolio evaluation will encourage growth in self-evaluation:

- Discuss the contents of the portfolio as you examine it with each child.
- Encourage and reward each child by emphasizing growth, original thinking, and completion of tasks.
- Reinforce and adjust instruction of the broad goals you want to accomplish as you evaluate the portfolios.
- Examine each portfolio on the basis of individual growth rather than in comparison with other portfolios.
- Share the portfolio with family during conferences or send the portfolio home with the child.

Common Core Assessment Formats

Common Core Assessment consortia have developed assessments that contain item types beyond the traditional multiple-choice format. This allows for a more robust assessment of children's understanding of concepts. Common Core assessments will be administered via computers; and *California Go Math!* presents items in formats similar to what children will see on the tests. The following information is provided to help teachers familiarize children with these different types of items. Each item type is identified on pages (xii-xiii). You may want to use the examples to introduce the item types to children. The following explanations are provided to guide children in answering the questions. These pages describe the most common item types. You may find other types on some tests.

Example 1 Identify groups with a given number of objects.

Yes or No

For this type of item, children respond to a single question with for several examples. There will be a question and children will circle "Yes" or "No" to answer for each part. Some items will ask children to fill in a bubble for "Yes" or "No." It is important for children to know they must circle or fill in a bubble for each part.

Example 2 Choose groups that have more than a given group.

More Than One Correct Choice

This type of item will ask them to choose all of something. Explain that when the item asks them to find all, they should look for more than one correct choice. Tell them to carefully look at each choice and mark it if it is a correct answer. Some items will ask children to "choose all." They may need to fill in bubbles instead of circling.

Example 3 Choose a number for a given group.

Choose From a List

Sometimes when children take a test on a computer, they will have to select a word or number from a drop-down list. The *California Go Math!* tests show a list and ask children to choose the correct answer. Tell children to make their choice by circling the correct answer. There will only be one choice that is correct.

Example 4 Match numbers.

Matching

Some items will ask children to match numbers or objects that are the same or related in some way. The directions will specify what they should match. There will be dots to guide them in drawing lines. The matching may be between columns or rows.

Example 1

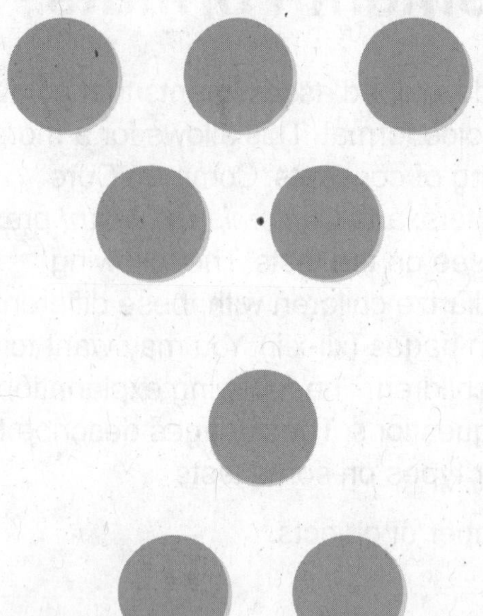

Yes No

Yes No

Yes No

Example 2

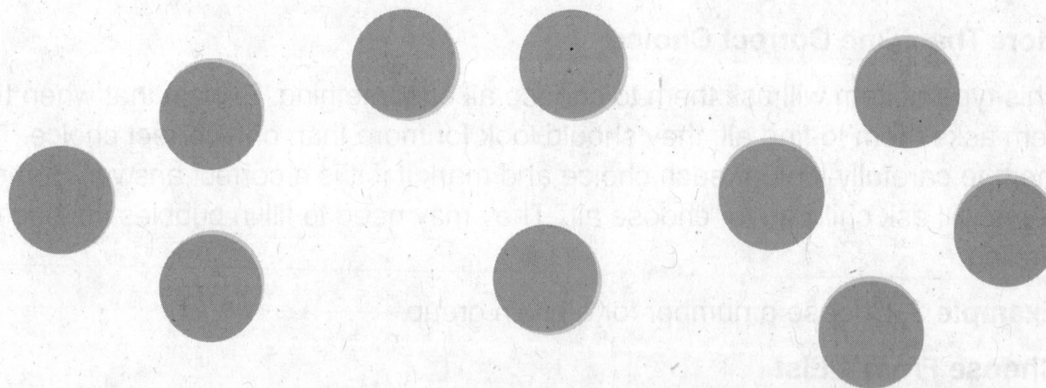

DIRECTIONS **1.** Are there three counters in the group? Circle Yes or No. **2.** Choose all the groups that show more.

Example 3

0

1

Example 4

0 3 5

3 0 5

DIRECTIONS **3.** How many counters are there? Circle the number. **4.** Draw lines to match the same numbers.

Child's Name ________________________

1

2

3

2

two

4

1 2 3 4 ____

6 5 4

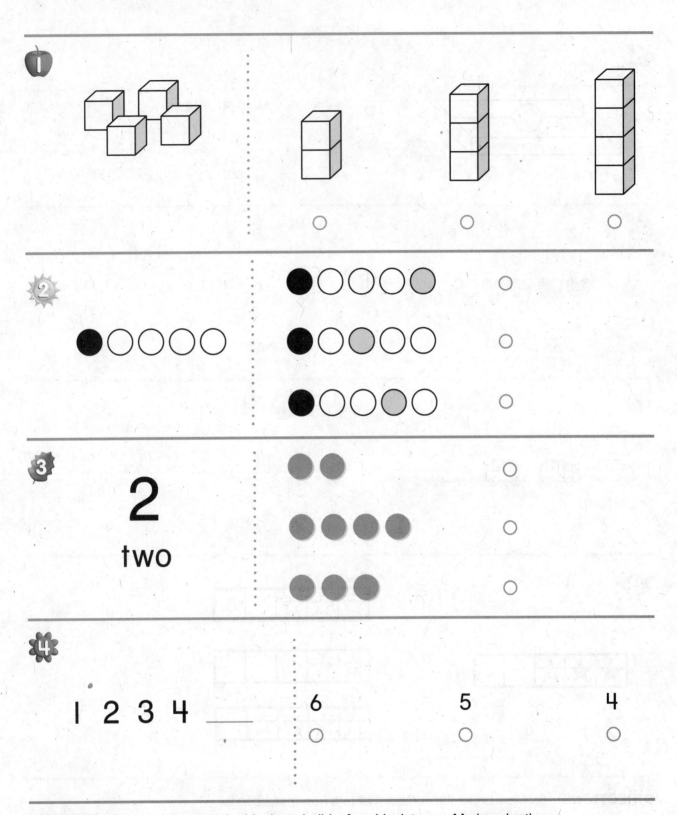

DIRECTIONS 1. Jake uses the blocks to build a four-block tower. Mark under the picture that shows his tower. 2. The first circle is colored black. Mark beside the picture that shows the fourth circle colored gray. 3. Mark beside the set that shows two. 4. Mark under the number that comes next.

Child's Name ______________________

5

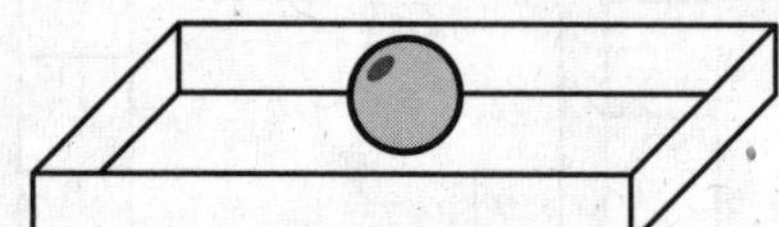

6 ○ 3 ○ 1 ○

6

4 ○ 5 ○ 6 ○

7

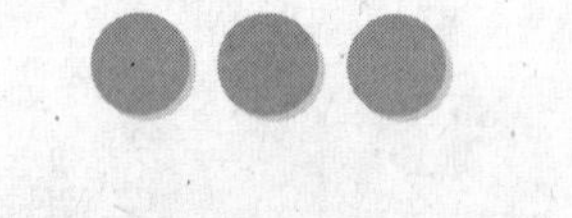

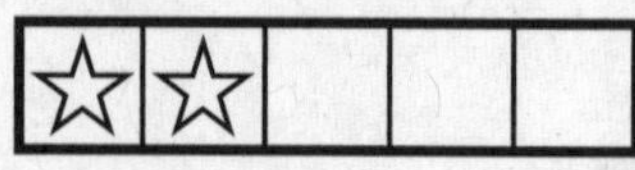 ○

 ○

○

DIRECTIONS **5.** Mark under the number that tells how many beads are in the box. **6.** Mark under the number that tells how many hearts there are. **7.** Mark beside the counters that show the same number of objects as there are in the set of toy trucks. **8.** Count the gray stars. Mark beside the set that shows more white stars.

Child's Name ______________________

9

○
○
○

10

○
○
○

11

○ ○ ○

12

first

○ ○ ○

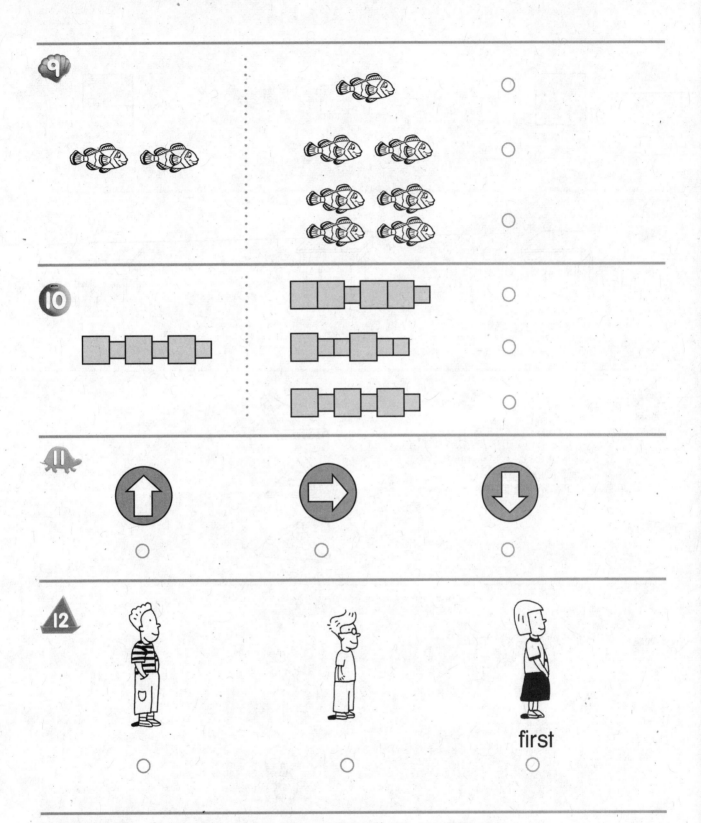

DIRECTIONS **9.** Mandy has 2 fish. The number of fish Ron has is less. Mark beside the number of fish Ron has. **10.** Mark beside the shape that is the same. **11.** Mark under the arrow that points down. **12.** Mark under the child that is last in line.

Child's Name ________________________________

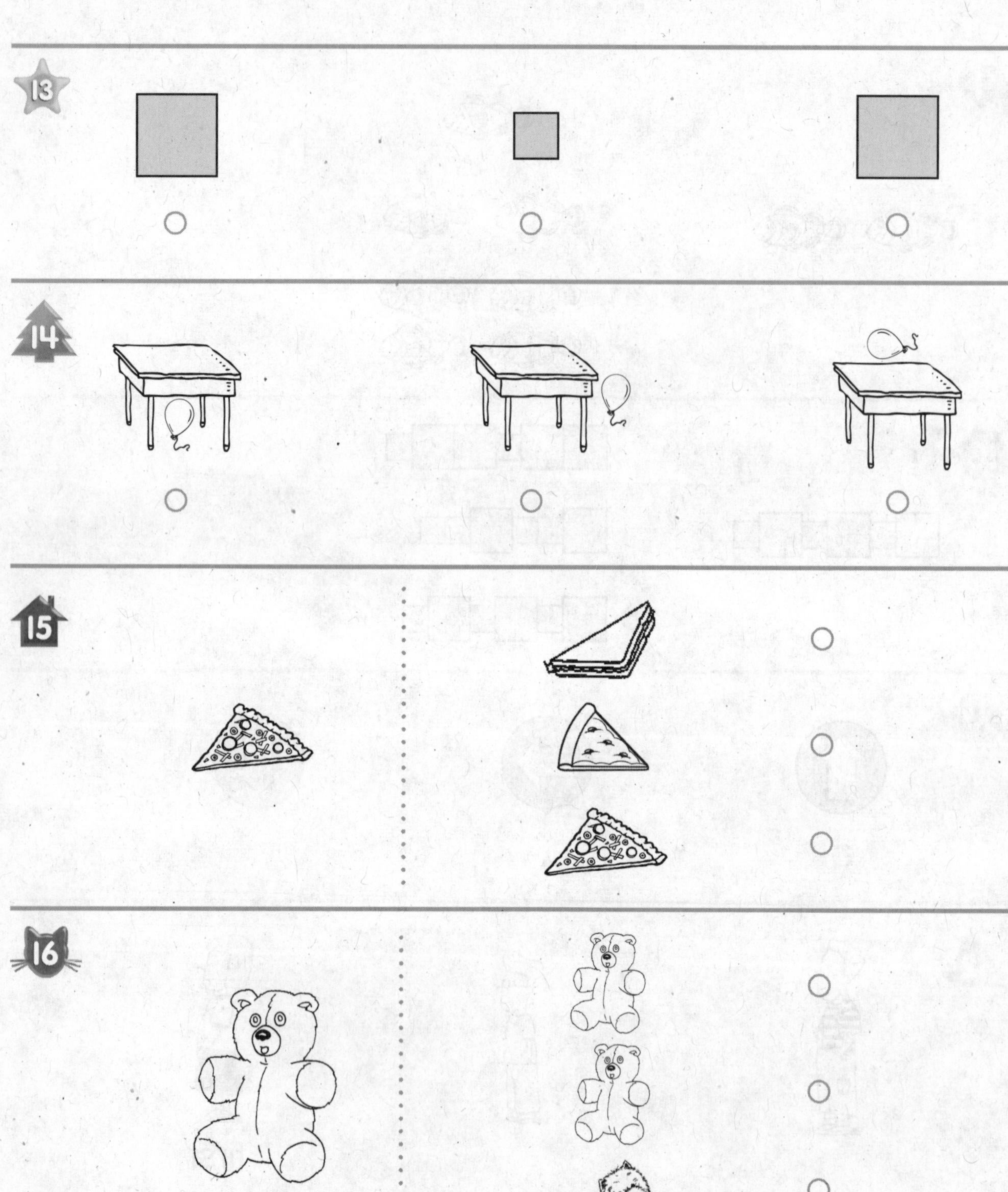

DIRECTIONS **13.** Mark under the small square. **14.** Mark under the picture that shows the balloon over the table. **15.** Mark beside the food that is alike. **16.** Mark beside the stuffed animal that is different.

GO ON

Child's Name ______________________

17

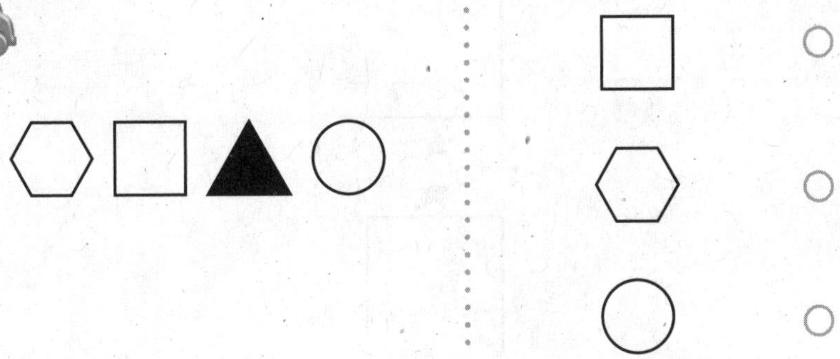

18

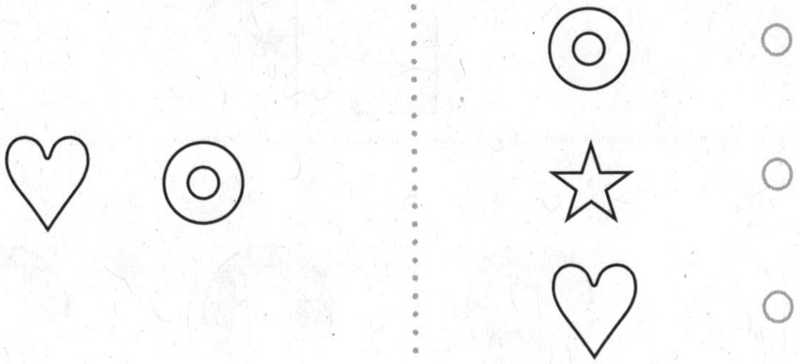

19

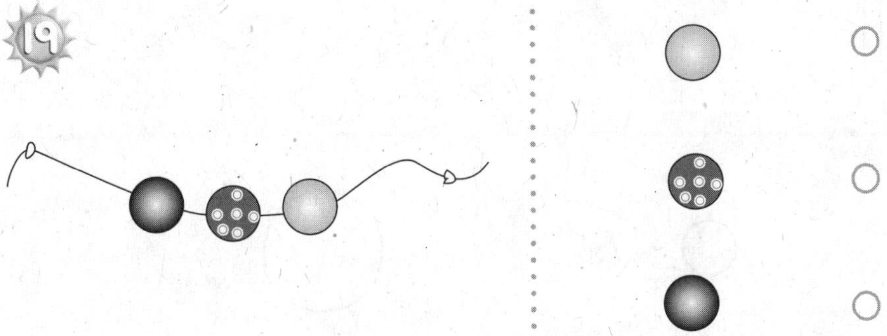

20

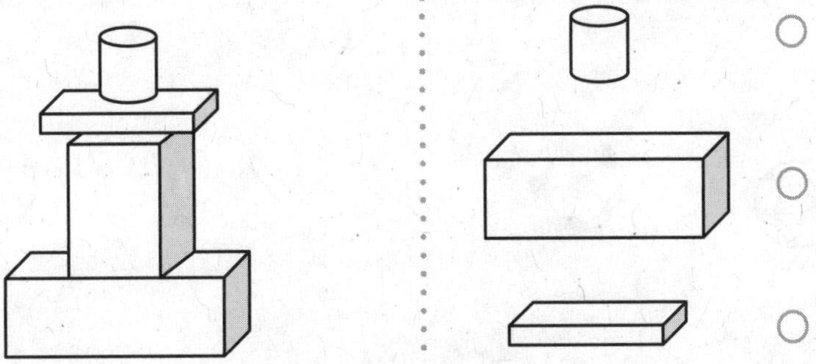

DIRECTIONS **17.** Mark beside the shape that is the same as the one to the right of the black triangle. **18.** Mark beside the shape that is the same as the one on the left at the beginning of the row. **19.** Mark beside the bead that is like the one in the middle. **20.** Mark beside the block that is the same as the one on the top of the tower.

Child's Name ______________________________

21

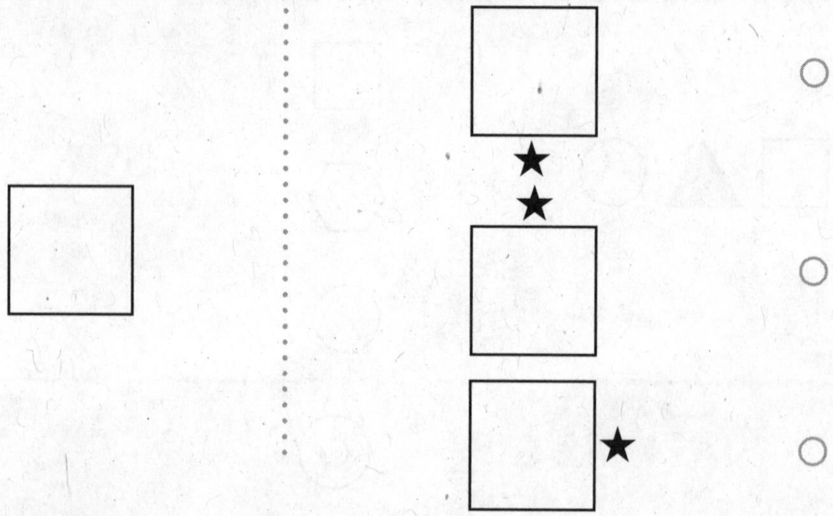

22

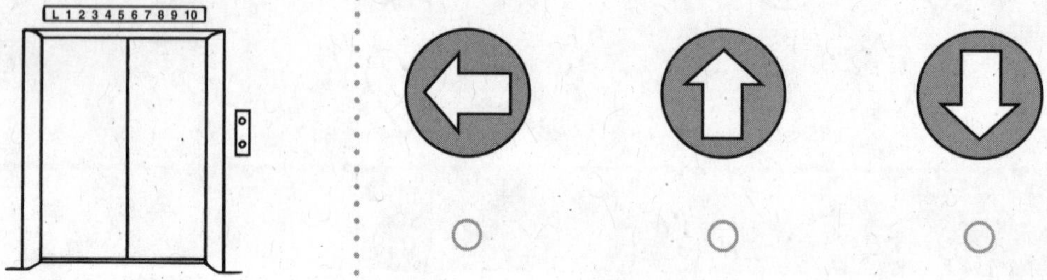

L 1 2 3 4 5 6 7 8 9 10

23

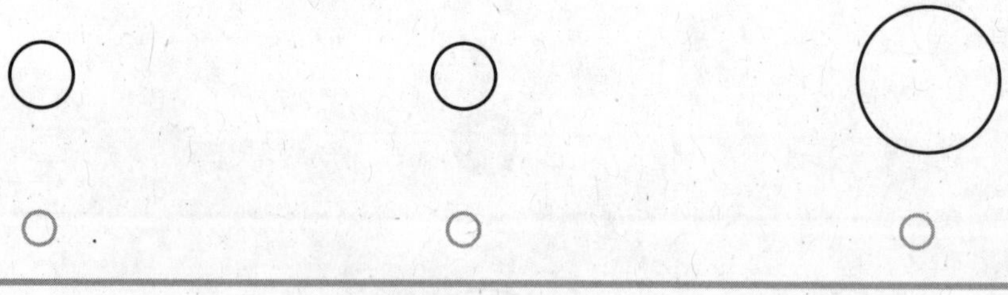

24

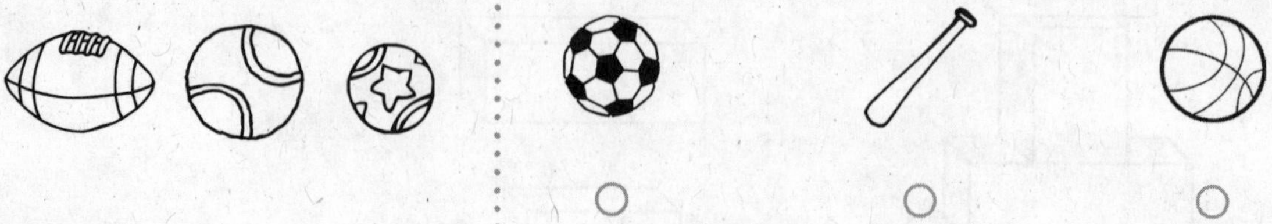

DIRECTIONS **21.** Seth draws a square. Then he draws a star under the square. Mark beside the picture Seth draws. **22.** The man pushes a button to go up on the elevator. Mark under the button that has an arrow pointing up. **23.** Mark under the big circle. **24.** Mark under the object that does not belong in the group.

Prerequisite Skills Inventory Activities

Activity 1 Alike and Different

Objective: Identify and describe similarities and differences among objects
Materials: large sorting rings; collection of three types of small objects, such as toy cars, plastic fruit, and bear counters

Have the child use the sorting rings to sort the objects in different ways, such as *things we eat, things with wheels,* and *things that are red.*

Ask: **What words tell how the objects in this group are the same?**
Ask: **What words tell how these objects are different?**

Encourage the child to explore different ways to sort the same collection of objects. Each time, encourage the child to describe how the objects in one group are the *same,* or *alike,* and how the others are *different.*

Activity 2 Does Not Belong

Objective: Identify objects that do not belong to a group.
Materials: collection of objects in two sizes, such as crayons, toy cars, blocks, or balls

Display a group of at least four objects of which one is a different size, such as three small crayons and one large crayon.

Ask: **How are these objects alike?**
Ask: **Which one does not belong in the group?**

Discuss with the child why the object does not belong in the group. Invite the child to name another object that would belong in the group.

Activity 3 Big and Small

Objective: Identify and describe the size of an object using the words *big* and *small*
Materials: two large sorting rings; collection of objects in two sizes, such as paper clips, blocks, balls, or toy animals

Have the child use two sorting rings to sort the objects by size.

Point to one ring of objects. Ask: **How are the objects in this ring alike?** Then point to the other ring of objects. Ask: **How are the objects in this ring alike?**

Hold up one object. Ask: **Is this object *big* or *small*?** Invite the child to hold a similar object for comparison.

Prerequisite Skills Inventory Activities

Activity 4 Ordinal Numbers

Objective: Identify the ordinal position of an object
Materials: collection of toy animals, such as stuffed animals or bear counters

Arrange 5 animals in a row and facing to the left.

Ask: **Which animal is *first*?**
Ask: **Which animal is *last*?**

Have the child point to the *first* animal and name the position of each animal in order. Then randomly ask the child to point to a particular position, such as the *third* animal, the *fifth* animal, and so on.

Next, have the child rearrange the order of the animals. Have the child identify the *first* animal. Ask the child to put that animal *fourth*.

Ask: **Which animal is *first*?**
Ask: **Which animal is *last*?**

Encourage the child to tell about the new order of the animals. Repeat the activity, asking the child to change the order by putting a specific animal in a different position. Discuss how the order has changed.

Activity 5 Count Objects to 5

Objective: Count aloud up to five objects
Materials: paper or plastic cup: collection of 5 objects, such as counters, buttons, dry beans, or coins

Place the objects in the cup. Spill the objects onto the table.

Ask: **How many objects are there?**

Encourage the child to touch each object and either move it aside or place it back into the cup as he or she counts aloud. Repeat the activity, spilling only some objects onto the table.

Prerequisite Skills Inventory Activities

Activity 6 More, Less, or the Same

Objective: Compare two or more groups of objects using the words *more, less,* or *the same*
Materials: collection of small objects, such as connecting cubes, counters, buttons, or coins

Arrange objects into three groups to show two, three, and four objects. Then count aloud three more objects and place them in a group in front of you.

Ask: **Which group has *the same* number of objects?**

Have the child compare the objects in the group in front of you with the objects in each of the other groups. Help the child line up pairs of objects to determine which group has *the same* number of objects.

Then, ask: **Which group has *more* objects?**
Ask: **Which group has *less*?**

Encourage the child to explain how to tell if the group has *more* or *less* objects.

Invite the child to choose one group and to make new groups that show *more, less,* and *the same.*

Activity 7 Over and Under

Objective: Use the position words *over* and *under* to describe the location of objects
Materials: collection of small objects, such as toy cars, plastic fruit, or bear counters; basket

Hold a bear *over* the basket. Ask: **Where is the bear?**

Then lift the basket and place the bear *under* the basket. Ask: **Now where is the bear?**

Leave the bear under the basket and hold a toy car over the basket. Ask: **What is another way to tell the location of the bear?**

Next, have the child place on object *under* the basket and hold another object *over* the object. Have the child use the words *under* and *over* to describe the position of each object.

Prerequisite Skills Inventory Activities

Activity 8 Top and Bottom

Objective: Use the position words *top* and *bottom* to describe the location of objects
Materials: collection of blocks, cans, or other stackable objects

Stack two blocks of different colors, such as a red block and a blue block. Have the child describe where each block is.

Ask: **Which block is on *top*?**
Ask: **Which block is on the *bottom*?**

Place a different colored block on top. Ask: **Now which block is on top?**

Activity 9 Left, Middle, Right

Objective: Use the position words *left, right,* and *middle* to describe the location of objects
Materials: three different classroom objects, such as a crayon, a pencil, and an eraser

Arrange three objects in a row in front of the child.

Ask: **Which object is on the *left*?**
Ask: **Which object is on the *right*?**
Ask: **Which object is in the *middle*?**

Invite the child to rearrange the objects and describe each object's location using the words *left, middle,* and *right.*

Activity 10 Up and Down

Objective: Use the words *up* and *down* to describe the movement of an object
Materials: two different classroom objects, such as a book and a block

Set both objects on the table.

Say: **Move the book *up.* Move the book *down.***
Say: **Move the book and the block *up.* Now move the block *down.***

Invite the child to move an object and describe how it is being moved.

Name ____________________

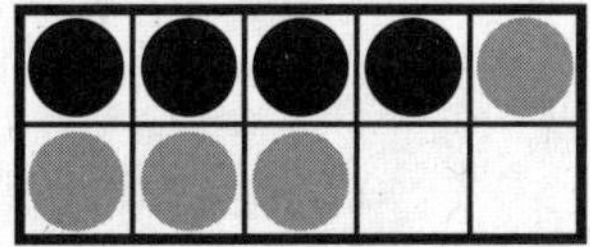
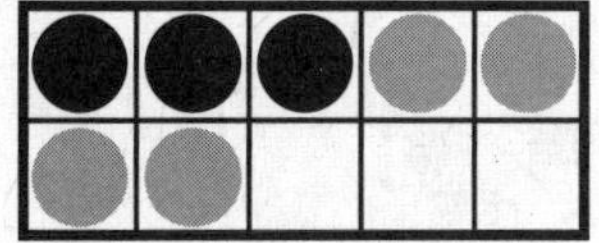
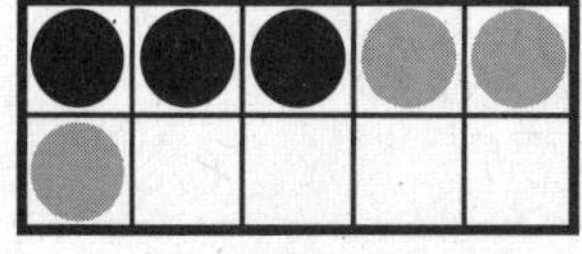

○ ○ ○

9

seven ○ eight ○ nine ○

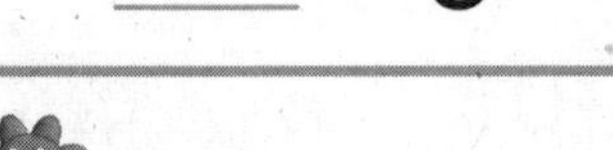

____ − 3 = 5

3 ○ 5 ○ 8 ○

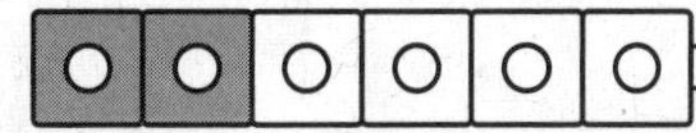

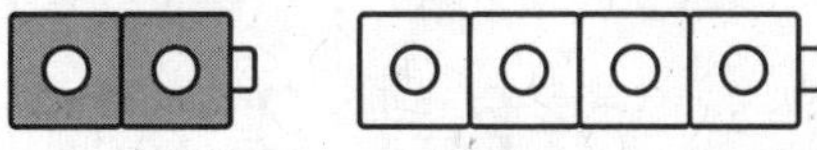

○ 6 − 4 = 2 ○ 6 − 3 = 3 ○ 5 − 4 = 1

DIRECTIONS **1.** Mark under the set that models a way to make seven. **2.** Mark under the word that matches the number at the beginning of the row. **3.** Mark under the number that shows how many you started with. **4.** Mark beside the subtraction sentence that shows the cube train being taken apart.

GO ON

5

12 13 14 ____

14	15	16
○	○	○

6

71	72	73	74	75	76	77	78	79	80
81	82	83	84	85	86	87	88	89	90
91	92	93	94	___	96	97	98	99	100

90	95	100
○	○	○

7

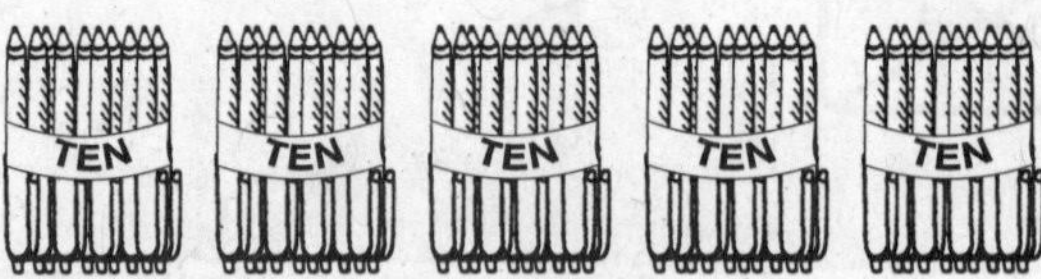

60	50	40
○	○	○

8

○ 2 + 3

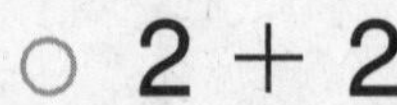
○ 2 + 2

○ 1 + 3

DIRECTIONS **5.** Mark under the number that comes next. **6.** Begin with 71 and count to 100. Mark under the number that completes the counting order. **7.** Count the pens by tens. Mark under the number that shows how many pens in all. **8.** Mark beside the addition that shows the counters put together.

GO ON

Name ________________________________

___ + 6 = 9

3 ○ 6 ○ 9 ○

○ 8 = 4 + 4

○ 7 = 3 + 4

○ 4 = 2 + 2

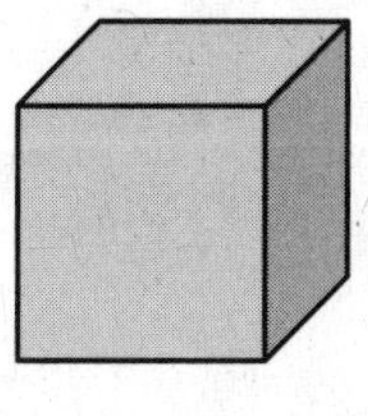

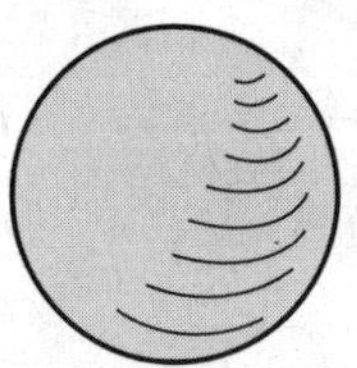

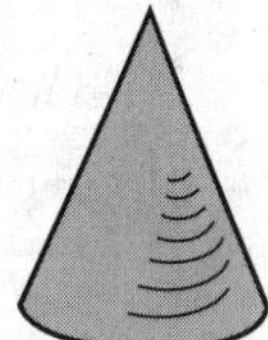

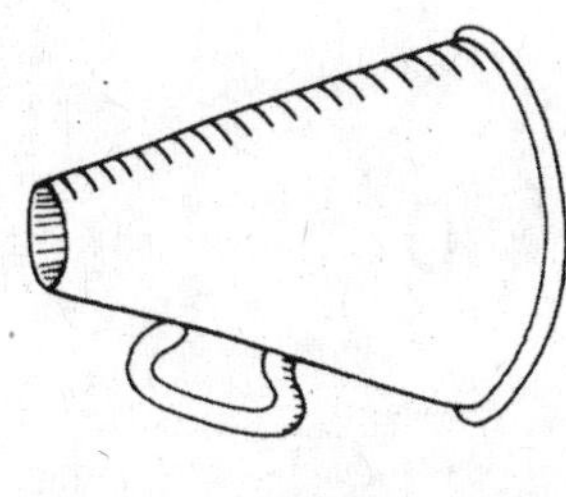

○ ○ ○

DIRECTIONS **9.** There are some birds. 6 more birds join them. Now there are 9 birds. How many birds were in the set to start? Mark under the number that completes the addition sentence. **10.** Mark beside the addition sentence that shows the number pair for the cube train. **11.** Mark under the shape that stacks. **12.** Mark under the object that is shaped like a cylinder.

GO ON

Name ____________________

13

Soup

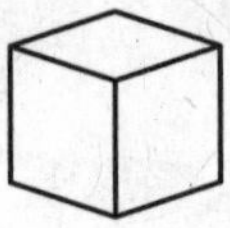

14

3

15

five

2 4 5

16

0 1 2

DIRECTIONS **13.** Mark under the object that is next to the object shaped like a cube. **14.** Mark under the set of strawberries that shows the number at the beginning of the row. **15.** Mark under the number that matches the word at the beginning of the row. **16.** Mark under the number that shows how many flowers are in the vase.

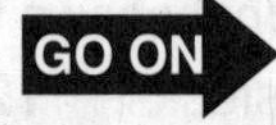

Name ______________________________

17

○

○

○

18

3 4 ____ 6

5	6	7
○	○	○

19

8

10	8	6
○	○	○

20

6	4	2
○	○	○

DIRECTIONS **17.** Mark beside the cube train that shows a way to make ten. **18.** Count forward. Mark under the missing number that fills the space. **19.** Mark under the number that is greater than the number at the beginning of the row. **20.** Look at the graph. Mark under the number that shows how many white cubes.

GO ON

Name ____________________

21

○ ○ ○

22

○ ○ ○

23

16 15 14

○ ○ ○

24

○ ○ ○

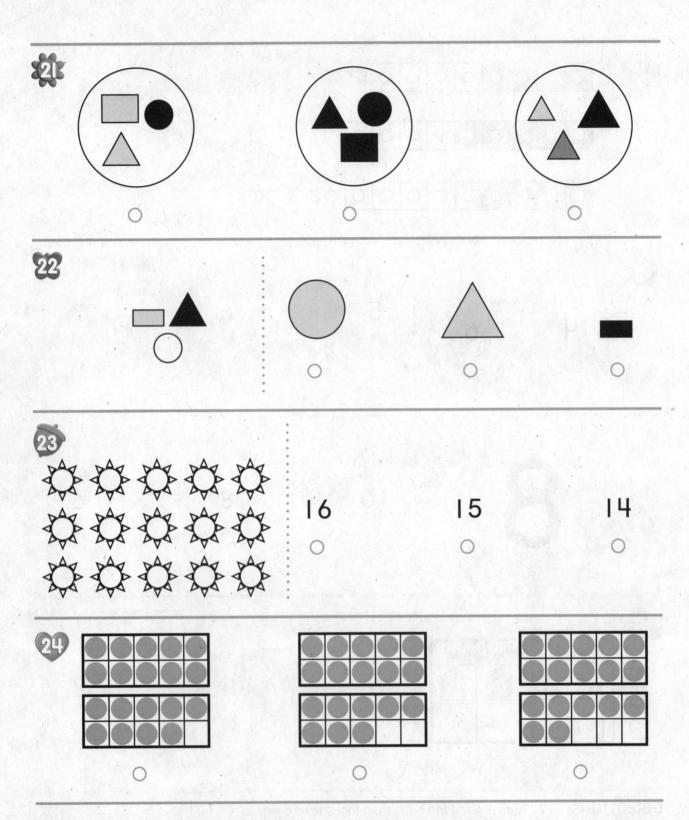

DIRECTIONS **21.** Mark under the shapes that are sorted and classified by triangles. **22.** Look at the set at the beginning of the row. Mark under the shape that belongs in that set. **23.** Mark under the number that shows how many. **24.** Mark under the set that shows 18.

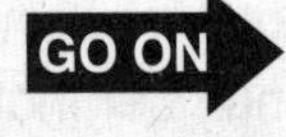

Name ______________________________

25

2 ○ 3 ○ 4 ○

26

○ ○ ○

27

○ ○ ○

28

○ ○ ○

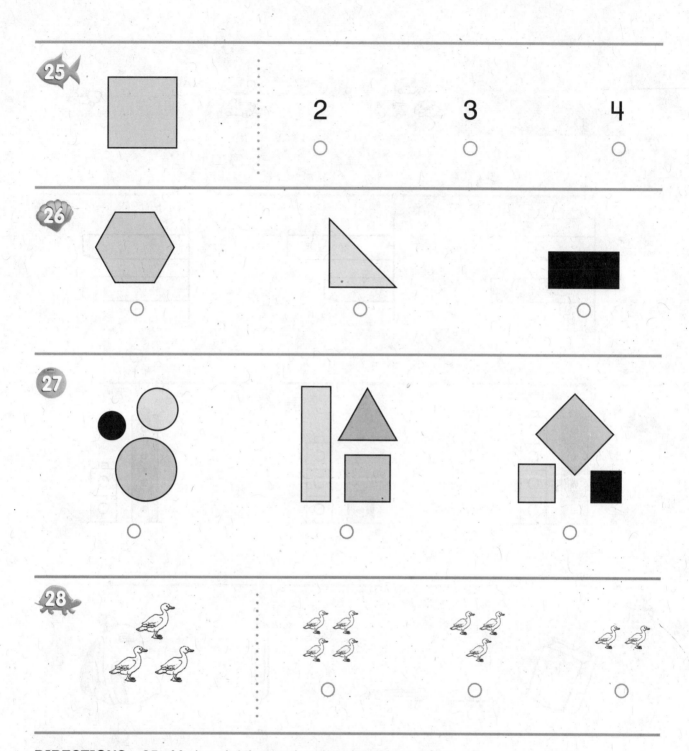

DIRECTIONS **25.** Mark under the number that shows how many vertices or corners the square has. **26.** Mark under the shape that is a hexagon. **27.** Mark under the set of shapes that have curves. **28.** Mark under the set that has a number of ducks less than the number of ducks at the beginning of the row.

Name ____________________

29

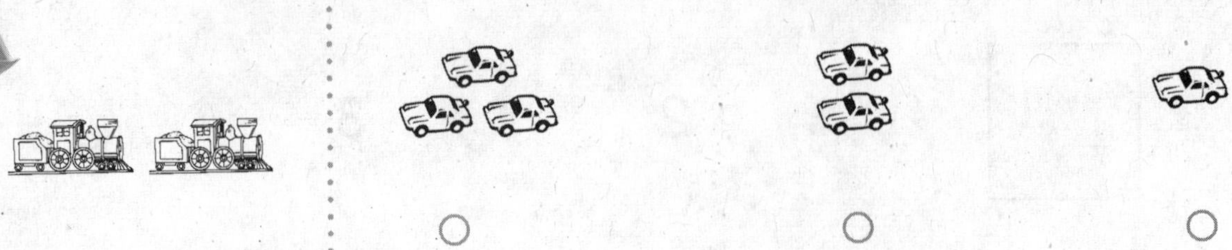

30

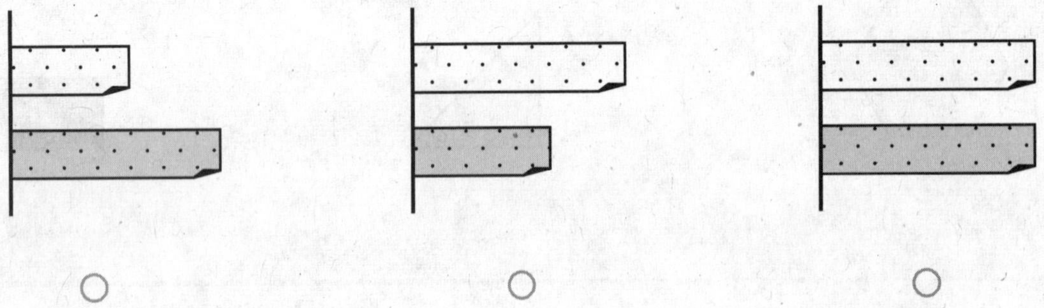

31

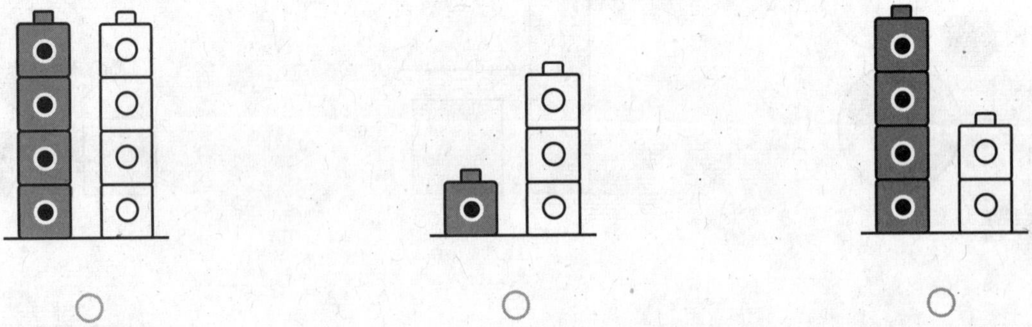

32

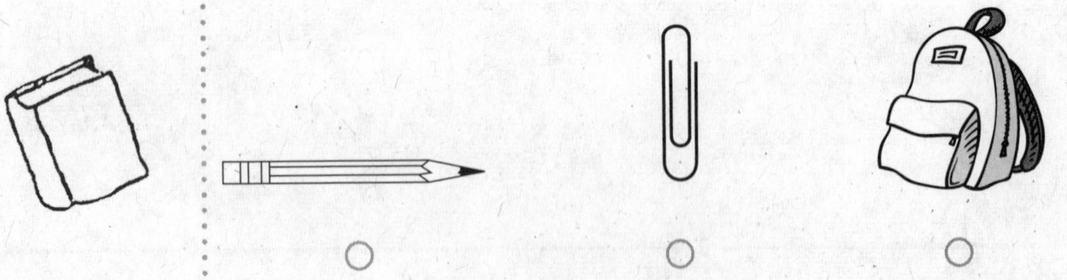

DIRECTIONS **29.** Mark under the set that has the same number of cars as the number of trains at the beginning of the row. **30.** Mark under the set that shows the white ribbon is shorter than the gray ribbon. **31.** Mark under the set that shows the white cube tower is taller than the gray cube tower. **32.** Mark under the object that is heavier than the object at the beginning of the row.

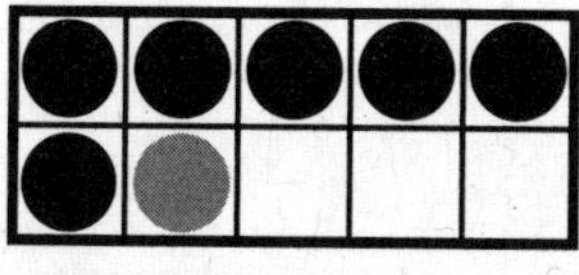
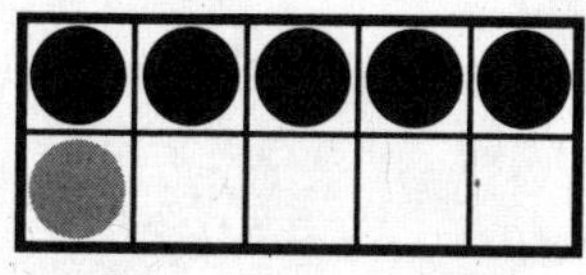
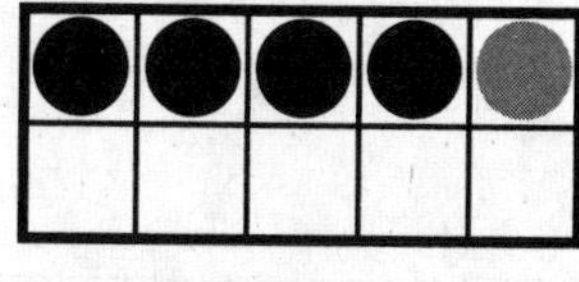

○  

nine

6 ○ 8 ○ 9 ○

___ − 2 = 6

6 ○ 8 ○ 9 ○

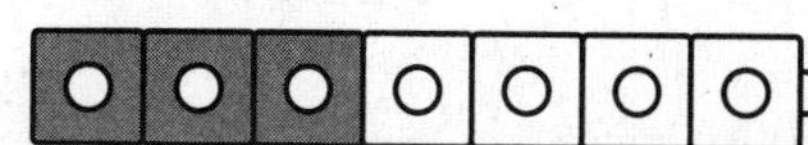

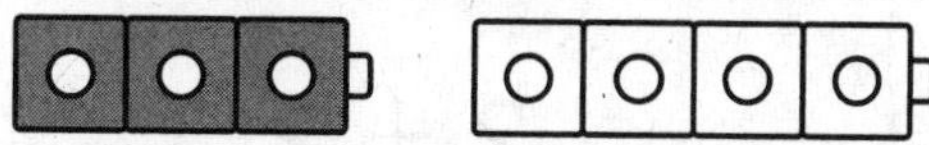

○ 7 − 5 = 2 ○ 7 − 4 = 3 ○ 6 − 4 = 2

DIRECTIONS 1. Mark under the set that models a way to make seven. 2. Mark under the number that matches the word at the beginning of the row. 3. Mark under the number that shows how many suns you started with. 4. Mark beside the subtraction sentence that shows the cube train being taken apart.

GO ON

Name ______________________________

5

17 18 19 ____

16	19	20
○	○	○

6

71	72	73	74	75	76	77	78	79	80
81	82	83	84	85	86	87	88	___	90
91	92	93	94	95	96	97	98	99	100

79	80	89
○	○	○

7

TEN TEN TEN TEN

4	40	50
○	○	○

8

○ 2 + 2

○ 1 + 3

○ 1 + 2

DIRECTIONS **5.** Mark under the number that comes next. **6.** Begin with 71 and count to 100. Mark under the number that completes the counting order. **7.** Count the pens by tens. Mark under the number that shows how many pens in all. **8.** Mark beside the addition that shows the counters put together.

Name ________________________________

___ + 2 = 6

2 ○   4 ○   8 ○

10

○ 9 = 6 + 3

○ 6 = 4 + 2

○ 8 = 5 + 3

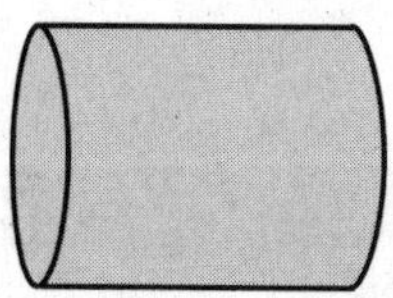

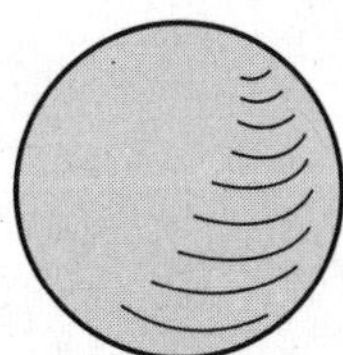

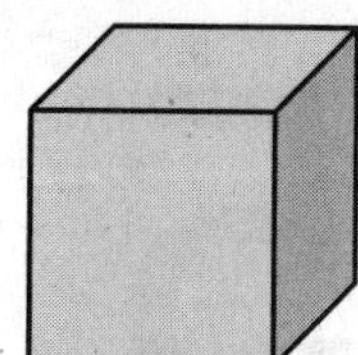

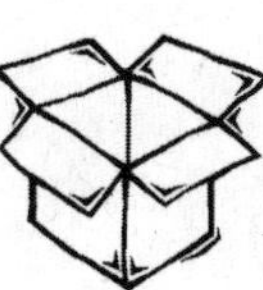

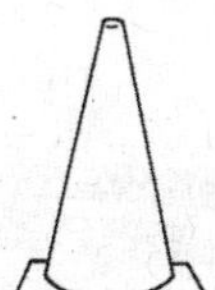

○

DIRECTIONS 9. There are some penguins. 2 more penguins join them. Now there are 6 penguins. How many penguins were in the set to start? Mark under the number that completes the addition sentence. **10.** Mark beside the addition sentence that shows the number pair for the cube train. **11.** Mark under the shape that rolls and stacks. **12.** Mark under the object that is shaped like a cylinder.

GO ON

Name ______________________________

13

two four five

14

4

15

5

two four five

16

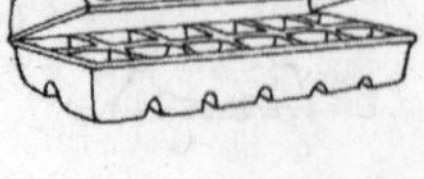

0 1 2

DIRECTIONS 13. Mark under the object that is next to the object shaped like a cylinder. 14. Mark under the set of butterflies that shows the number at the beginning of the row. 15. Mark under the word that matches the number at the beginning of the row. 16. Mark under the number that shows how many eggs are in the carton.

Name ________________________________

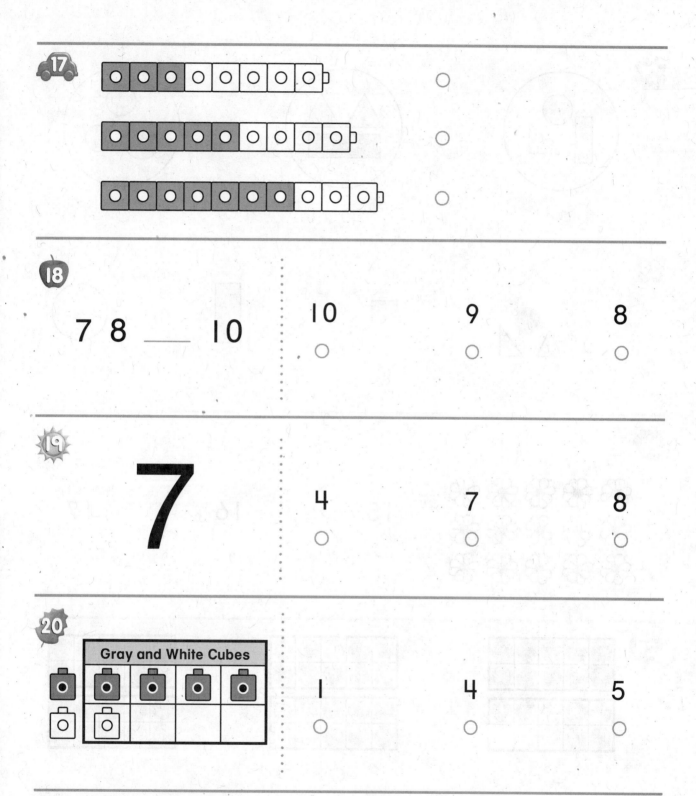

17

○

○

○

18

7 8 ___ 10

10	9	8
○	○	○

19

7

4	7	8
○	○	○

20

Gray and White Cubes

1	4	5
○	○	○

DIRECTIONS **17.** Mark beside the cube train that shows a way to make ten. **18.** Count forward. Mark under the number that fills the space. **19.** Mark under the number that is greater than the number at the beginning of the row. **20.** Look at the graph. Mark under the number that shows how many white cubes.

Name ______________________________

21

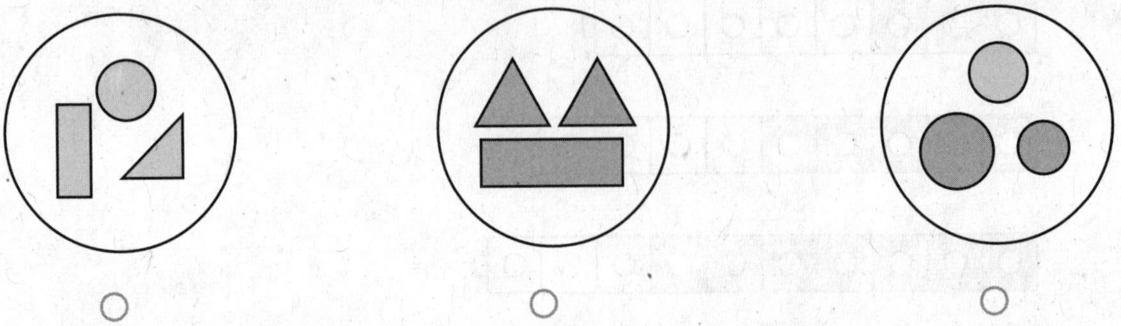

○ ○ ○

22

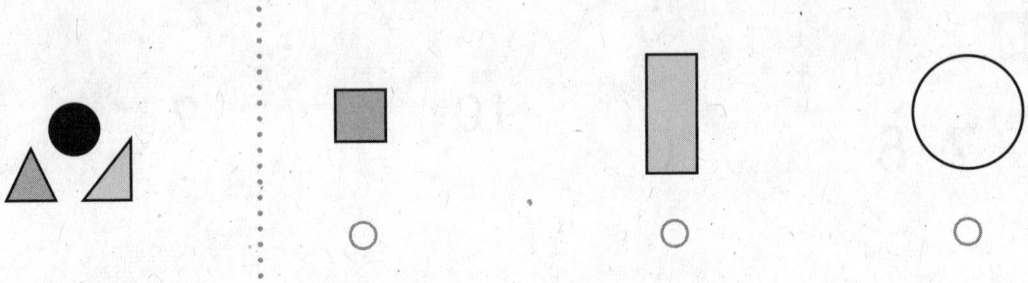

○ ○ ○

23

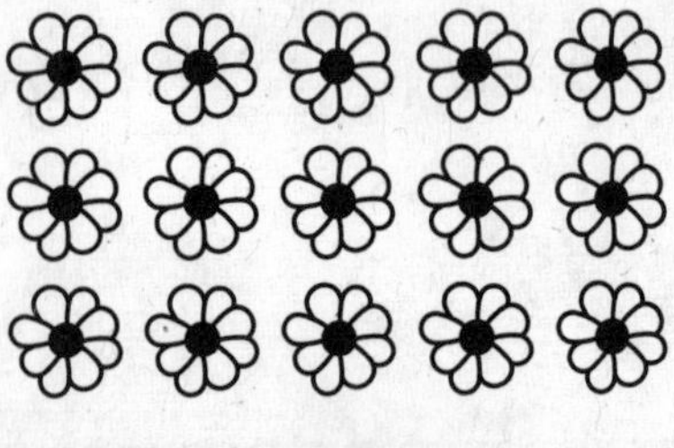

15 16 17

○ ○ ○

24

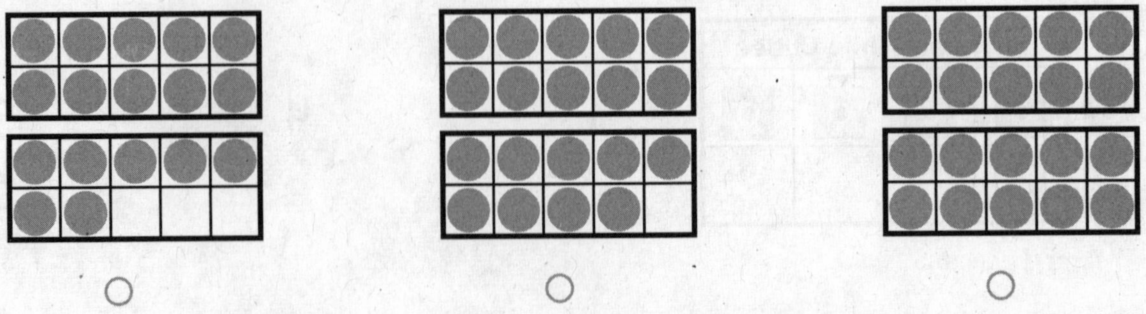

○ ○ ○

DIRECTIONS **21.** Mark under the shapes that are sorted and classified by circles. **22.** Look at the set at the beginning of the row. Mark under the shape that belongs in that set. **23.** Mark under the number that shows how many. **24.** Mark under the set that shows 19.

Name ________________________________

25

6 4 3

26

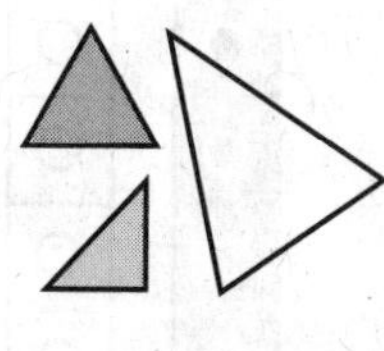

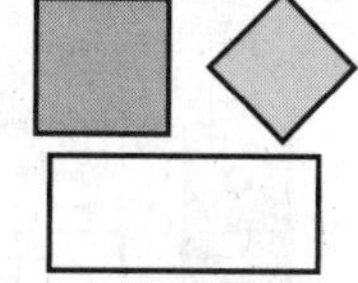

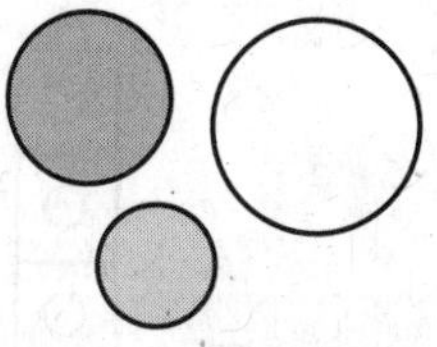

DIRECTIONS **25.** Mark under the number that shows how many sides the square has. **26.** Mark under the shape that is a hexagon. **27.** Mark under the set of shapes that have 3 vertices or corners. **28.** Mark under the set that has a number of cars greater than the number of cars at the beginning of the row.

GO ON

29

30

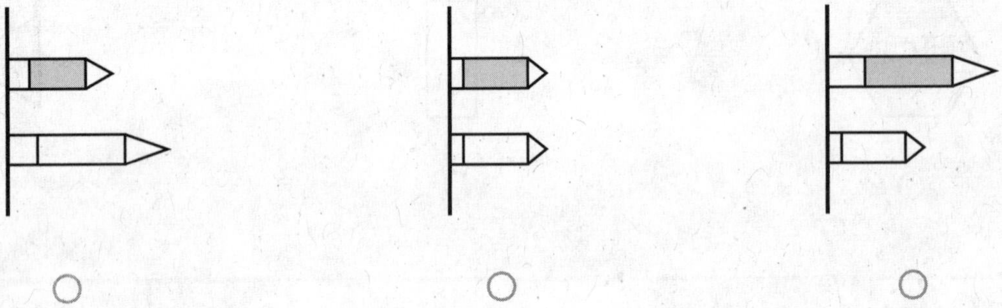

31

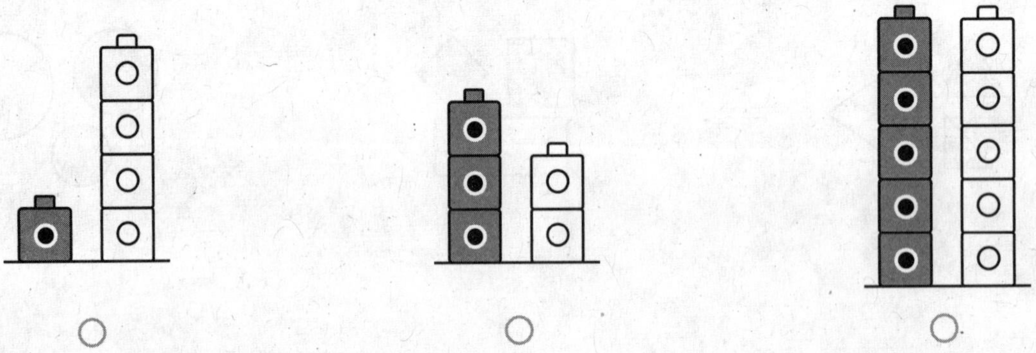

32

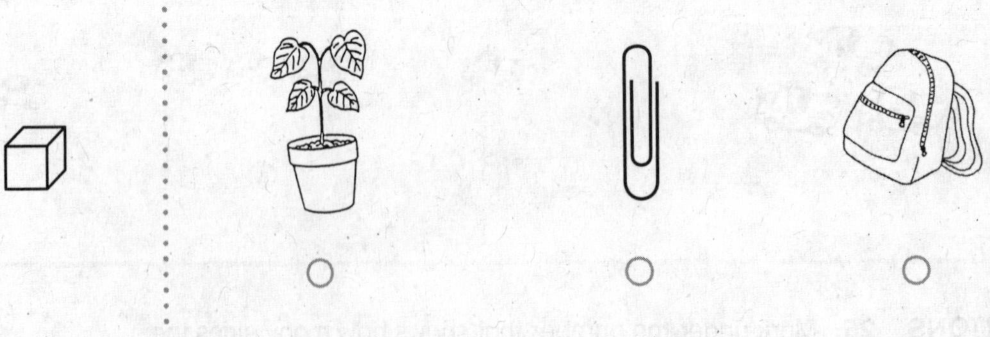

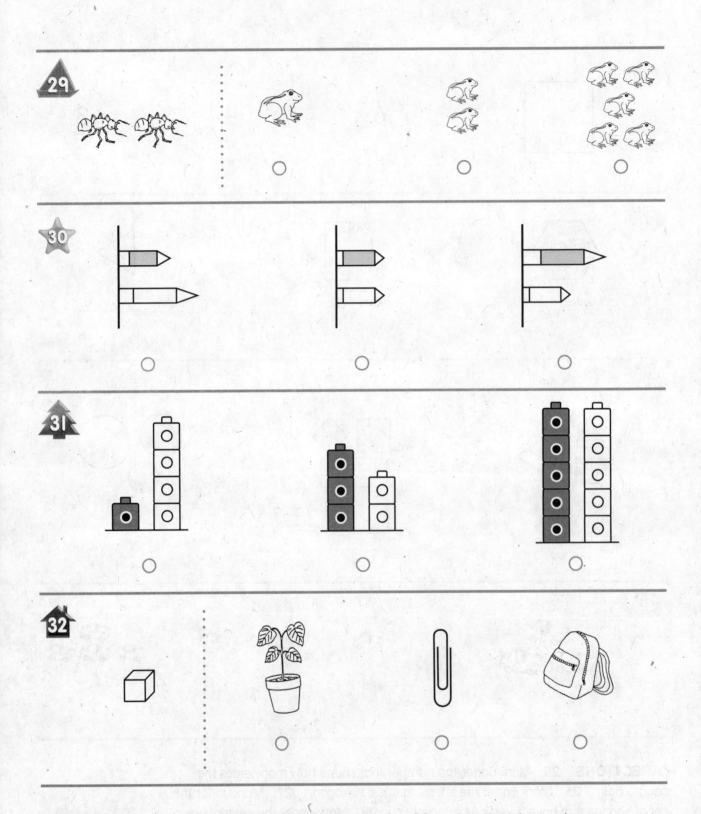

DIRECTIONS **29.** Mark under the set that has a number of frogs less than the number of ants at the beginning of the row. **30.** Mark under the set that shows the white pencil is longer than the gray pencil. **31.** Mark under the set that shows the white cube tower is taller than the gray cube tower. **32.** Mark under the object that is lighter than the object at the beginning of the row.

Name ______________________________

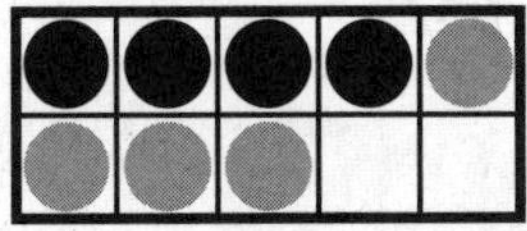

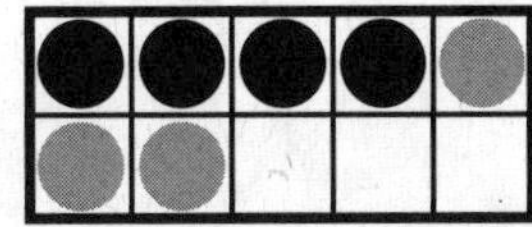

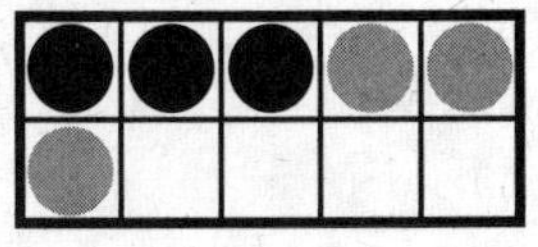

○ ○ ○

nine

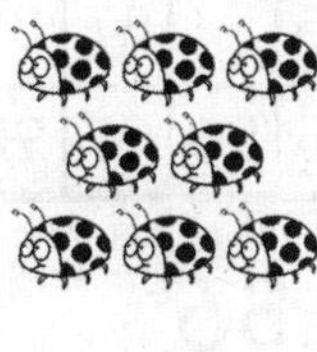

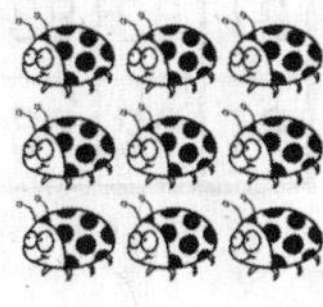

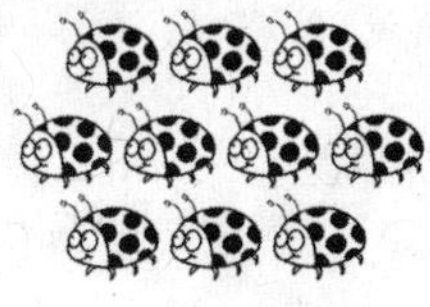

○ ○ ○

3

____ − 1 = 5

5 6 7

○ ○ ○

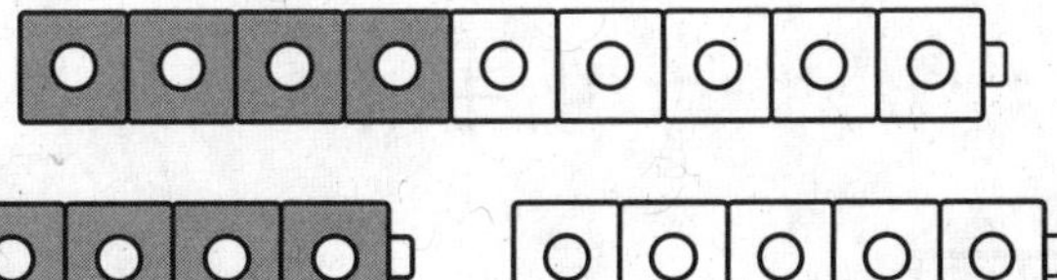

○ 8 − 5 = 3 ○ 9 − 6 = 3 ○ 9 − 5 = 4

DIRECTIONS **1.** Mark under the set that models a way to make seven. **2.** Mark under the set that matches the word at the beginning of the row. **3.** Mark under the number that shows how many stars you started with. **4.** Mark beside the subtraction sentence that shows the cube train being taken apart.

5

16 17 18 ____

18	19	20
○	○	○

71	72	73	74	75	76	77	78	79	80
81	82	83	84	85	___	87	88	89	90
91	92	93	94	95	96	97	98	99	100

77	86	90
○	○	○

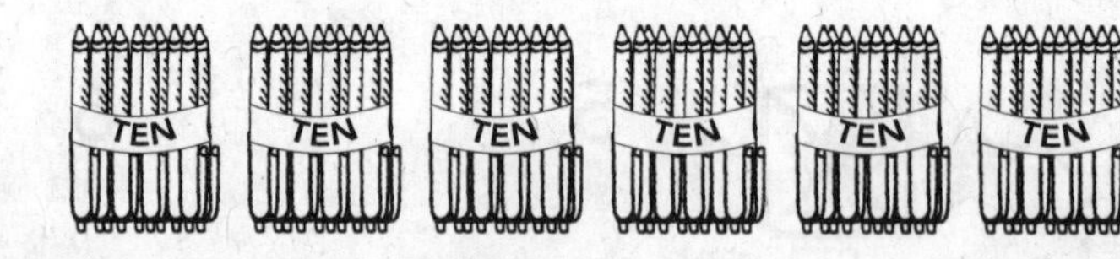

60	50	6
○	○	○

○ 4 + 1

○ 3 + 2

○ 3 + 1

DIRECTIONS **5.** Mark under the number that comes next. **6.** Begin with 71 and count to 100. Mark under the number that completes the counting order. **7.** Count the pens by tens. Mark under the number that shows how many pens in all. **8.** Mark beside the addition that shows the counters put together.

Name ______________________________

____ + 3 = 6

2	3	6
○	○	○

○ 4 = 2 + 2

○ 8 = 6 + 2

○ 9 = 5 + 4

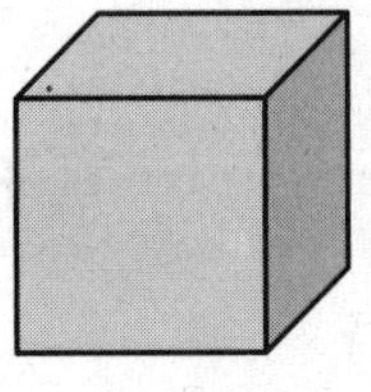

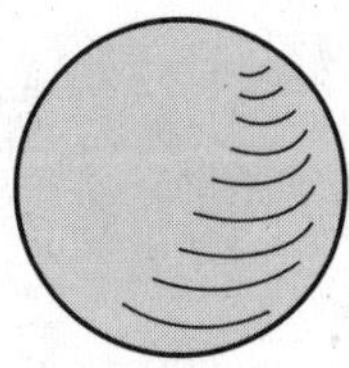

DIRECTIONS **9.** There are some fish. 3 more fish join them. Now there are 6 fish. How many fish were in the set to start? Mark under the number that completes the addition sentence. **10.** Mark beside the addition sentence that shows the number pair for the cube train. **11.** Mark under the shape that stacks and slides. **12.** Mark under the object that is shaped like a cylinder.

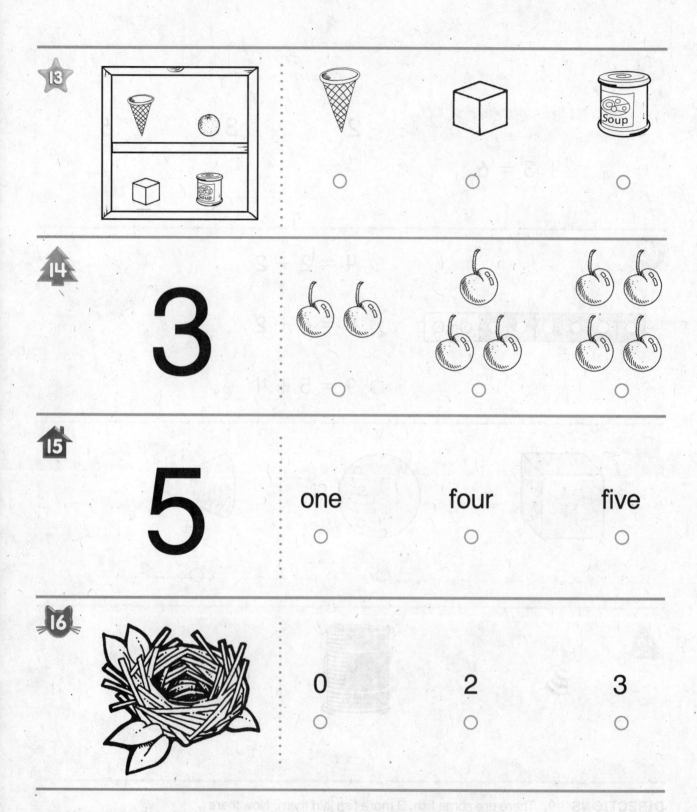

13

Soup

○ ○ ○

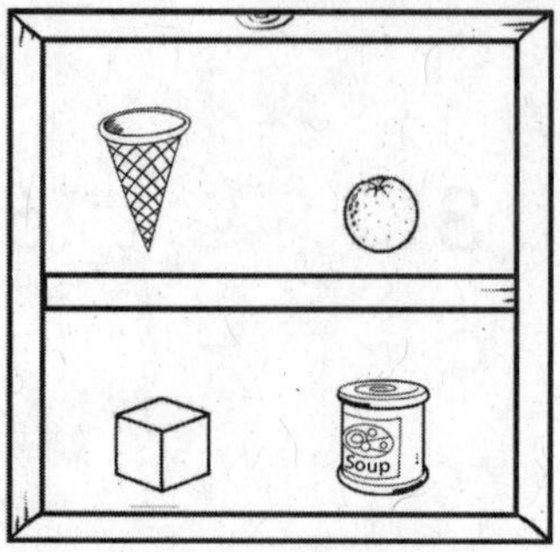

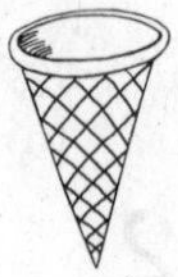

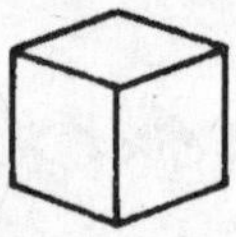

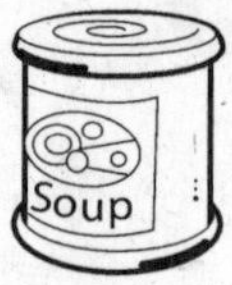

14

3

○ ○ ○

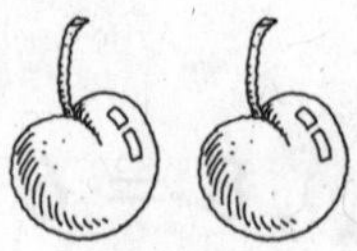

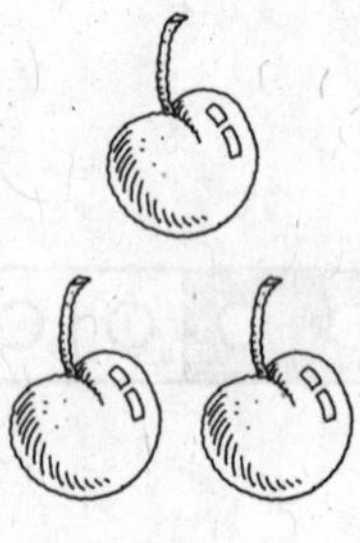

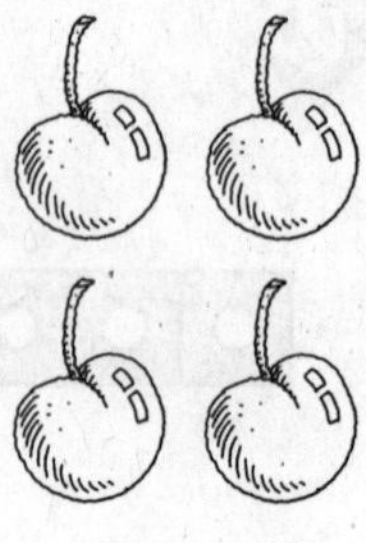

15

5

one four five

○ ○ ○

16

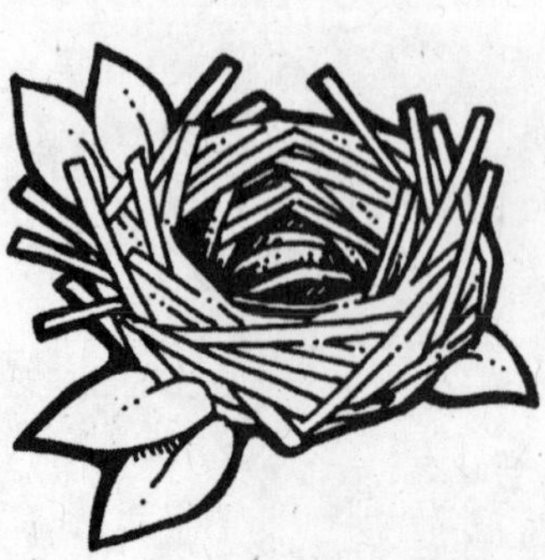

0 2 3

○ ○ ○

DIRECTIONS **13.** Mark under the object that is next to the object shaped like a cylinder. **14.** Mark under the set of cherries that shows the number at the beginning of the row. **15.** Mark under the word that matches the number at the beginning of the row. **16.** Mark under the number that shows how many birds are in the nest.

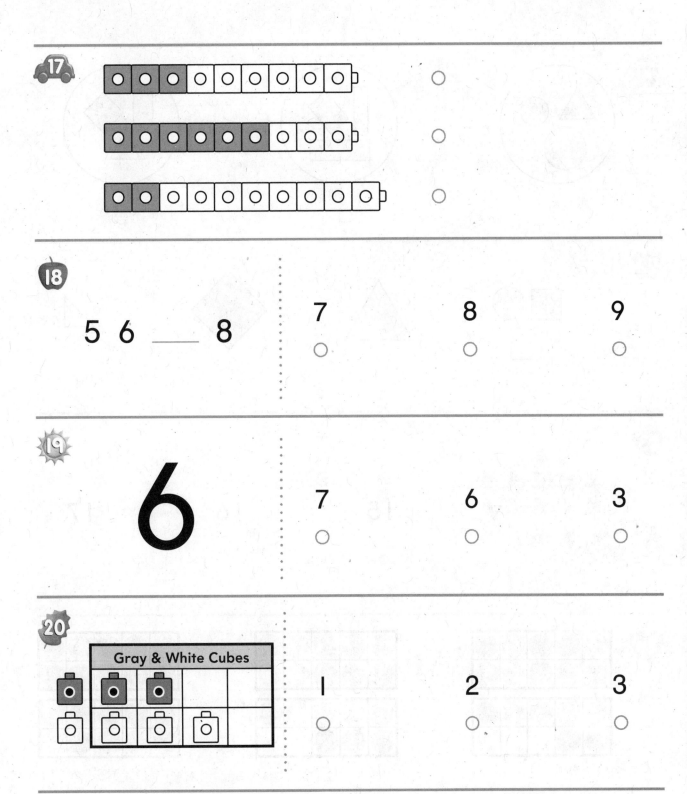

Name ______________________________

17

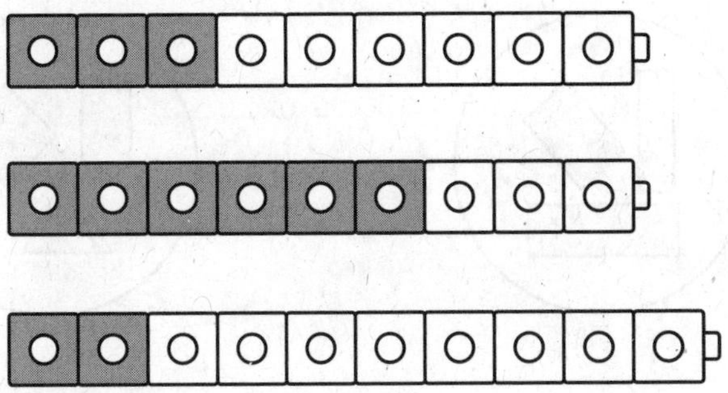

18

5 6 ____ 8

7	8	9
○	○	○

19

6

7	6	3
○	○	○

20

Gray & White Cubes

1	2	3
○	○	○

DIRECTIONS **17.** Mark beside the cube train that shows a way to make ten. **18.** Count forward. Mark under the number that fills the space. **19.** Mark under the number that is less than the number at the beginning of the row. **20.** Look at the graph. Mark under the number that shows how many white cubes.

21

22

23

15 16 17

24

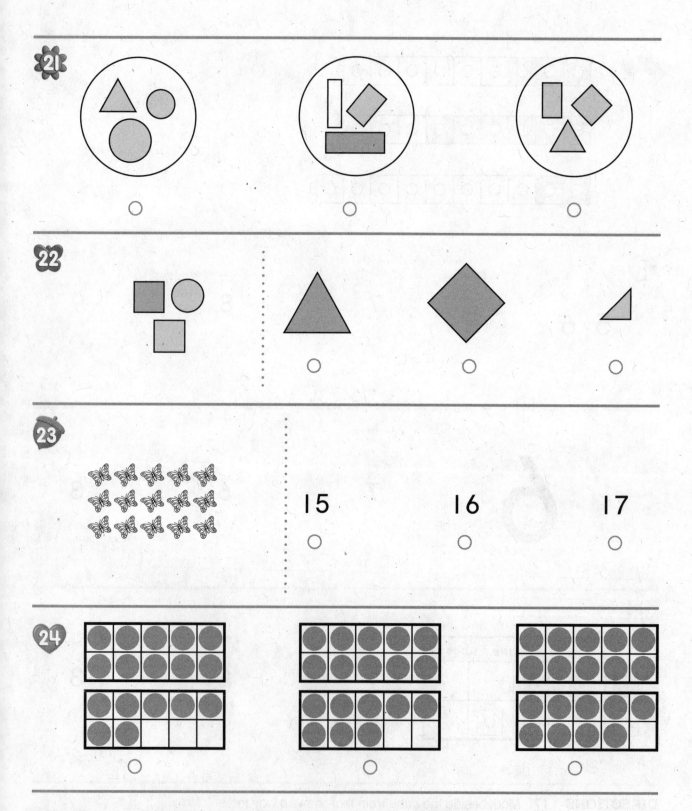

DIRECTIONS **21.** Mark under the shapes that are sorted and classified by rectangles. **22.** Look at the set at the beginning of the row. Mark under the shape that belongs in that set. **23.** Mark under the number that shows how many. **24.** Mark under the set that shows 18.

Name ______________________________

25

3 ○ 4 ○ 8 ○

26

○ ○ ○

27

○ ○ ○

28

○ ○ ○

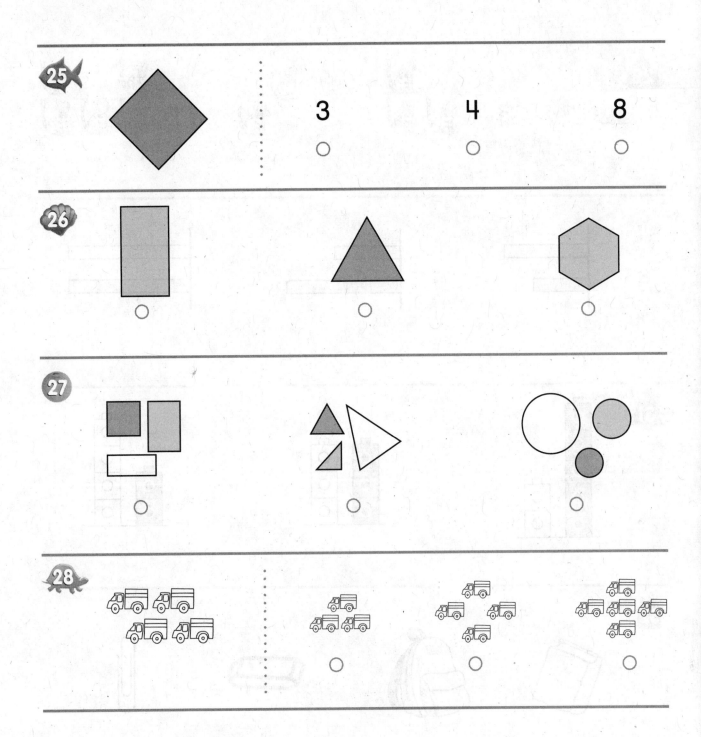

DIRECTIONS **25.** Mark under the number that shows how many sides the square has. **26.** Mark under the shape that is a hexagon. **27.** Mark under the set of shapes that have 4 vertices or corners. **28.** Mark under the set that has a number of trucks greater than the number of trucks at the beginning of the row.

Name ______________________________

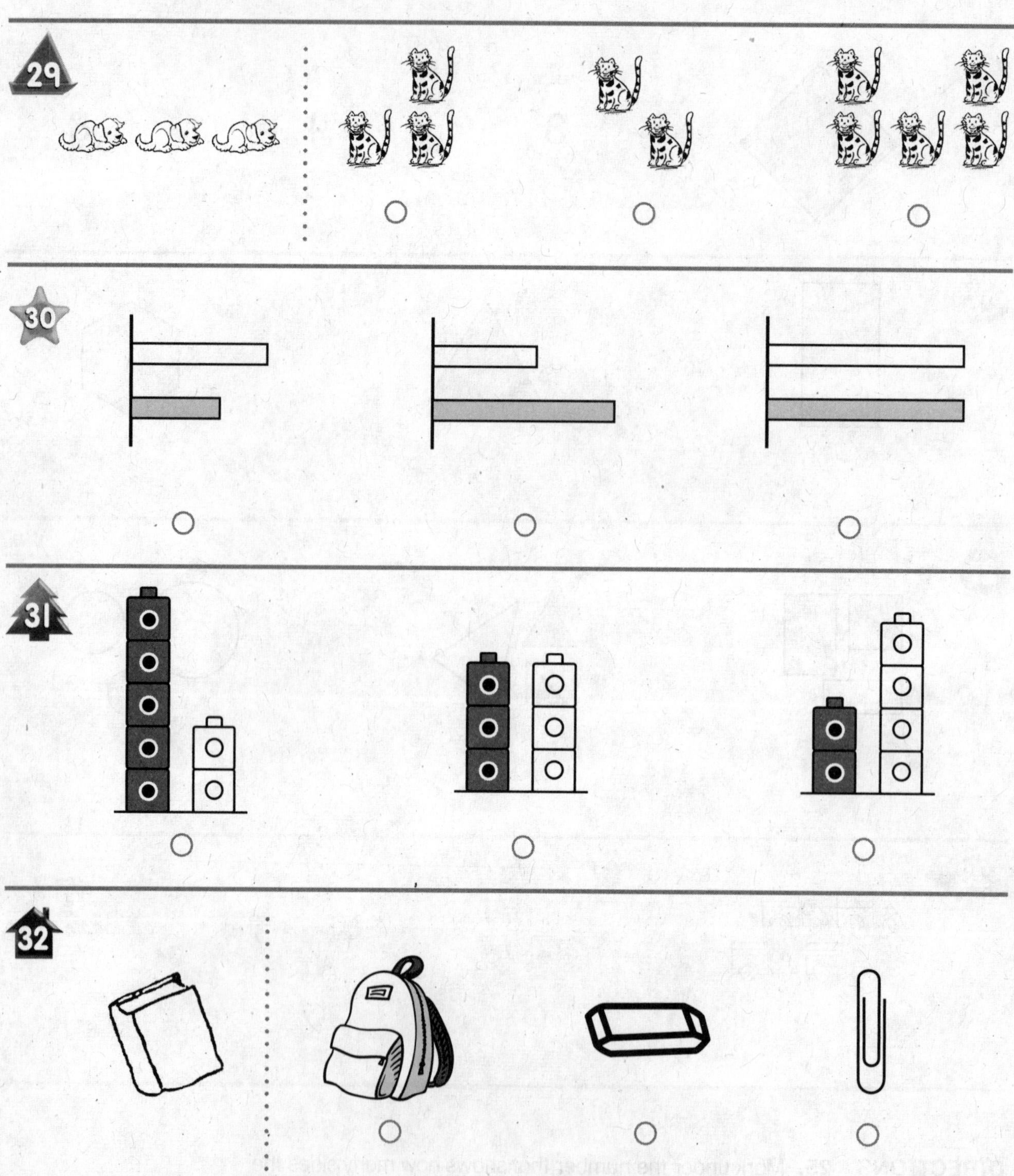

DIRECTIONS **29.** Mark under the set that has a number of cats greater than the number of dogs at the beginning of the row. **30.** Mark under the set that shows the white string is shorter than the gray string. **31.** Mark under the set that shows the white cube tower is taller than the gray cube tower. **32.** Mark under the object that is heavier than the object at the beginning of the row.

STOP

Name ______________________

○ 2
○ two

○ 5
○ five
○ 4

5

DIRECTIONS **1–2.** Choose all the answers that tell how many. **3.** How many muffins are on the plate? Write the number. **4–5.** Count how many. Write the number.

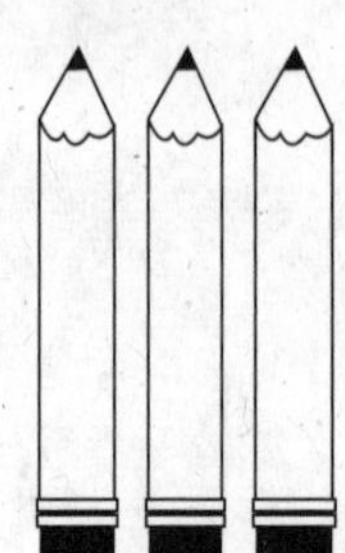

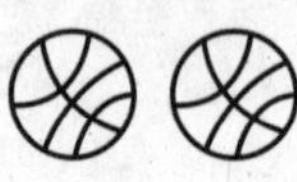

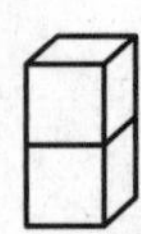

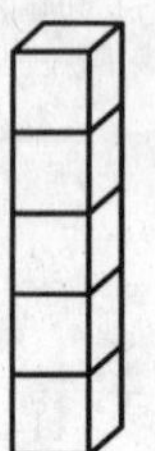

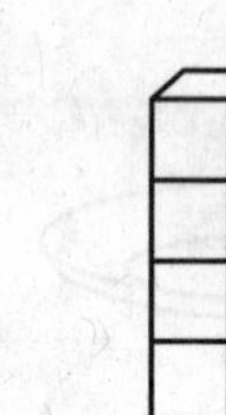

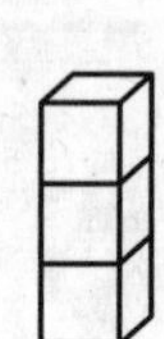

8

DIRECTIONS **6.** Circle all the sets that show 3. **7.** Count the cubes in each tower. Write the number. **8.** Write the numbers 1 to 5 in counting order.

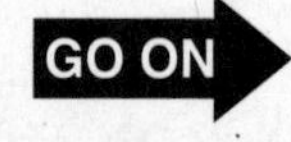

2	3	4	○ Yes	○ No
4	3	5	○ Yes	○ No
3	4	5	○ Yes	○ No

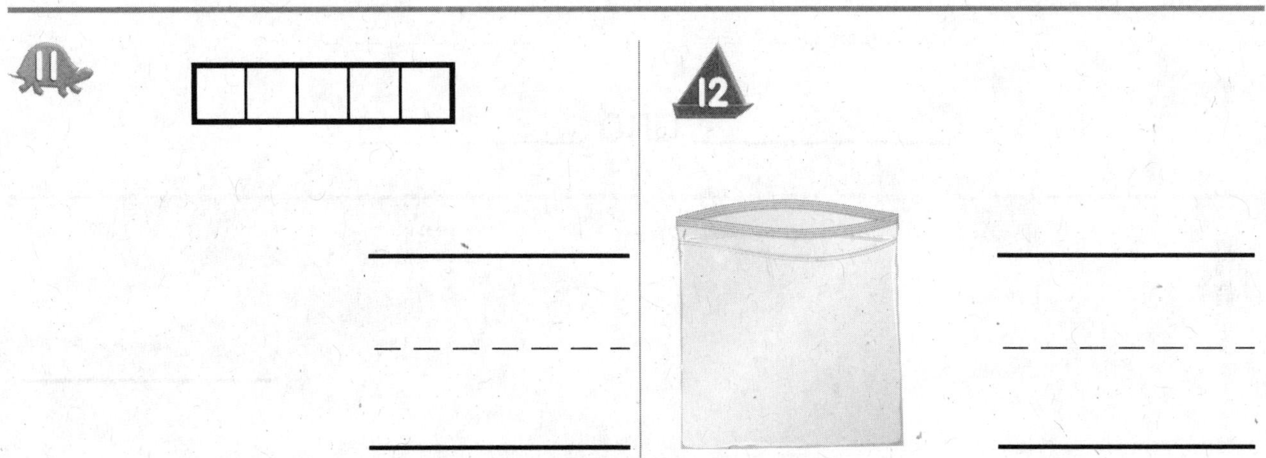

DIRECTIONS **9.** Are the numbers in counting order? Choose Yes or No. **10.** Four children each have one doll. Draw counters to show the dolls. Write the number. **11.** Anna put no counters in a five frame. How many counters did she put in the five frame? Write the number. **12.** There are three carrot sticks in a bag. Joey eats all three carrots. How many carrots are in the bag now? Write the number.

GO ON

Name ______________________

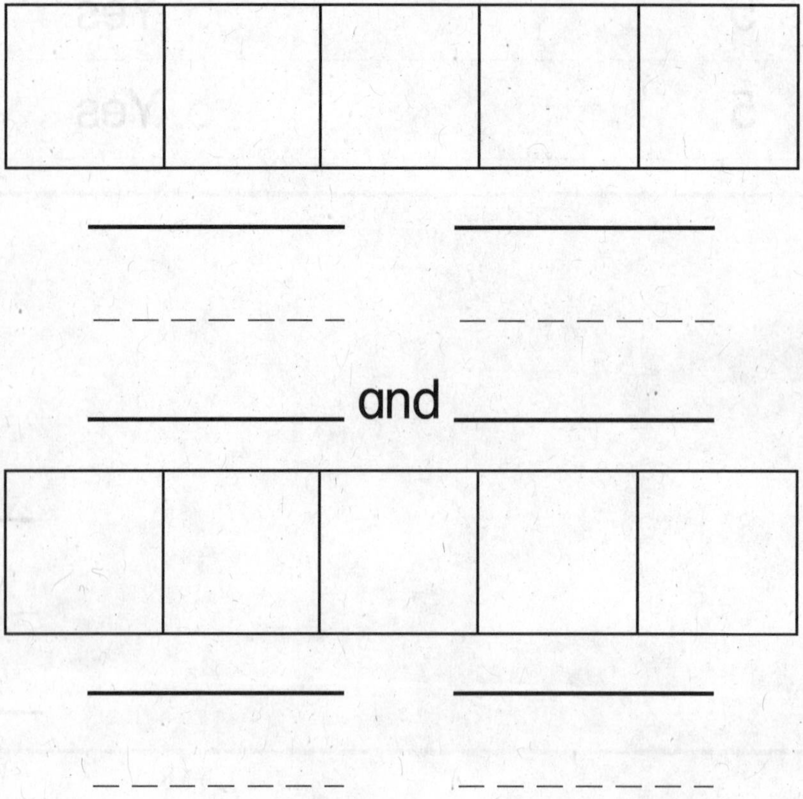

_______ and _______

_______ and _______

____

DIRECTIONS 13. Show 2 ways to make 5. Color some boxes red. Color some boxes yellow. Write the numbers. 14. Write the number that comes after 4 in counting order. Draw counters to show the number.

Name ____________________

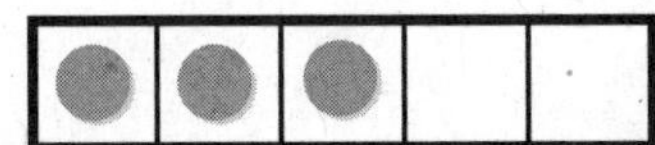

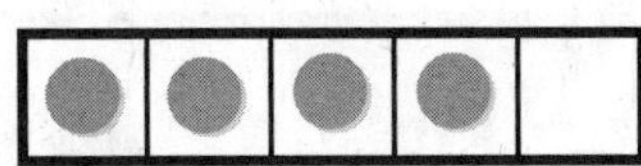

DIRECTIONS **1.** Draw a counter below each kitten to show the same number of counters as kittens. Write how many kittens. Write how many counters. **2.** How many counters are there in each row? Write the numbers. Compare the sets by matching. Circle the number that is greater.

3

○ ○ ○

4

○ ○ ○

5

○ ○ ○

6

○ 2 ○ 3 ○ 5

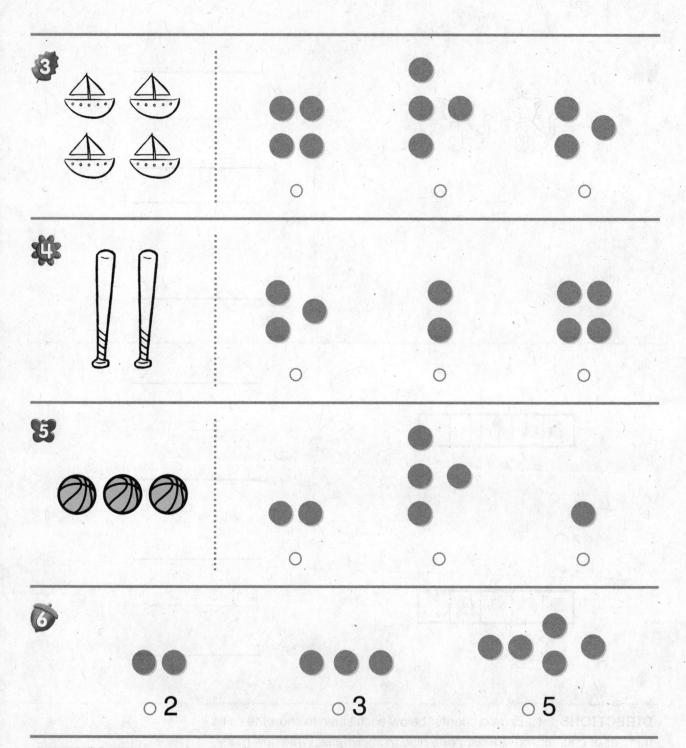

DIRECTIONS **3.** Mark under all the sets that have the same number of counters as the number of boats. **4.** Mark under all the sets that have a number of counters greater than the number of bats. **5.** Mark under all the sets that have a number of counters less than the number of basketballs. **6.** Mark all the numbers less than 5.

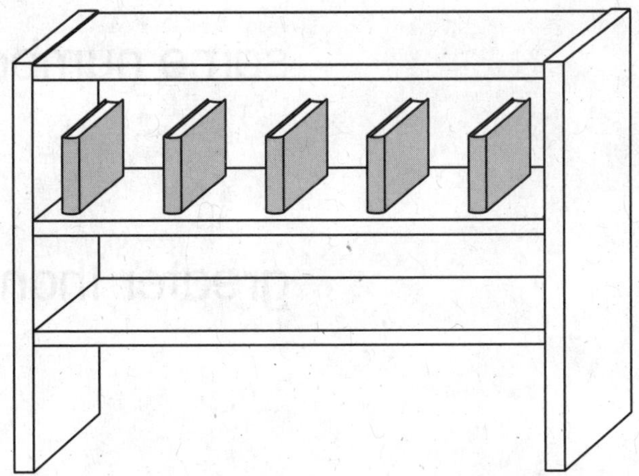

DIRECTIONS **7.** Maria has these books. Draw a set of books on the shelf below that has the same number. Compare the sets by matching. Write how many books in each set. **8.** Raul has three flowers. Draw Raul's flowers. Jenna has a number of flowers that is one less than the number of flowers Raul has. How many flowers does Jenna have? Draw her flowers. Write how many in each set.

GO ON

 • • same number

 • • greater than

 • • less than

DIRECTIONS 9. Compare the number of counters in each set to the number of stars. Draw lines from the sets of counters to the words that show *same number*, *greater than*, or *less than*. **10.** Draw five counters. Now draw a set that has a number of counters that is less. How many are in each set? Write the numbers. Use red to color the set with a greater number of counters. Use blue to color the set with a number of counters that is less.

Name ____________________

 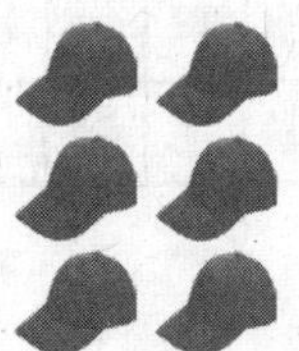 

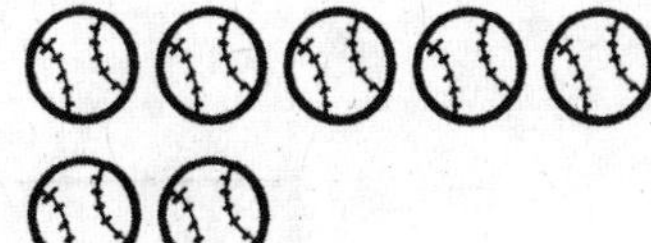 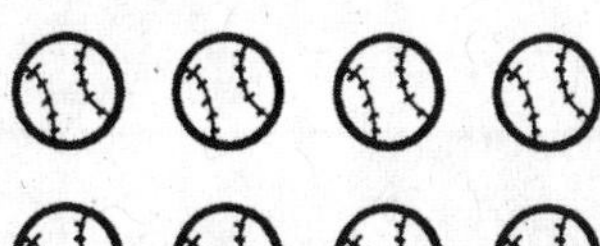 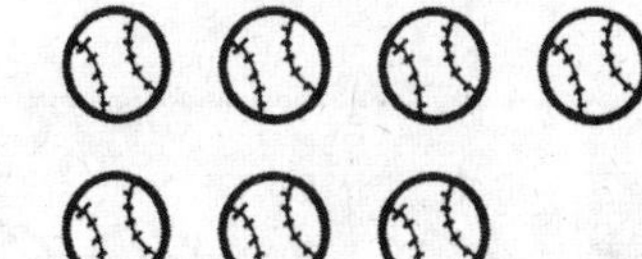

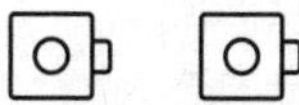

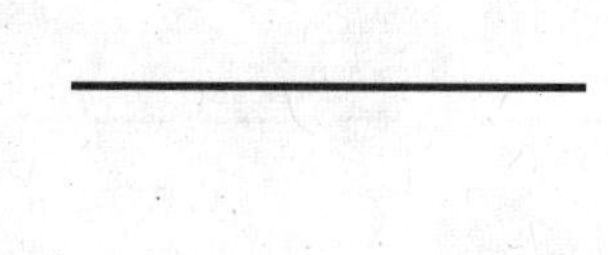

DIRECTIONS **1.** Circle all the sets that show 6. **2.** Circle all the sets that show 7. **3–4.** Count and tell how many. Write the number.

GO ON

5

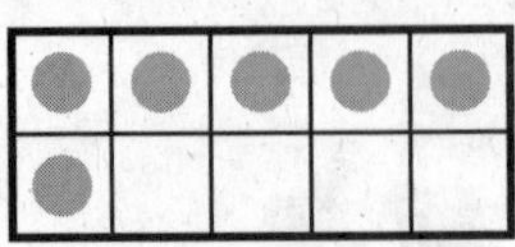
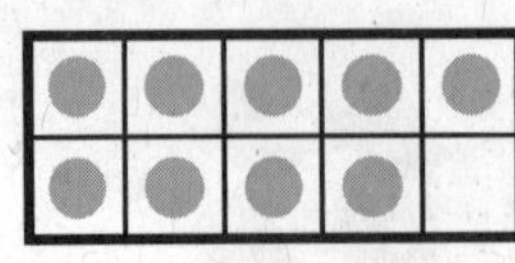
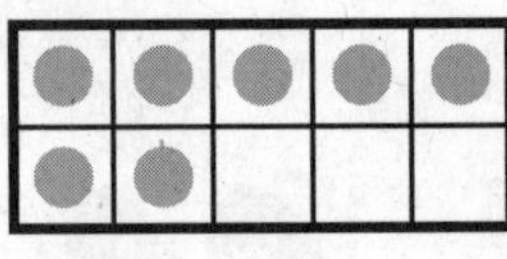

9 7 6

7

8

9

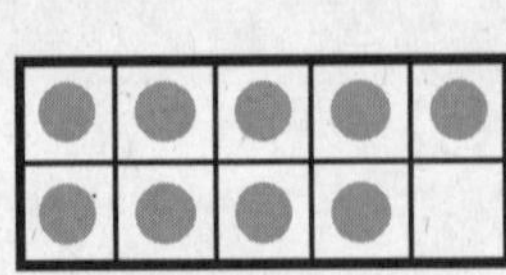

4 and
4
5
more

DIRECTIONS **5.** Match each set to the number that tells how many. **6–7.** Count to tell how many. Write the number. **8.** The ten frame shows 4 counters on the bottom and some on the top. Four and how many more make 9? Choose the number.

GO ON

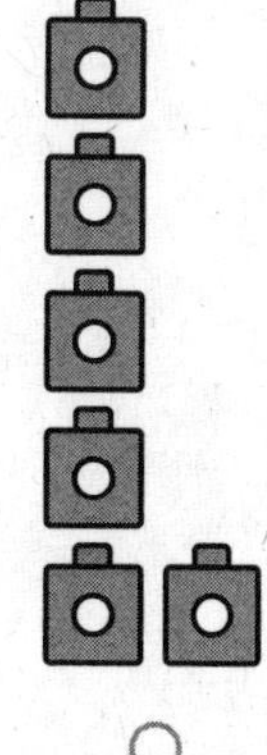

DIRECTIONS 9. Mike has 7 boxes. Daisy has a number of boxes that is one greater than 7. Draw the boxes. Write the number for each set of boxes. **10.** Choose all the cube towers that have a number of cubes greater than 6.

GO ON

Name ______

11

DIRECTIONS 11. The number of birds in a tree is 2 more than 5. Draw counters to show the birds. Write the number. 12. Draw a set that has a number of objects that is 2 more than 4. Write the number.

Name ____________________

○ ○ ○

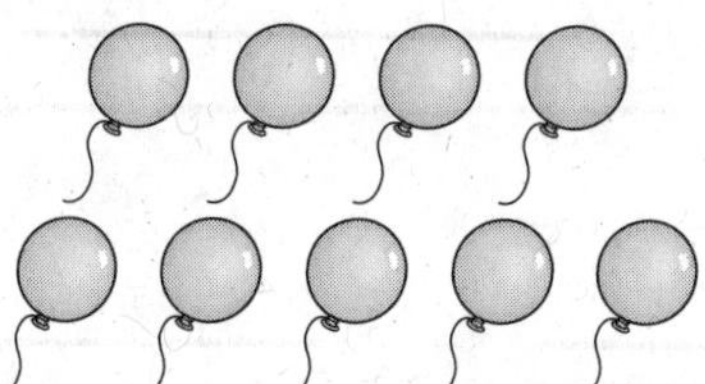

five
six

DIRECTIONS **1.** Mark under all the sets that have 10 items. **2.** How many balloons are shown? Write the number. **3.** What is another way to write 6? Circle the word.

GO ON

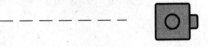

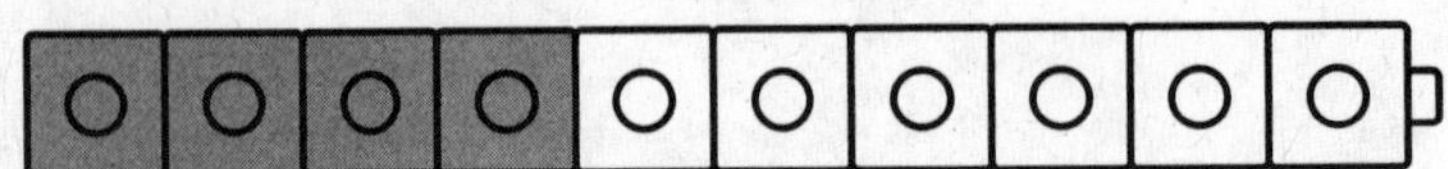

cubes

5

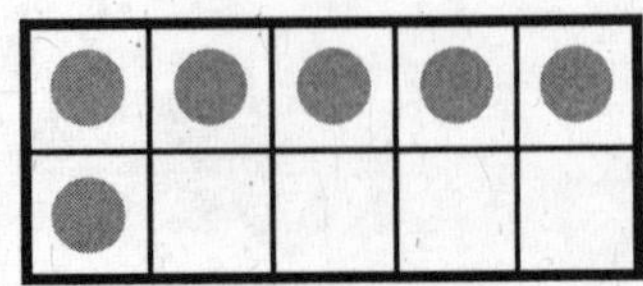

6

5 7 6 8	○ Yes	○ No
7 8 9 10	○ Yes	○ No
5 6 7 8	○ Yes	○ No

DIRECTIONS 4. Write how many gray cubes. Write how many white cubes. Write how many cubes in all. 5. How many counters are there? Write the number. How many more counters do you need to make 10? Write the number. 6. Are the numbers in counting order? Choose Yes or No.

 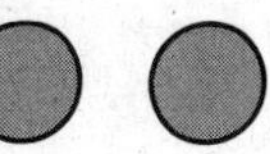     

8 ○ 5 ○ 6 ○

DIRECTIONS **7.** Write how many counters are in the set. Use matching lines to draw a set of counters less than the number of counters shown. Circle the number that is less. **8.** Count how many in each set. Write the numbers. Circle the greater number. **9.** Think about counting order. Choose the number that is more than 7.

GO ON

Name ______________________________

9 10 8

DIRECTIONS **10.** How many flowers are there? Write the number. **11.** Max has 6 stones. Draw Max's stones. The number of stones Pat has is one less than Max's. Draw Pat's stones. How many stones does Pat have? Write how many in each set. Circle the number that is less. **12.** Match sets to the numbers that show how many fish.

Name ______________________

______ and ______

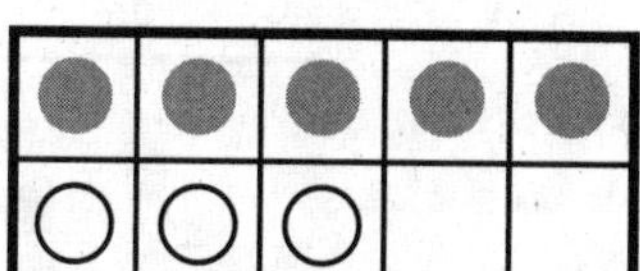

- ○ 5 plus 1
- ○ 5 plus 3
- ○ 5 + 3

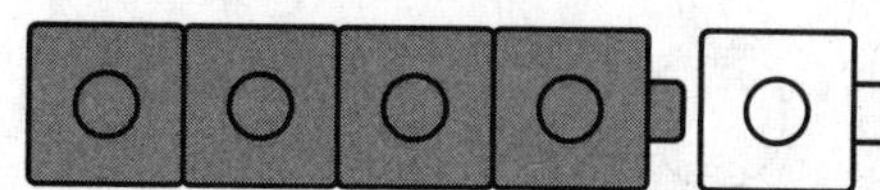

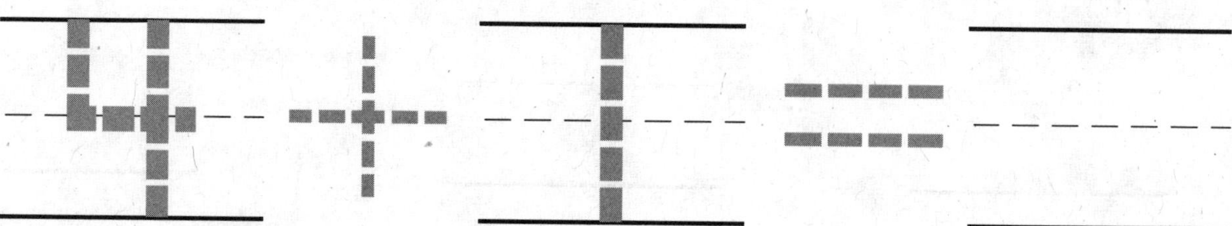

DIRECTIONS 1. How many children are facing right? How many children are being added to the group? Write the numbers. **2.** Keri put 5 gray counters in the ten frame. Then she put 3 white counters in the ten frame. Choose all the ways that show the counters being put together. **3.** How many of each color cube is being added? Trace the numbers and symbols. Write the number that shows how many cubes in all.

GO ON

Name ________________________________

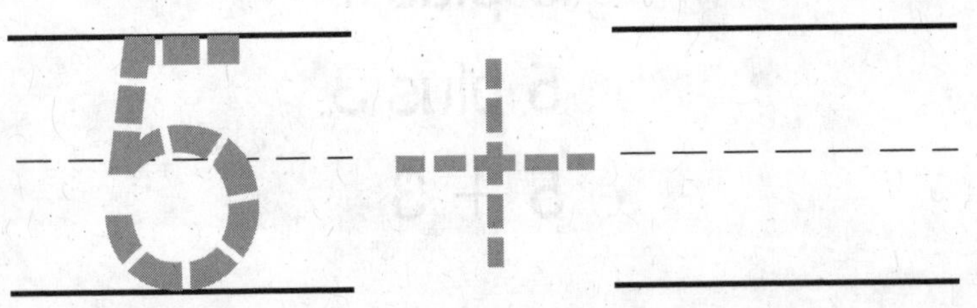

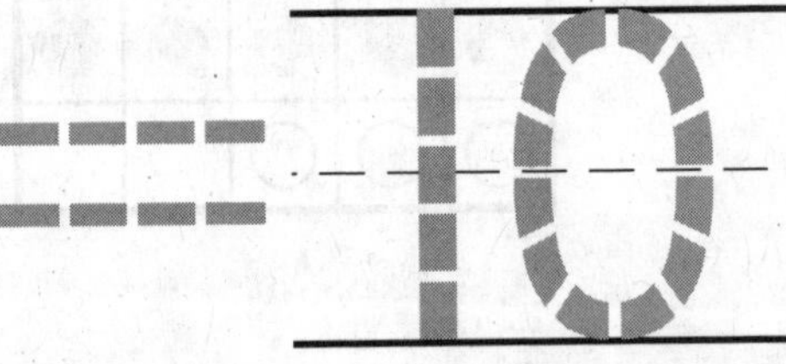

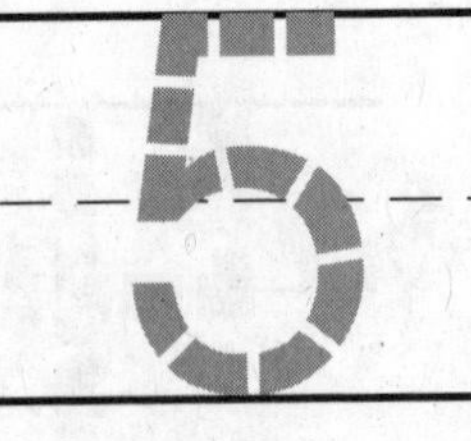

DIRECTIONS 4. Jeff has 2 red cubes. He has 3 yellow cubes. How many cubes does he have? Draw the cubes. Trace the numbers and symbols. Write how many in all. 5. Look at the cube train. How many gray cubes do you see? How many more cubes are added to make 10? Draw the cubes. Write and trace to show this in an addition sentence. 6. Write and trace to complete the addition sentence.

Name ______________________________

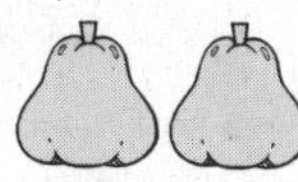

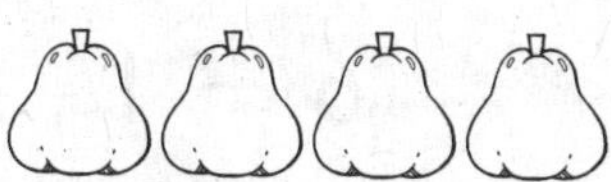

 + ______ = 6

 ______ 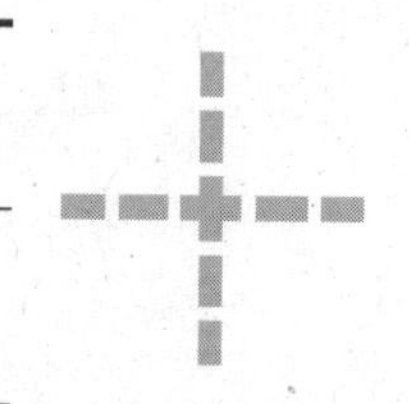 ______

1 + 7	○ Yes	○ No
4 + 4	○ Yes	○ No
5 + 1	○ Yes	○ No

DIRECTIONS **7.** Write the numbers and trace the symbols to complete the addition sentence. **8.** Ryan has 2 big marbles. Dani has some small marbles. Together they have 5 marbles. Draw to show how many small marbles Dani has. Complete the number pair. **9.** Does the number pair make a number greater than 6? Choose Yes or No.

GO ON

8 + 0   6 + 1   5 + 3

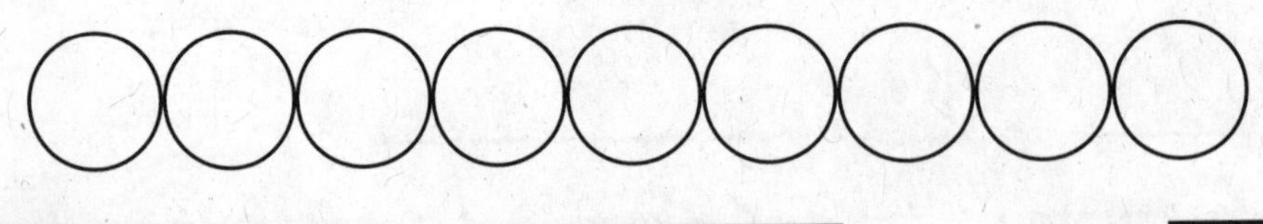

9 = ______ + ______

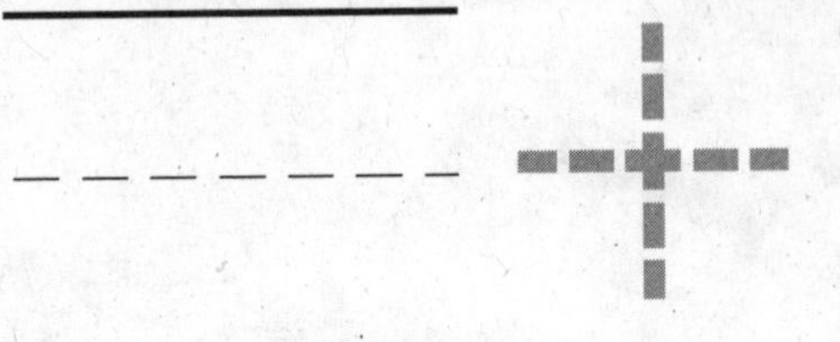

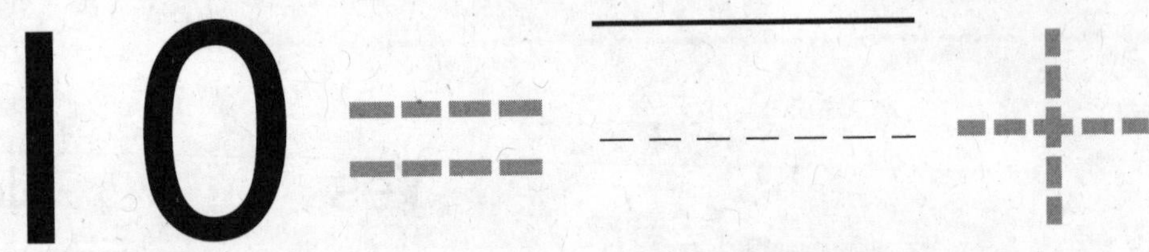

10 = ______ + ______

DIRECTIONS **10.** Circle all the number pairs for 8. **11.** Paul has 9 tokens. Each token is either red or blue. How many red and blue tokens could he have? Color the tokens to show the number of red and blue tokens. Write the numbers to complete the addition sentence. **12.** Complete the addition sentence to show a number pair for 10.

Name ______________________

______ ______

______ take away ______

______

______

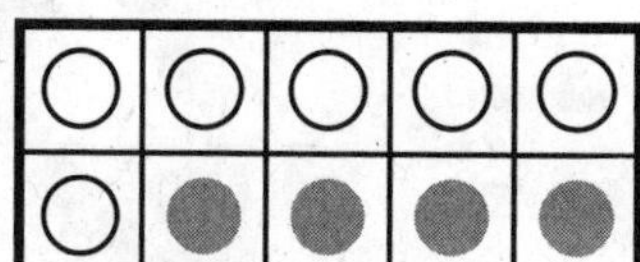

10 − 4	○ Yes	○ No
6 − 4	○ Yes	○ No
10 − 1	○ Yes	○ No

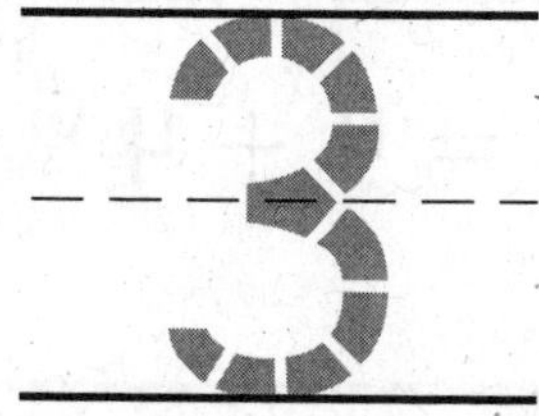

______

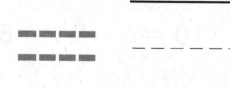

DIRECTIONS **1.** Write how many people there are. Write how many people are leaving. Write how many people are left. **2.** Which answers show how many counters are white? Choose Yes or No. **3.** Model a five-cube train. Three cubes are gray and the rest are white. Take apart the cube train to show how many are white. Draw the cube trains. Trace and write to complete the subtraction sentence.

4
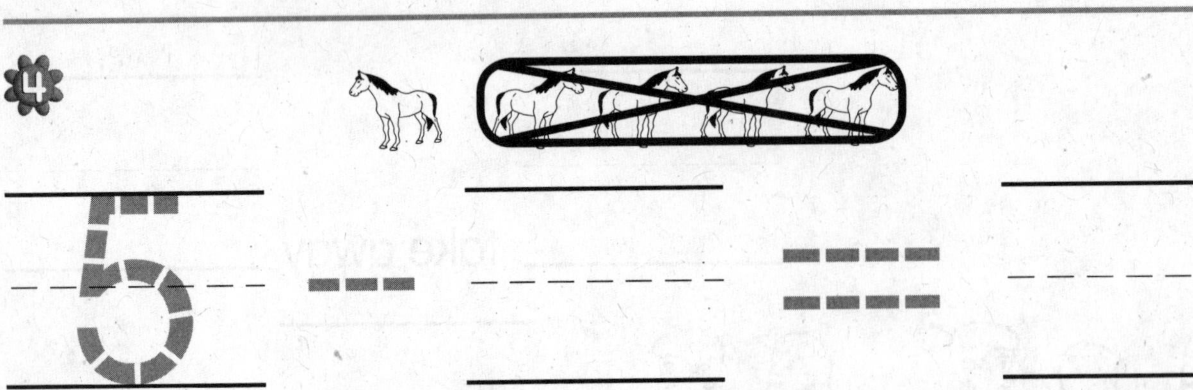

5
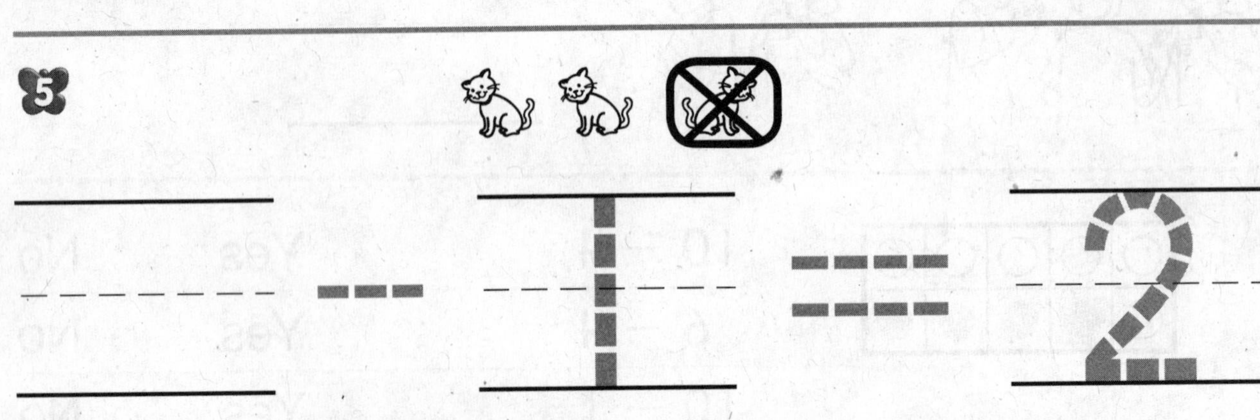

6
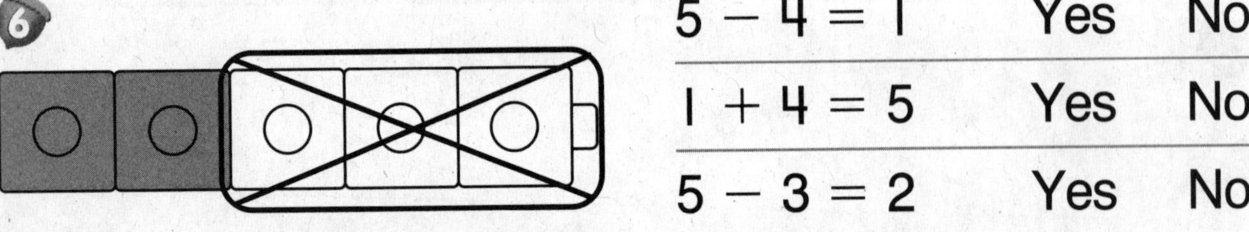

5 − 4 = 1	Yes	No
1 + 4 = 5	Yes	No
5 − 3 = 2	Yes	No

7
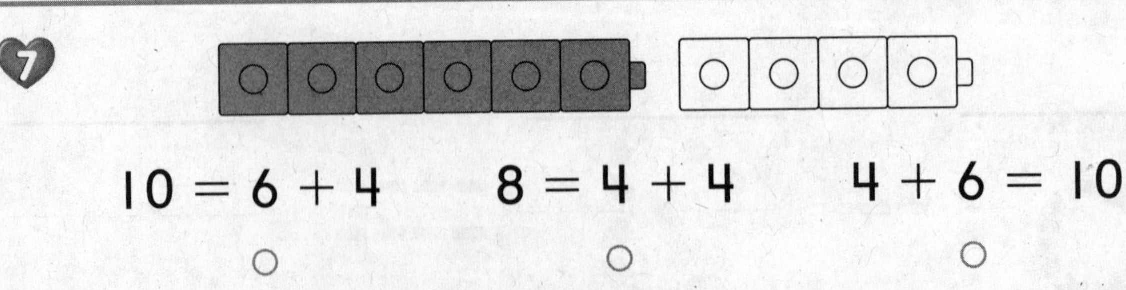

10 = 6 + 4 ○   8 = 4 + 4 ○   4 + 6 = 10 ○

DIRECTIONS 4. There are 5 horses. Some horses are taken from the set. Trace and write to complete the subtraction sentence. 5. There are some cats. One is taken from the set. How many cats were there to start? Write and trace to complete the subtraction sentence. 6. Does the number sentence match the picture? Circle Yes or No. 7. Mark under all the number sentences that match the cubes.

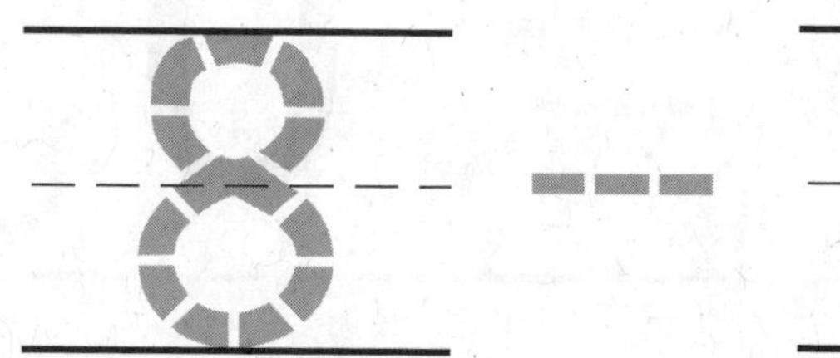

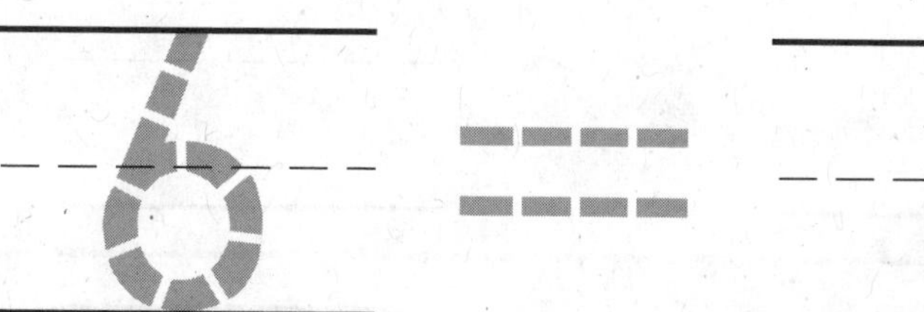

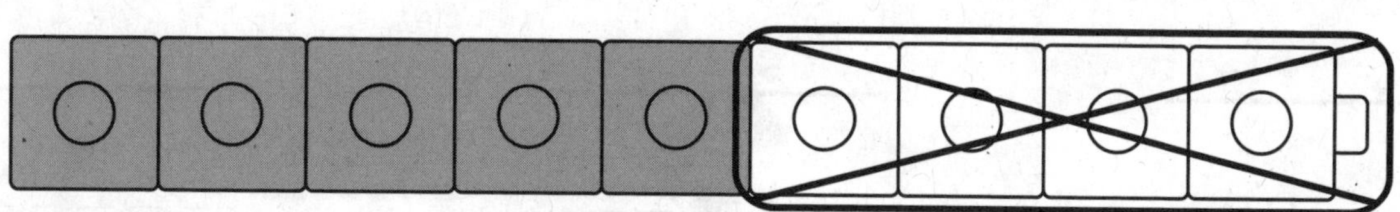

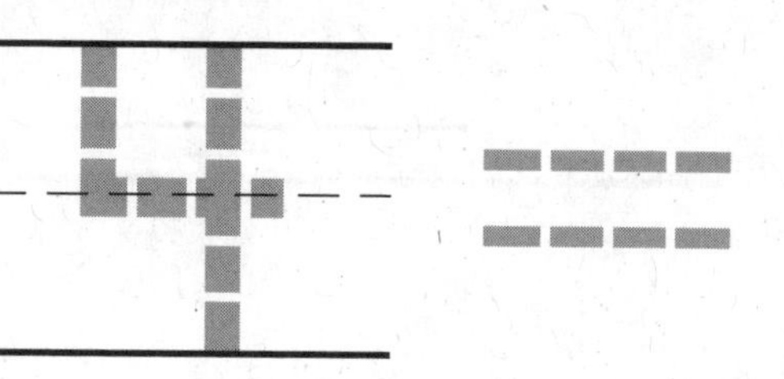

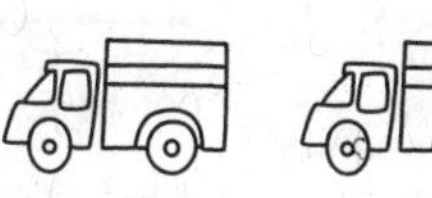

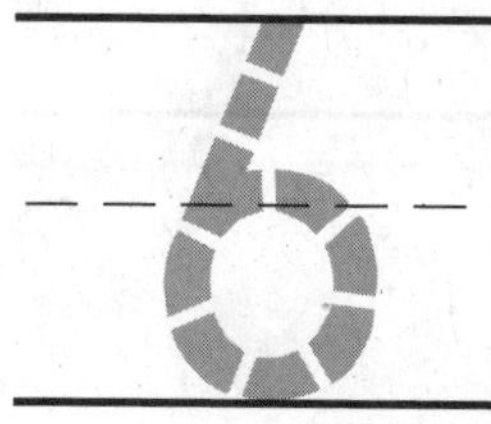

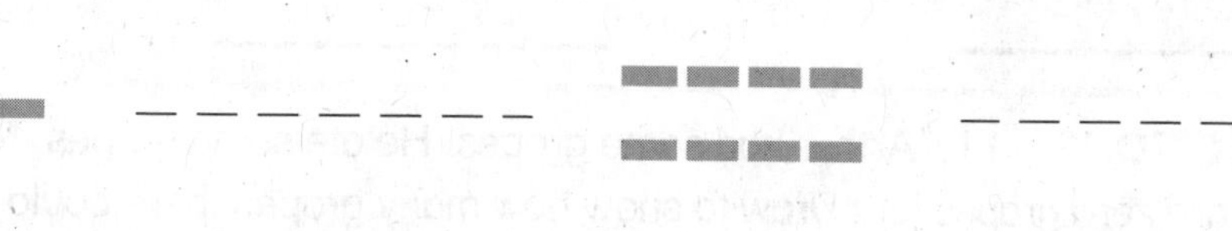

DIRECTIONS **8.** Model an eight-cube train. Six cubes are gray and the rest are white. Take apart the cube train to show how many are white. Draw the cube trains. Complete the subtraction sentence. **9–10.** Complete the subtraction sentence to match the picture.

GO ON

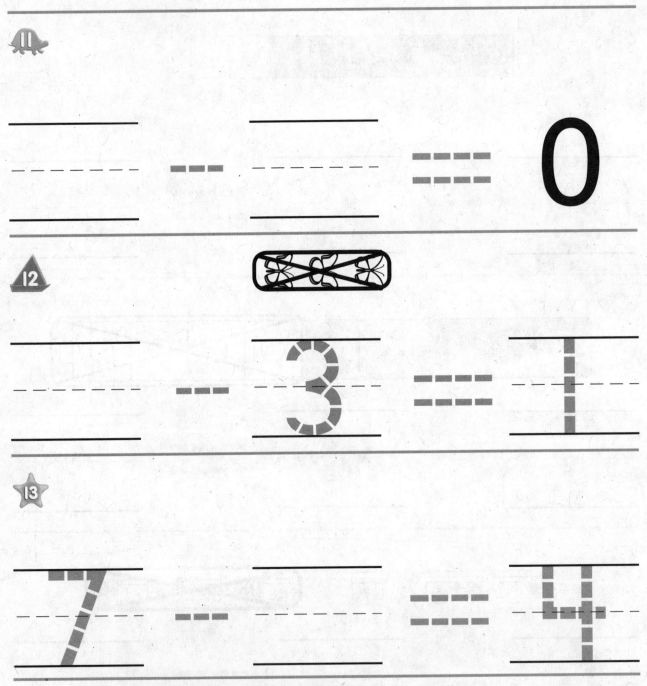

Name ______________________________

11

______ – ______ = 0

12

______ – 3 = 1

13

7 – ______ = 4

DIRECTIONS **11.** Arthur had some grapes. He ate some grapes. Now there are zero grapes left. Draw to show how many grapes there could have been to start. Cross out grapes to show how many were eaten. Complete the subtraction sentence. **12.** There are some butterflies. Three of the butterflies are taken from the set. Draw more butterflies to show how many butterflies there were to start. Write the number to complete the subtraction sentence. **13.** Mabel started a game with 7 baseballs. Some of the baseballs were lost. Now Mabel has 4 baseballs. How many baseballs were lost? Draw to solve the problem. Complete the subtraction sentence.

Name ______________________

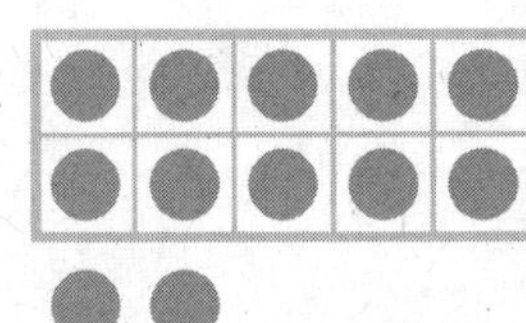

3

10 + 1

15	○ Yes	○ No
14	○ Yes	○ No
10 + 4	○ Yes	○ No

DIRECTIONS **1–2.** How many objects are there? Write the number. **3.** Choose all the ways that show 11. **4.** Is this a way to write the number of bears in the set? Choose Yes or No.

Name ______________________________

5

10 + 7 = ____

6

____ + ____ = ____

7

16   17

8

____ hats

DIRECTIONS 5–6. Count how many. Write the number. Complete the addition sentence. **7.** Draw lines to match the ten frames to the numbers they show. **8.** There are 6 green hats and 7 blue hats. Draw the hats. Circle a group of 10. How many hats are there in all?

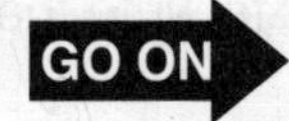

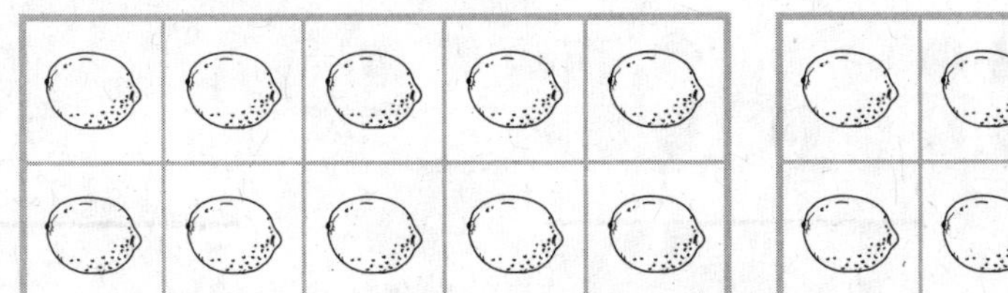

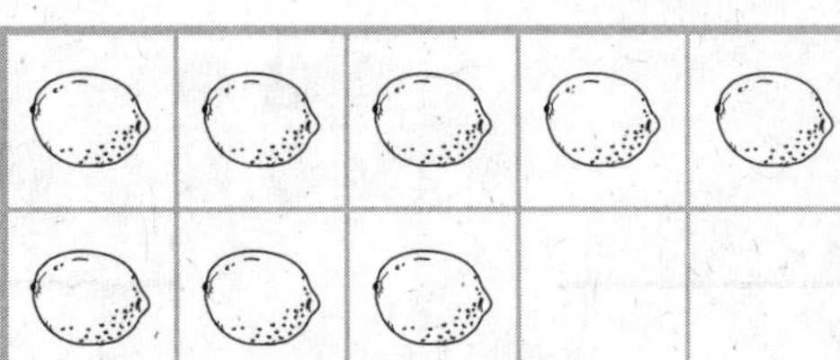

10 ones and [8 / 9] ones

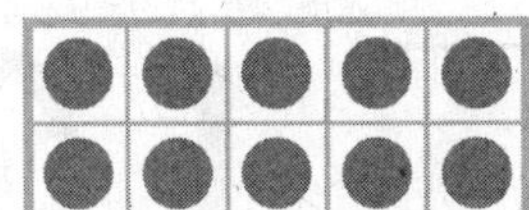

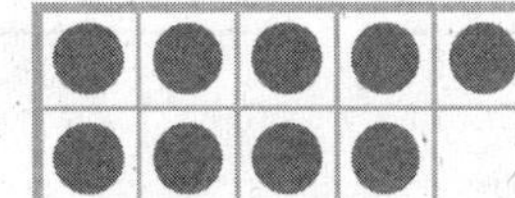

____ + ____ = ____

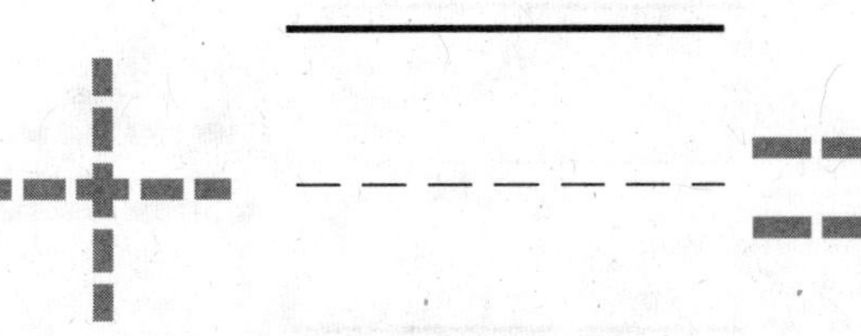

10 + ____ = ____

DIRECTIONS **9.** How many more ones are needed to show the number of lemons? Circle the number. **10.** Look at the ten frames. Complete the addition sentence. **11.** Vicki was told to pick up 10 sticks. She picked up one extra stick. How many sticks are there in all? Draw the sticks. Complete the addition sentence.

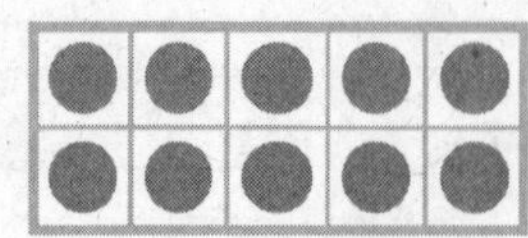 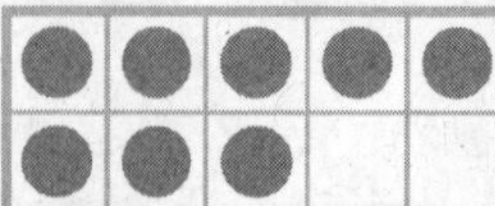

______   ______

10 ______ ______ 13 14

10 + ______  ______

DIRECTIONS **12.** What number do the ten frames show? Complete the addition sentence to show the number. **13.** Count in order. Fill in the missing numbers. **14.** Franklin has 8 blue buttons and 5 green buttons. Draw the buttons. Circle a group of 10 buttons. Count the remaining buttons starting from 10. Complete the addition sentence.

Name ______________________________

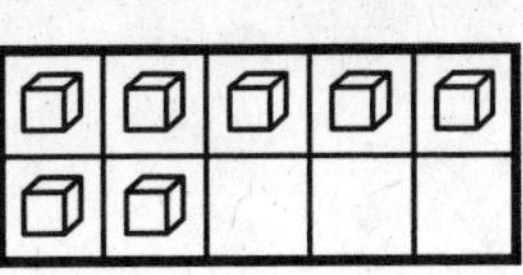

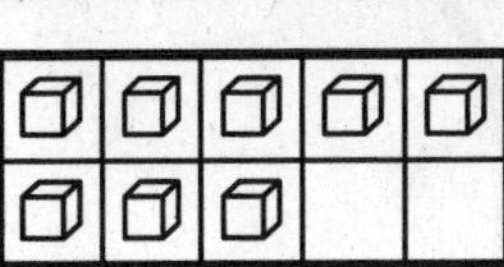

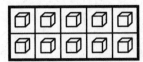

18 17 20

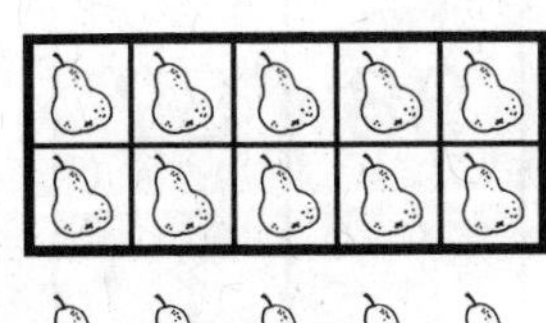

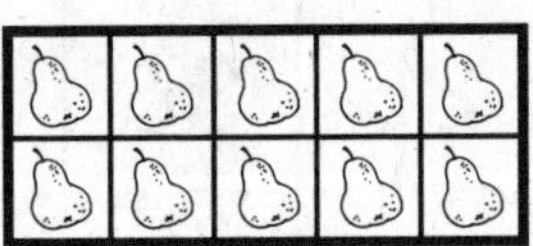

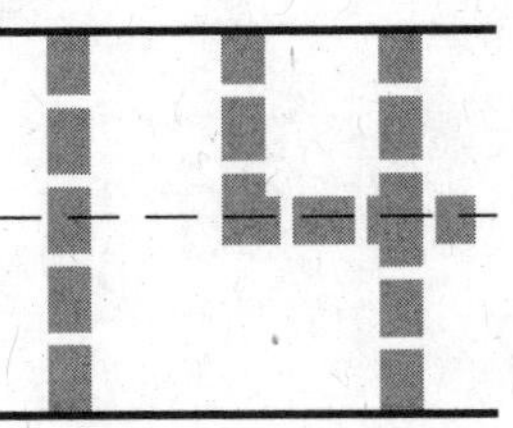

16

18

DIRECTIONS 1. Match the ten frames to the numbers that tell how many cubes. 2. Harry has 20 pears. Circle how many pears he has. Write the number of pears. 3. Start with 14. Count forward. Write the numbers in order.

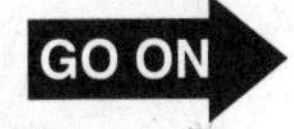

4

17

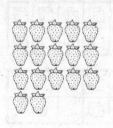

○ ○ ○ ○

5

21	22	23	24	25	26	27	28	29	30
31	32	33	34	35	36	37	38	39	40

83 84 85 86 87 [88 / 90] 89

DIRECTIONS 4. Mark under all the sets with a number of strawberries greater than 17. **5.** Begin with 21. Point to each number as you count. Draw a line under the number to complete the counting order. **6.** Point to each number as you count. Circle the number to complete the counting order.

GO ON

11	12	13	14	15	16	17	18	19	20
21	22	23	24	25	26	27	28	29	30

○ 40 ○ 50 ○ 60 ○ 70

DIRECTIONS 7. Circle the numbers that complete each row of 10.
8. Count the straws by tens. Mark the number that shows how many.
9. Barney has these rubber bands. How many rubber bands does he have? Write the number. Sarah has a number of rubber bands 2 less than Barney. Draw the number of rubber bands Sarah has. Write the number. Circle the number that is greater.

Name ____________________

10

17	18	19	Yes	No
10	11	12	Yes	No
20	14	16	Yes	No

11

30 ____ 50

____ 60 70

12

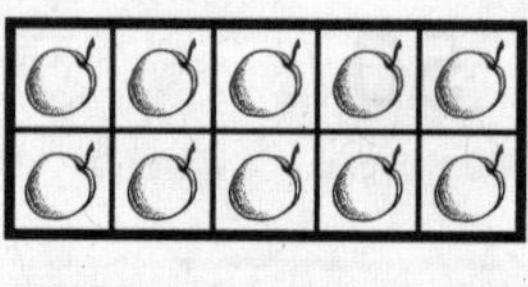

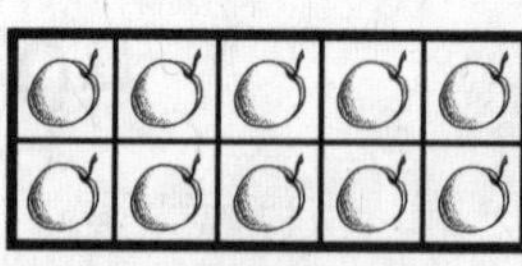

DIRECTIONS 10. Are the numbers in counting order? Circle Yes or No. 11. Count by tens. Write the missing number. 12. What number does each set show? Write the numbers. Then write the numbers in counting order.

○ Yes ○ No

○ Yes ○ No

○ Yes ○ No

______ squares

DIRECTIONS **1.** Is the shape a circle? Choose Yes or No. **2.** Mark under all of the shapes that have curves. **3.** How many squares are in the picture? Write the number.

GO ON

____

- - - - - - - - - -

______________ vertices

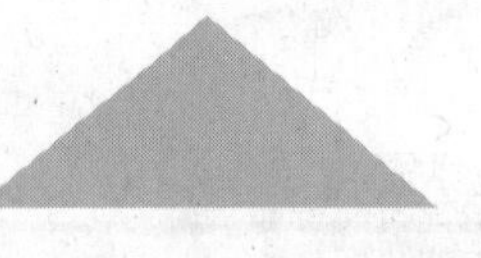

○ ○ ○ ○

DIRECTIONS **4.** Look at the square. Write the number of corners, or vertices, the square has. **5.** Mark under all of the shapes that are triangles. **6.** Mark an X on each shape that has 3 sides and 3 vertices.

GO ON

Name ______________________

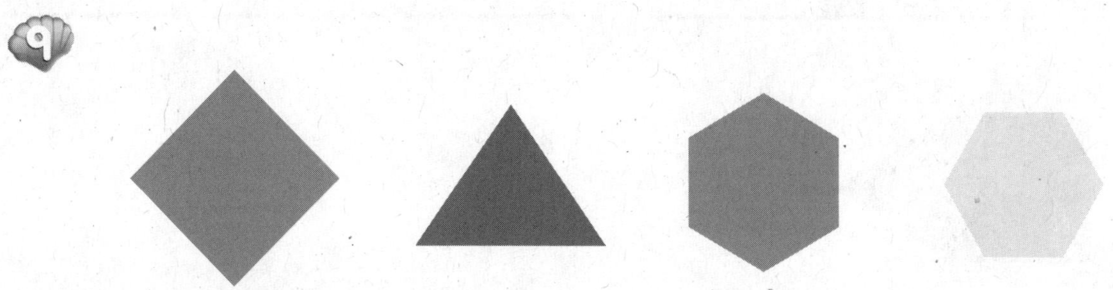

DIRECTIONS **7.** Mark an X on the shape that is not a rectangle. **8.** Draw a shape that is the same as the boxcars on the train. **9.** Mark an X on all of the hexagons.

Name ______________________________

10

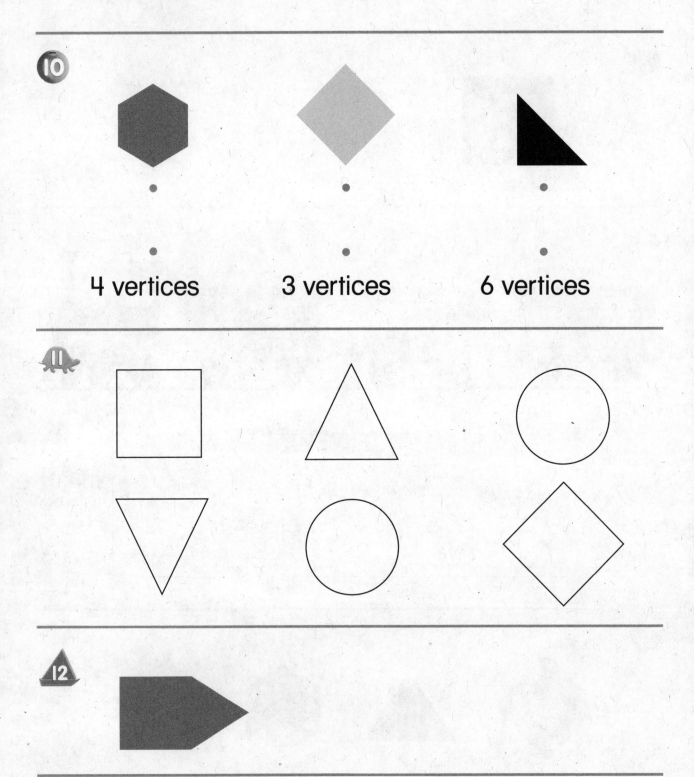

4 vertices   3 vertices   6 vertices

11

12

DIRECTIONS **10.** Match the shape to the number with that many corners, or vertices. **11.** Look at the shapes. Compare them to see how they are alike and how they are different. Color the shape with curves green. Color the shape with four vertices red. Color the shape with three sides blue. **12.** Draw the two shapes used to make the shape shown.

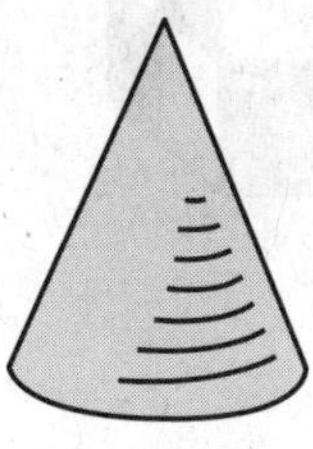 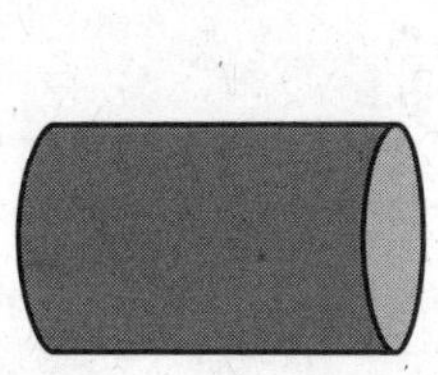 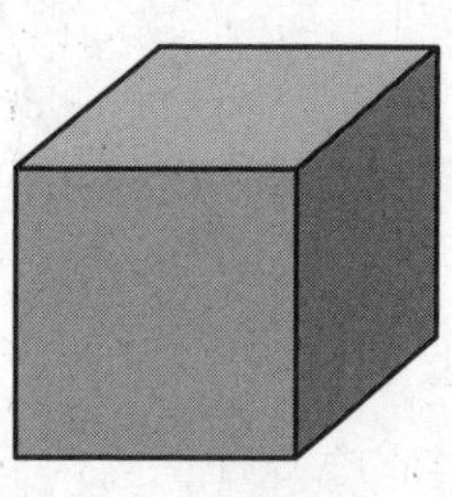 

○ ○ ○ ○

 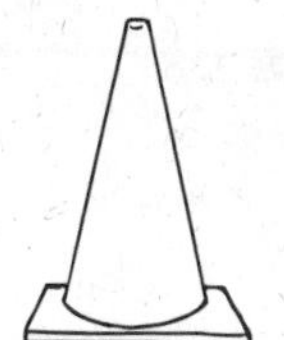 

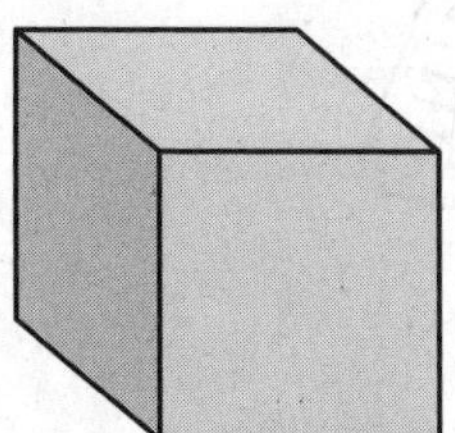

slides	Yes	No
stacks	Yes	No

DIRECTIONS **1.** Mark under all the shapes that roll. **2.** Which objects are shaped like a sphere? Mark an X on each of those objects. **3.** Do the words describe a cube? Circle Yes or No.

4

5

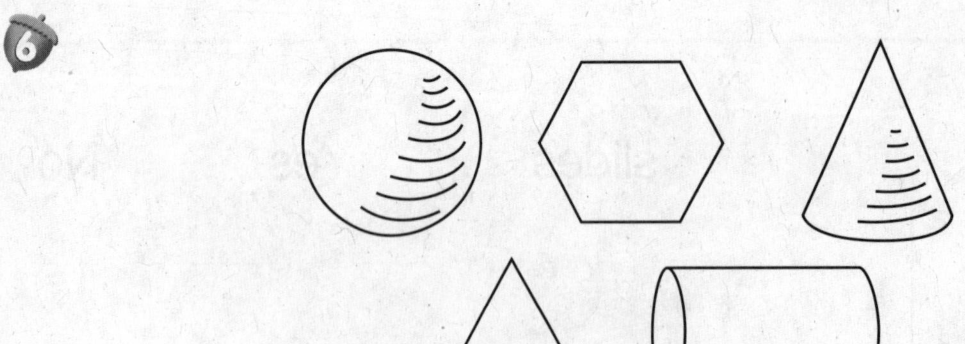

6

DIRECTIONS **4.** Draw lines to match the objects to their shapes. **5.** Which objects are shaped like cones? Mark an X on each of those objects. **6.** Color the solid shapes blue. Color the flat shapes red. Draw another flat shape that is different.

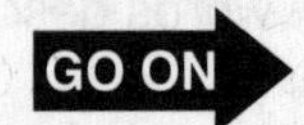

Name ______________________________

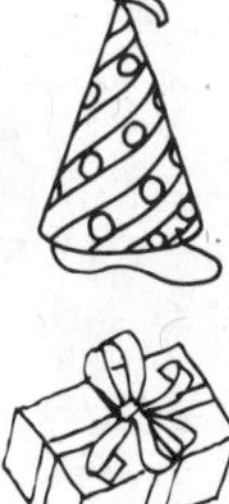

DIRECTIONS **7.** Draw an object that has the shape of a cone. **8.** Circle the shapes that show the cone above the cube. **9.** Mark an X on the shape that is next to the cylinder.

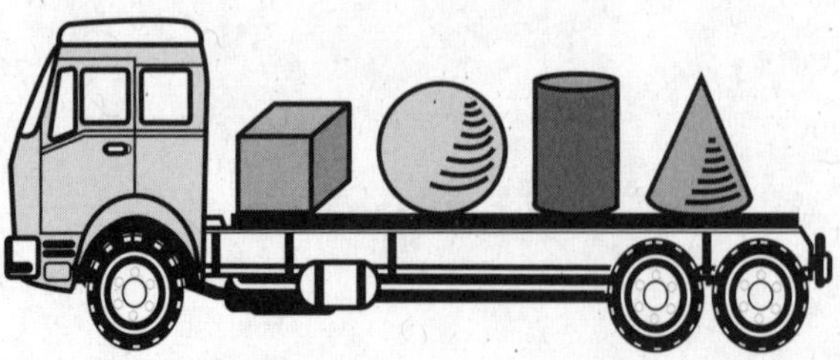

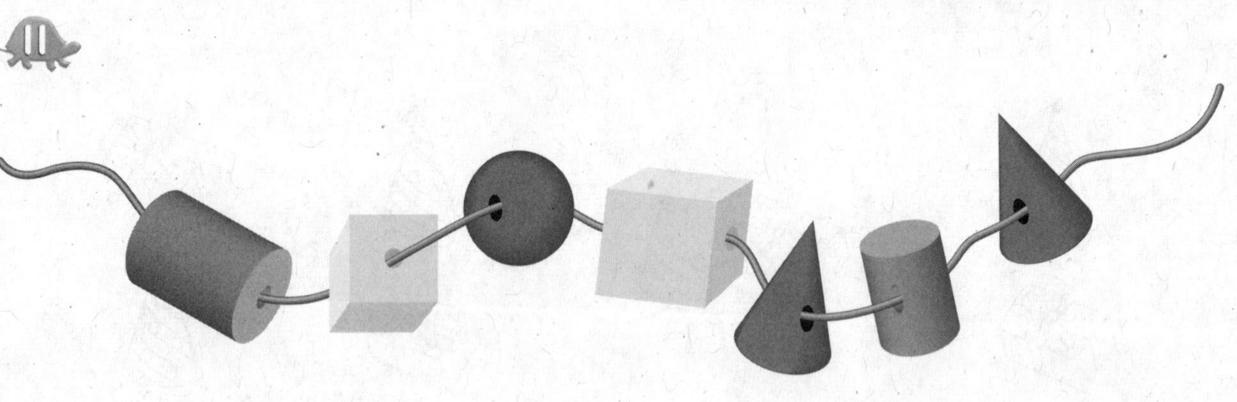

DIRECTIONS **10.** Mark an X on the shape that is behind the sphere. **11.** Mark an X on the bead shaped like a cylinder that is next to the bead shaped like a cone. **12.** Mark an X on the object that is above the basketball net.

Name ____________________

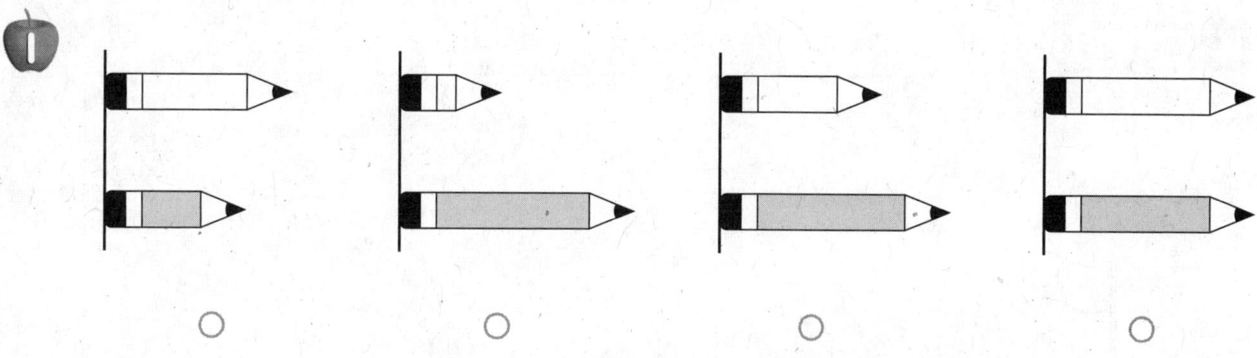

○ ○ ○ ○

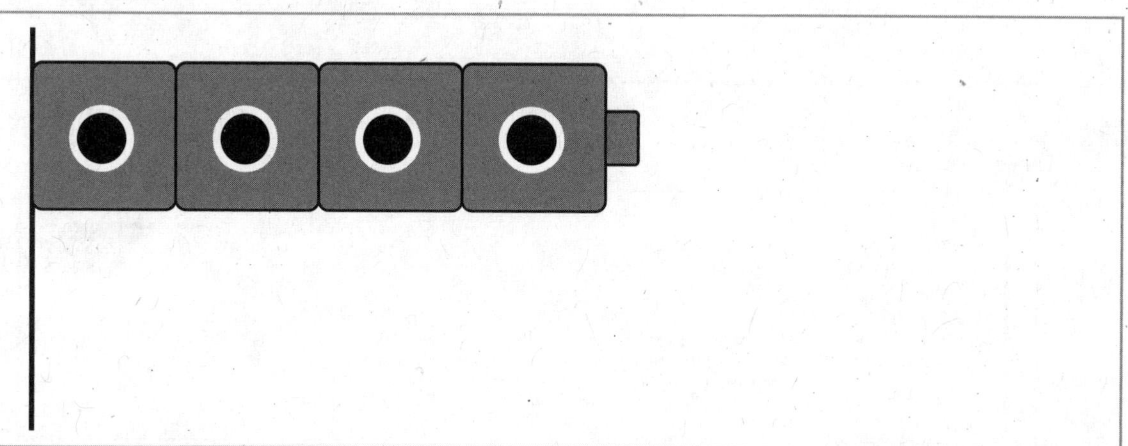

DIRECTIONS **1.** Choose all the sets that have a white pencil that is shorter than the gray pencil. **2.** Draw a cube train that is longer. **3.** Circle the flower that is shorter.

5

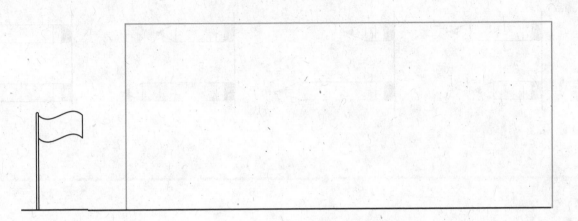

DIRECTIONS **4.** This flag is shorter than another flag. Draw to show the other flag. **5.** Draw two pieces of string of different lengths. Draw a circle around the string that is shorter. **6.** Which tree is shorter than the first tree? Color it red. Which tree is taller than the first tree? Color it blue.

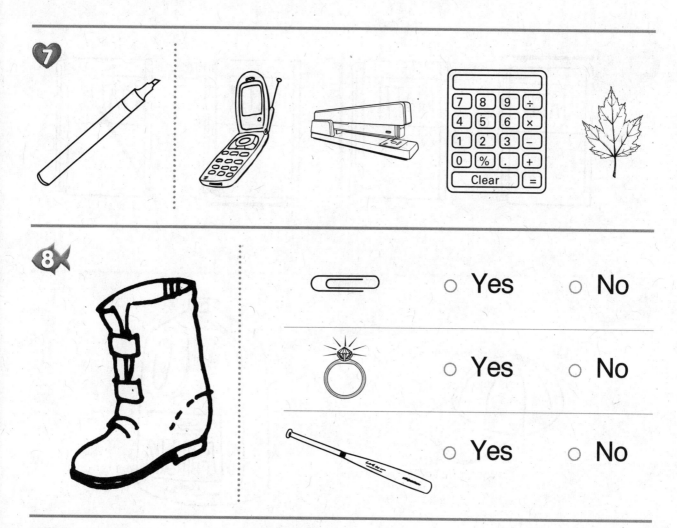

7

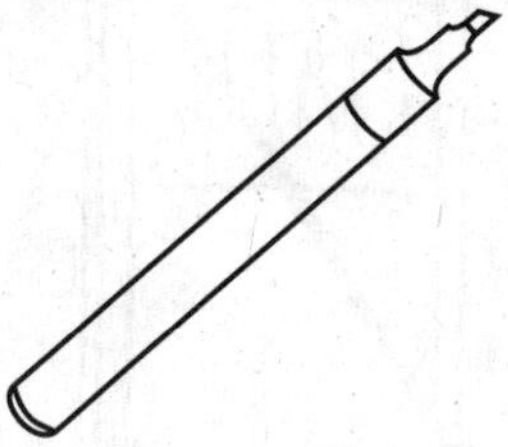

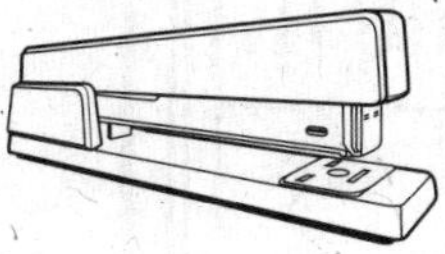

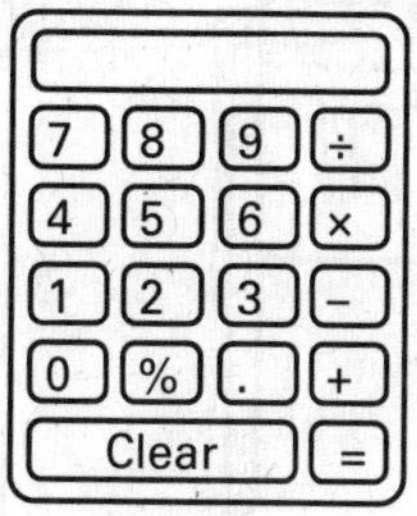

Clear

8

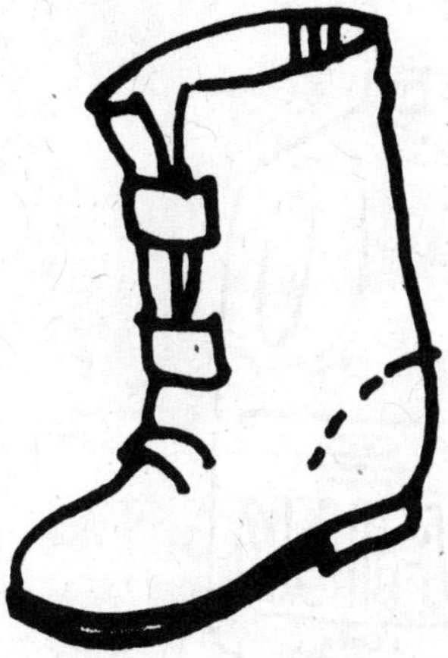

Yes No

Yes No

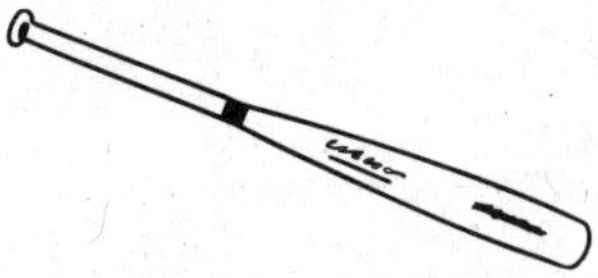

Yes No

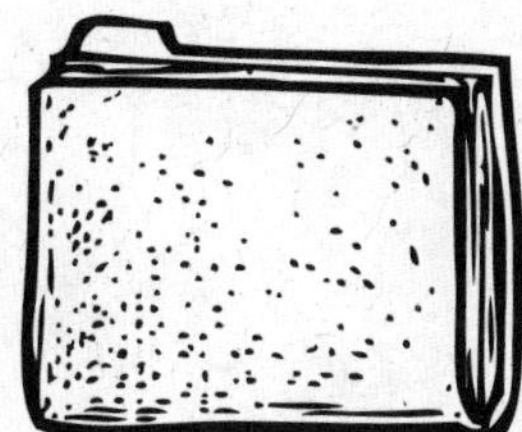

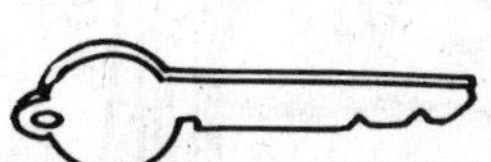

DIRECTIONS **7.** Circle all the objects that are heavier than a marker. **8.** Is the object lighter than the boot? Choose Yes or No. **9.** Draw a line to show the height of the folder. Draw a line to show the length of the key.

GO ON

Name ______________________________

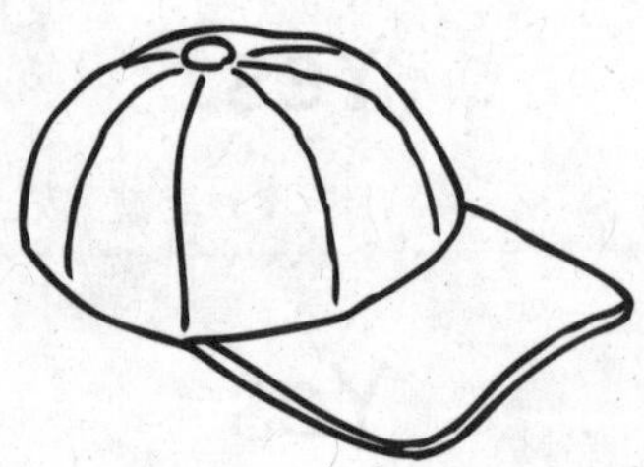

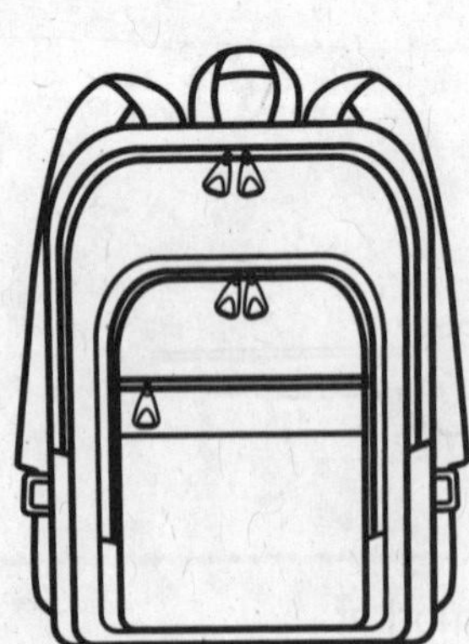

DIRECTIONS **10.** Choose all of the pictures that have lines that show how to measure length. **11.** Look at the objects. Circle the heavier object. Mark an X on the lighter object. **12.** Draw an object that is lighter than a backpack.

1

2

3

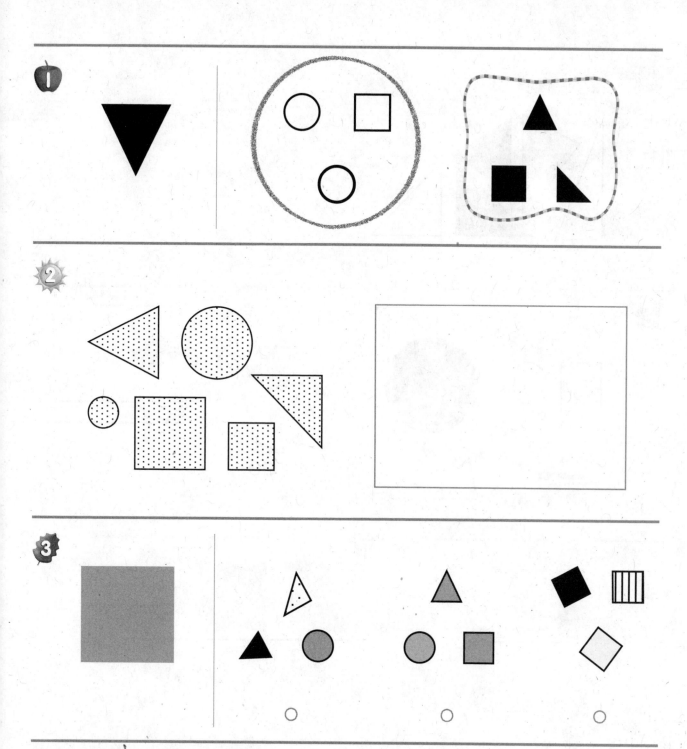

DIRECTIONS 1. Hani sorted some shapes into categories by color. Look at the shape at the beginning of the row. Mark an X on the category that shows where the shape belongs. 2. Draw and color a shape that belongs in this category. 3. Look at the shape at the beginning of the row. Mark under all of the categories where the shape can belong.

Name ________________

5

small ________

large ________

6

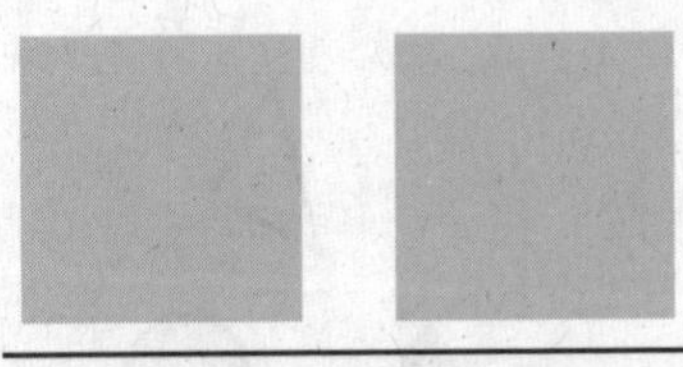

big

small

DIRECTIONS 4. Draw another object that belongs in this category. 5. Draw a circle around each small shape. Write how many small shapes. Mark an X on each big shape. Write how many large shapes. 6. Draw lines to match the shapes to the way they were sorted.

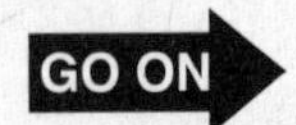

7

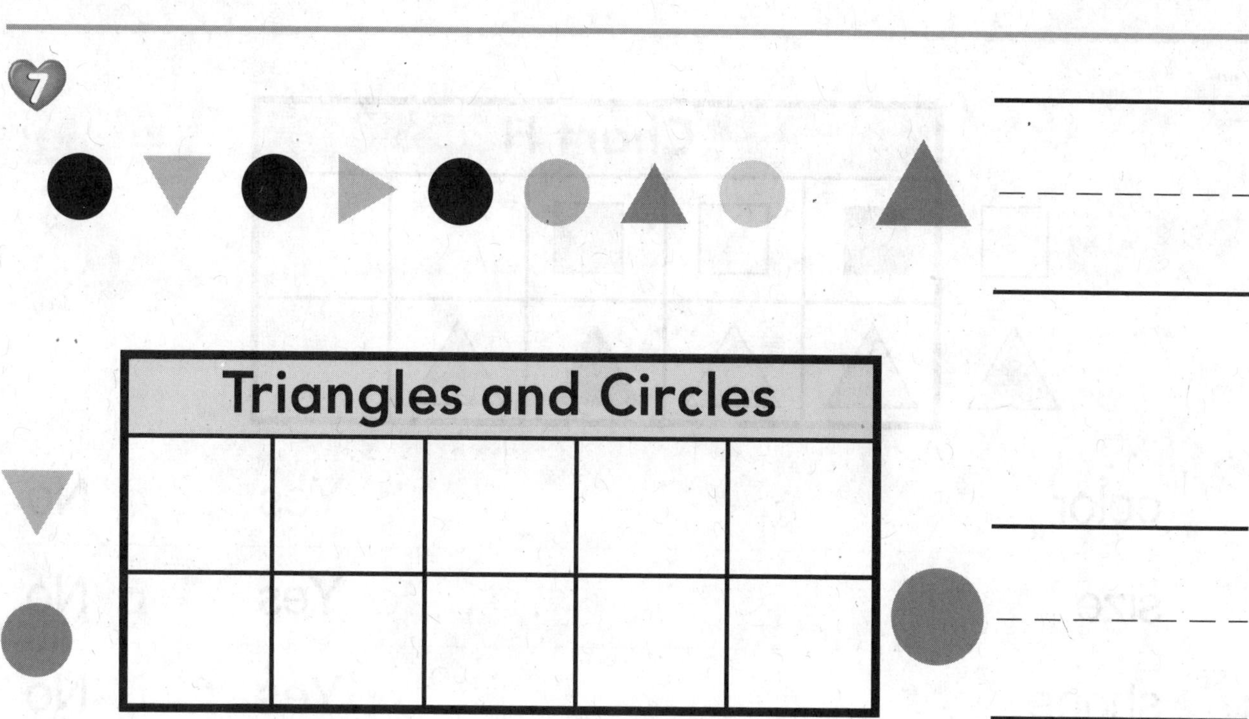

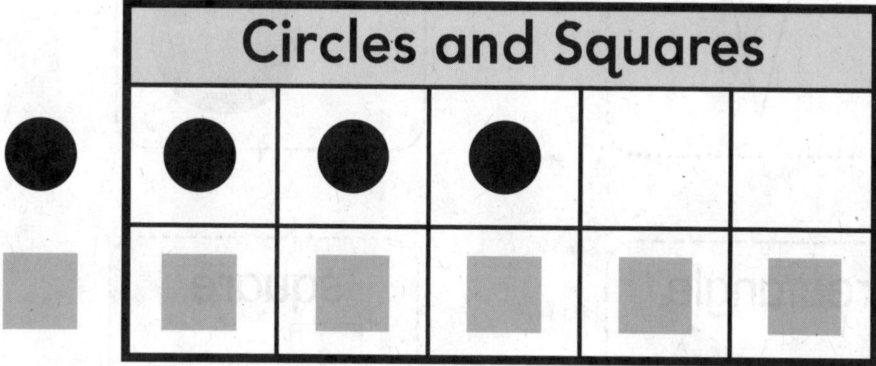

DIRECTIONS **7.** Sort and classify the shapes by category. Draw each shape on the graph. Write how many of each shape. **8.** Rita sorted some shapes. Then she made a graph. Count how many shapes there are in each category. Mark an X on the category that has more shapes.

GO ON

Name ____________________

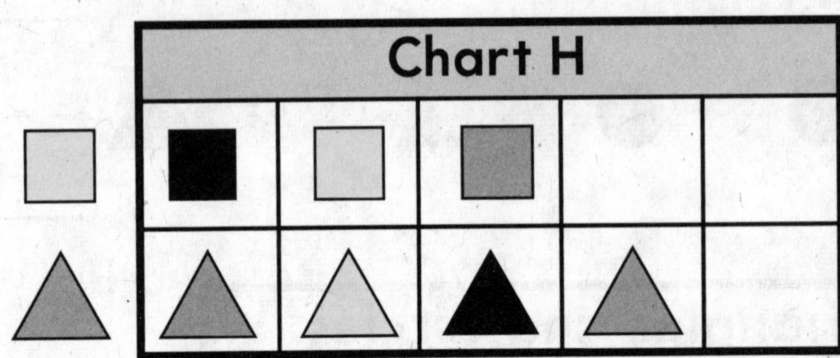

color	○ Yes	○ No
size	○ Yes	○ No
shape	○ Yes	○ No

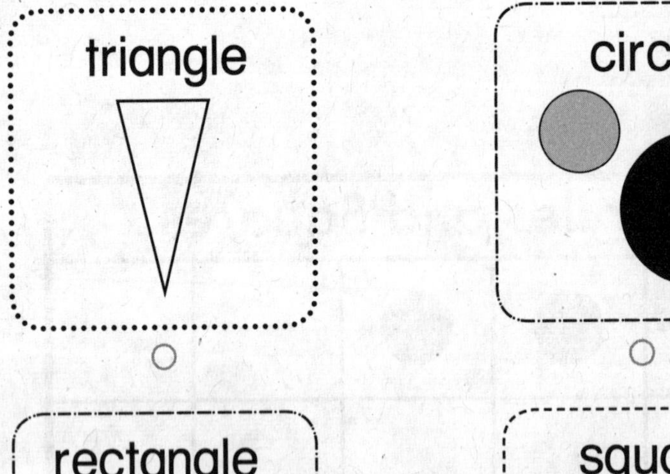

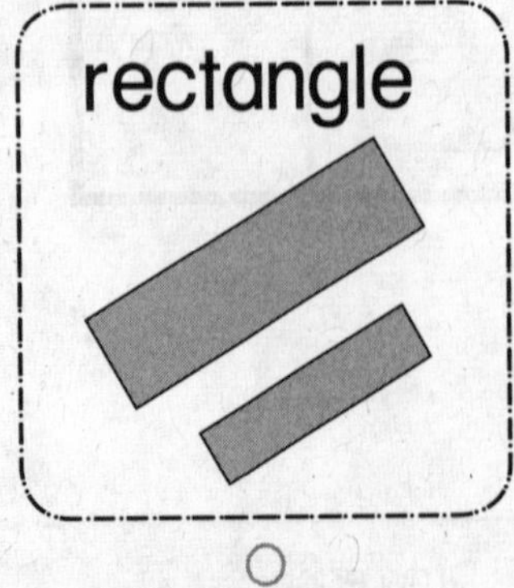

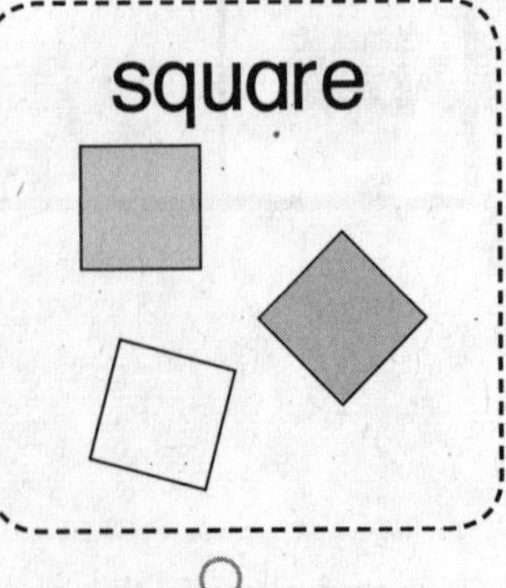

DIRECTIONS 9. Is this chart sorted by color, size, and shape? Choose Yes or No. **10.** Choose all of the sets with the same number of objects.

Name ___________________________________

Count on It

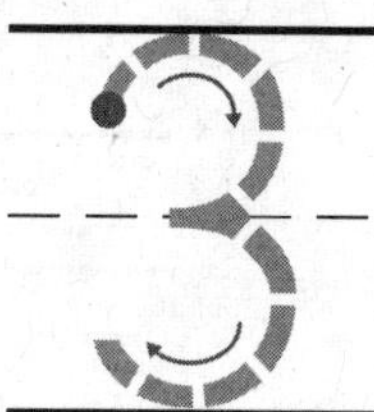

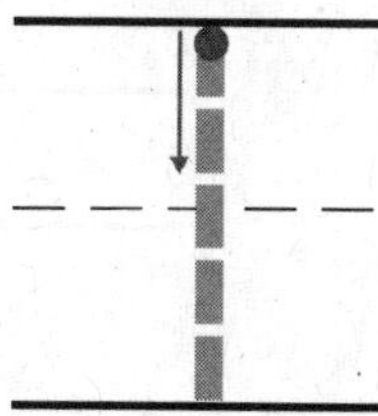

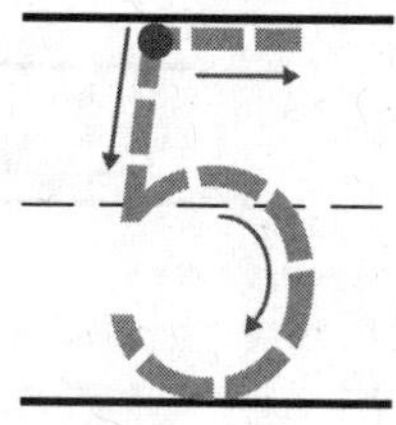

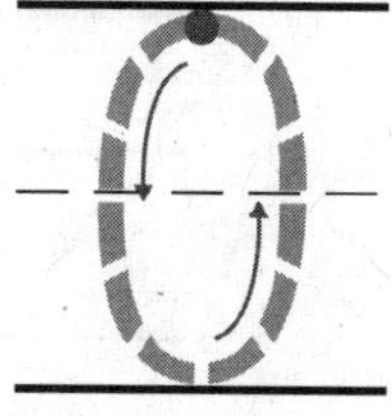

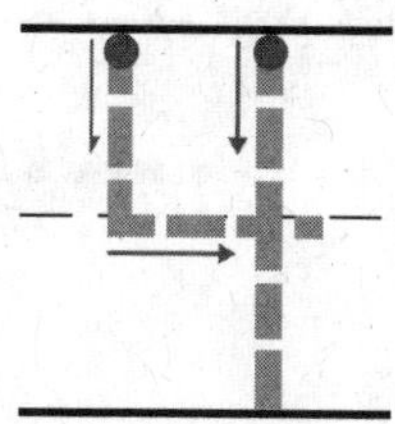

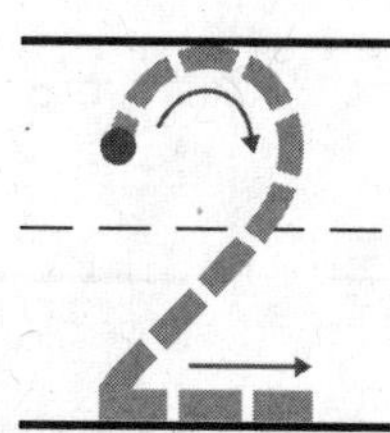

DIRECTIONS 1. Trace each number. Draw balloons to show that number. Circle the number that is 1 larger than 4.

2

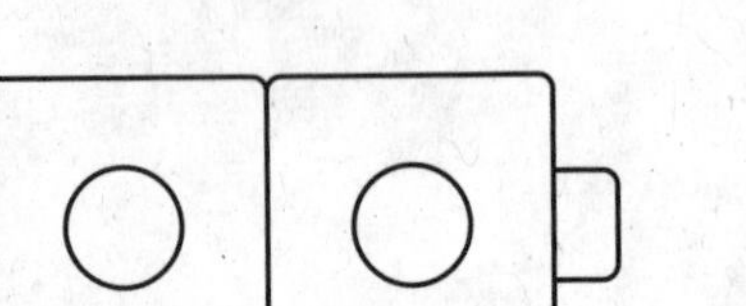

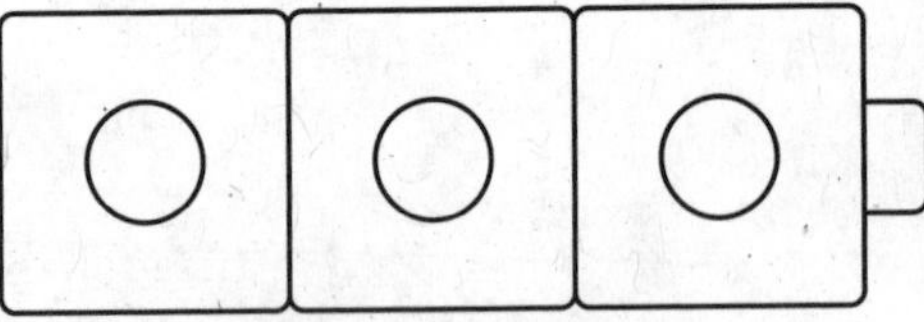

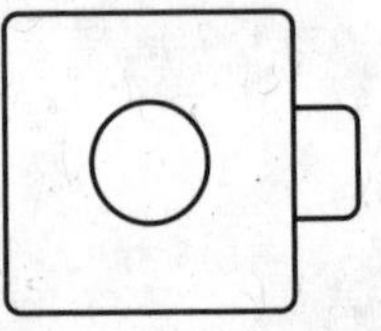

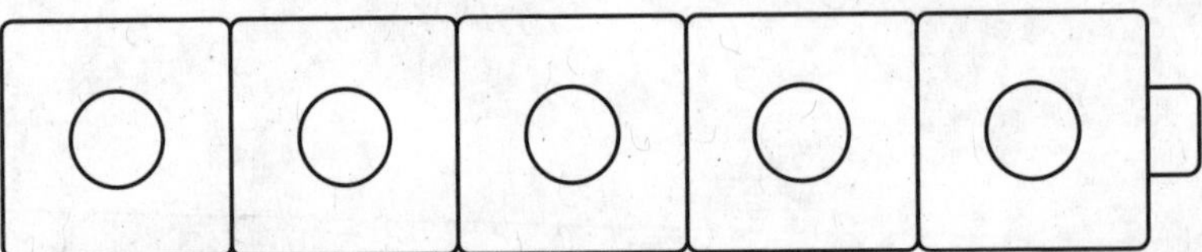

3

DIRECTIONS 2. Count the cubes in each set. Write that number of cubes.
3. Write the numbers in order at the bottom of the page.

Addition Concepts

Count on It

COMMON CORE STANDARDS

K.CC.3 Write numbers from 0 to 20. Represent a number of objects with a written numeral 0–20 (with 0 representing a count of no objects).

K.CC.4a When counting objects, say the number names in the standard order, pairing each object with one and only one number name and each number name with one and only one object.

K.CC.4b Understand that the last number name said tells the number of objects counted. The number of objects is the same regardless of their arrangement or the order in which they were counted.

K.CC.4c Understand that each successive number name refers to a quantity that is one larger.

PURPOSE

To assess the ability to model, count, and write numbers to 5 and to understand that each successive number refers to a quantity that is one larger.

TIME

25–30 minutes

GROUPING

Individuals

MATERIALS

- Performance Task, paper, pencil
- Connecting cubes (optional)

PREPARATION HINTS

- Review counting sets of objects to 5 with children before assigning the task.
- Review written numerals 0–5 with children before assigning the task.
- Review vocabulary, including *zero, one, two, three, four, five, larger*.

IMPLEMENTATION NOTES

- Read the task aloud to children and make sure that all children have a clear understanding of the task.
- Children may use manipulatives to complete the task.
- Allow children as much paper as they need to complete the task.
- Allow as much time as children need to complete the task.
- Children must complete the task individually, without collaboration.
- Collect all work when the task is complete.

TASK SUMMARY

Children use understanding of cardinality to model, count, and write numerals to represent quantities up to 5. They identify a number that is 1 larger than a given number and write numerals in standard order.

REPRESENTATION

In this task teachers can…

- Provide options for language, mathematical expressions and symbols by illustrating examples of terms used in directions.
- Provide options for comprehension by highlighting the relationship between numeric and pictorial representations.

ACTION and EXPRESSION

In this task teachers can…

- Provide options for physical action by allowing varied methods of response depending on motor skills.
- Provide options for physical action by offering connecting cubes to students while completing the task.

ENGAGEMENT

In this task teachers can…

- Sustain effort and persistence by providing specific feedback.

EXPECTED STUDENT OUTCOMES

- Complete the task within the time allowed
- Reflect engagement in a productive struggle
- Model, count, write, and order numbers to 5

SCORING

Use the associated Rubric to evaluate each child's work.

Performance Task Rubric

COUNT ON IT	
A level 3 response	• Indicates that the child has made sense of the task and persevered • Demonstrates an understanding of the relationship between numerals and the quantities they represent • Indicates an understanding that the last number name said tells the number of objects counted • Demonstrates an understanding that each successive number refers to a quantity that is one larger
A level 2 response	• Indicates that the child has made sense of the task and persevered • Demonstrates an understanding of the relationship between numerals and the quantities they represent • Indicates an understanding that the last number name said tells the number of objects counted • Demonstrates an understanding that each successive number refers to a quantity that is one larger • Addresses most or all aspects of the task, but there may be errors of omission
A level 1 response	• Shows that the child has made sense of at least some elements of the task • Shows evidence of understanding the relationship between numerals and quantities and that the last number name said tells the number of objects counted • May not indicate an understanding that each successive number refers to a quantity that is one larger • May contain errors in counting or in writing numerals
A level 0 response	• Shows little evidence that the child has made sense of the problems of the task • Reflects lack of understanding of the relationship between numerals and quantities • Shows little evidence of addressing the elements of the task

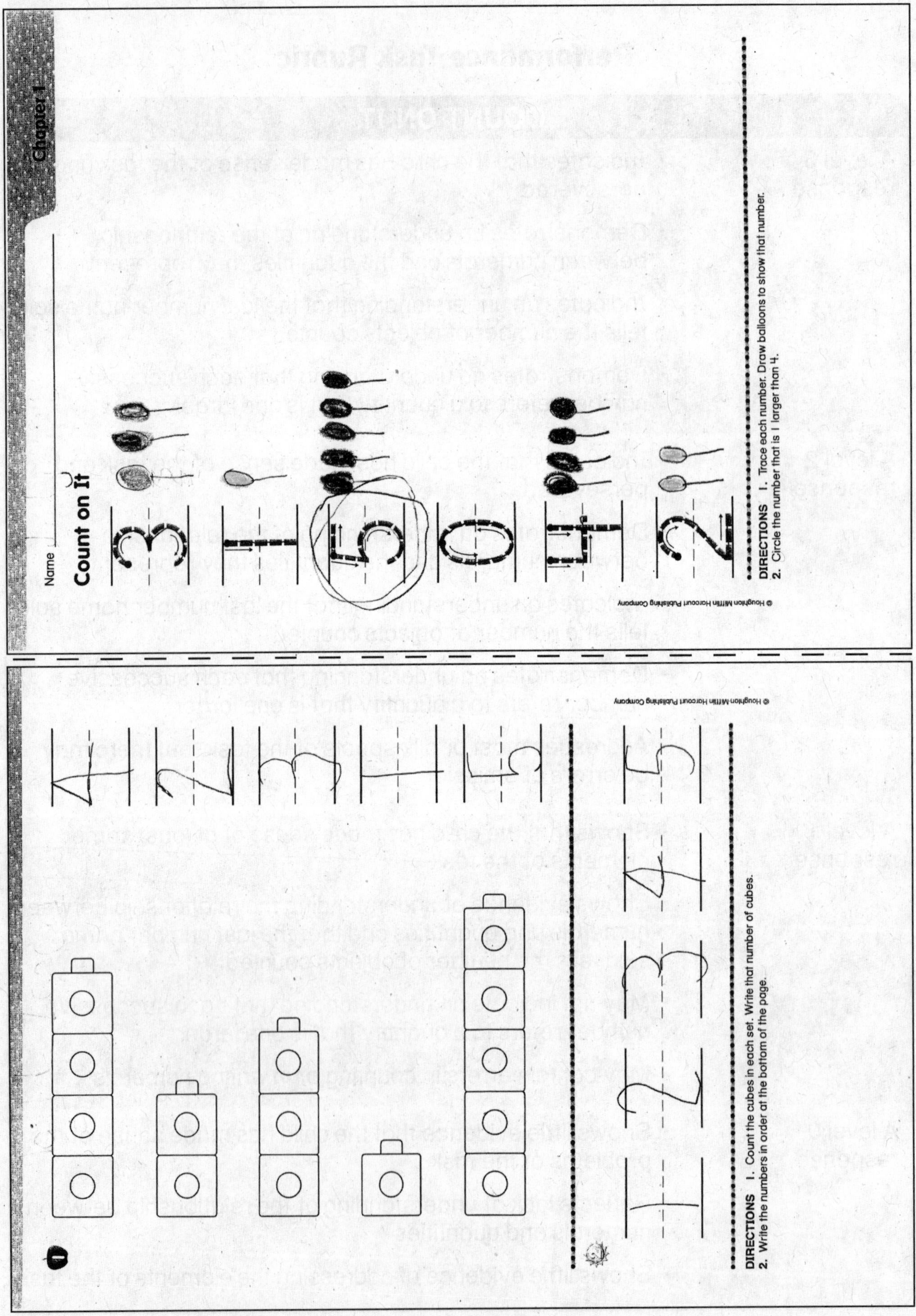

Chapter 1

Name

Count on It

3 1 5 0 4 2

DIRECTIONS 1. Trace each number. Draw balloons to show that number.
2. Circle the number that is 1 larger than 4.

DIRECTIONS 1. Count the cubes in each set. Write that number of cubes.
2. Write the numbers in order at the bottom of the page.

Name ______________________

Chapter 1

Count on It

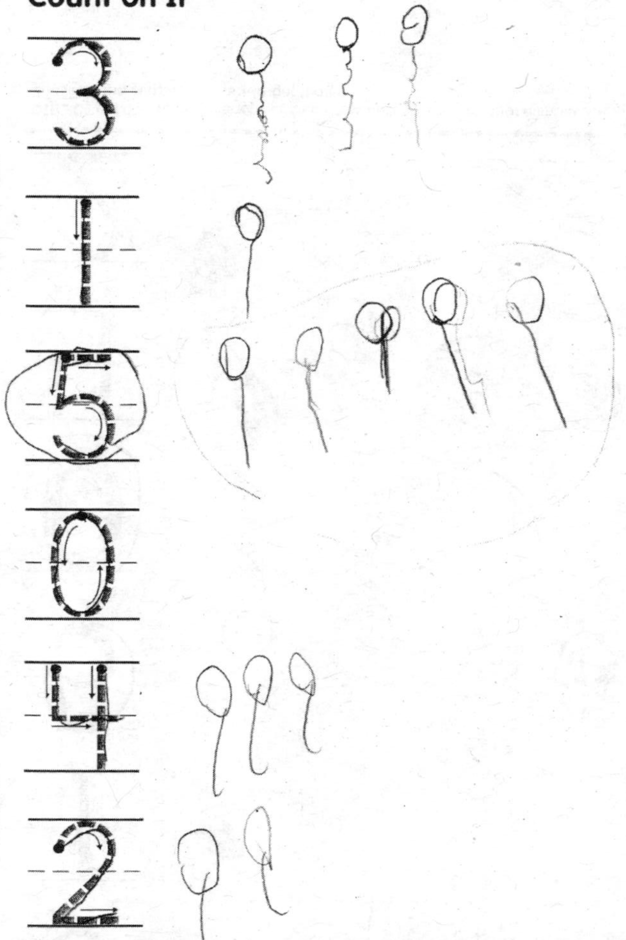

3

1

5

0

4

2

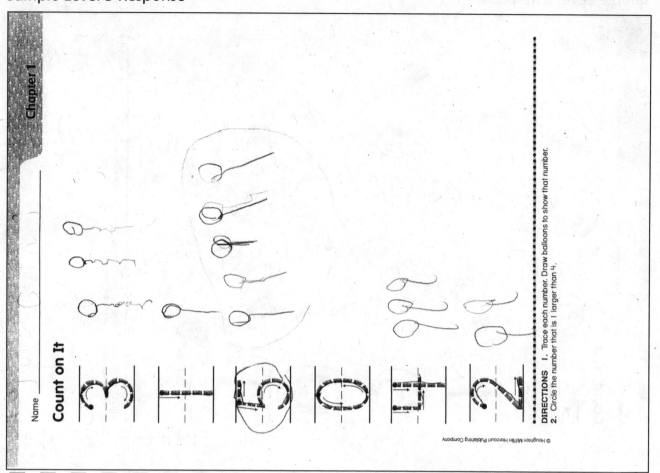

DIRECTIONS 1. Trace each number. Draw balloons to show that number.
2. Circle the number that is 1 larger than 4.

1

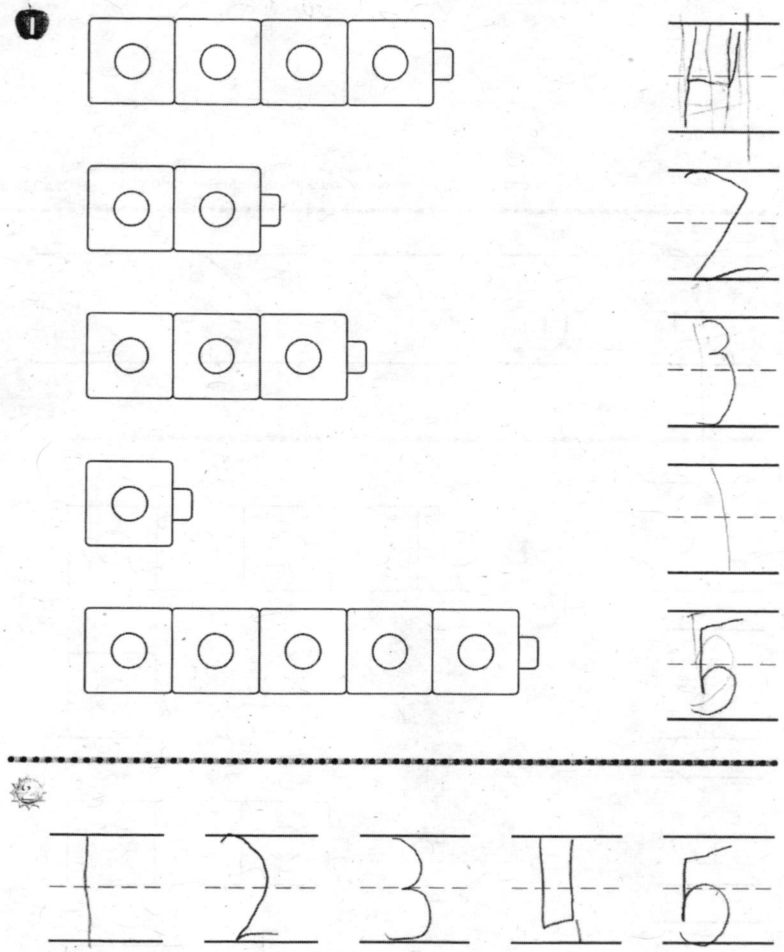

DIRECTIONS 1. Count the cubes in each set. Write that number of cubes.
2. Write the numbers in order at the bottom of the page.

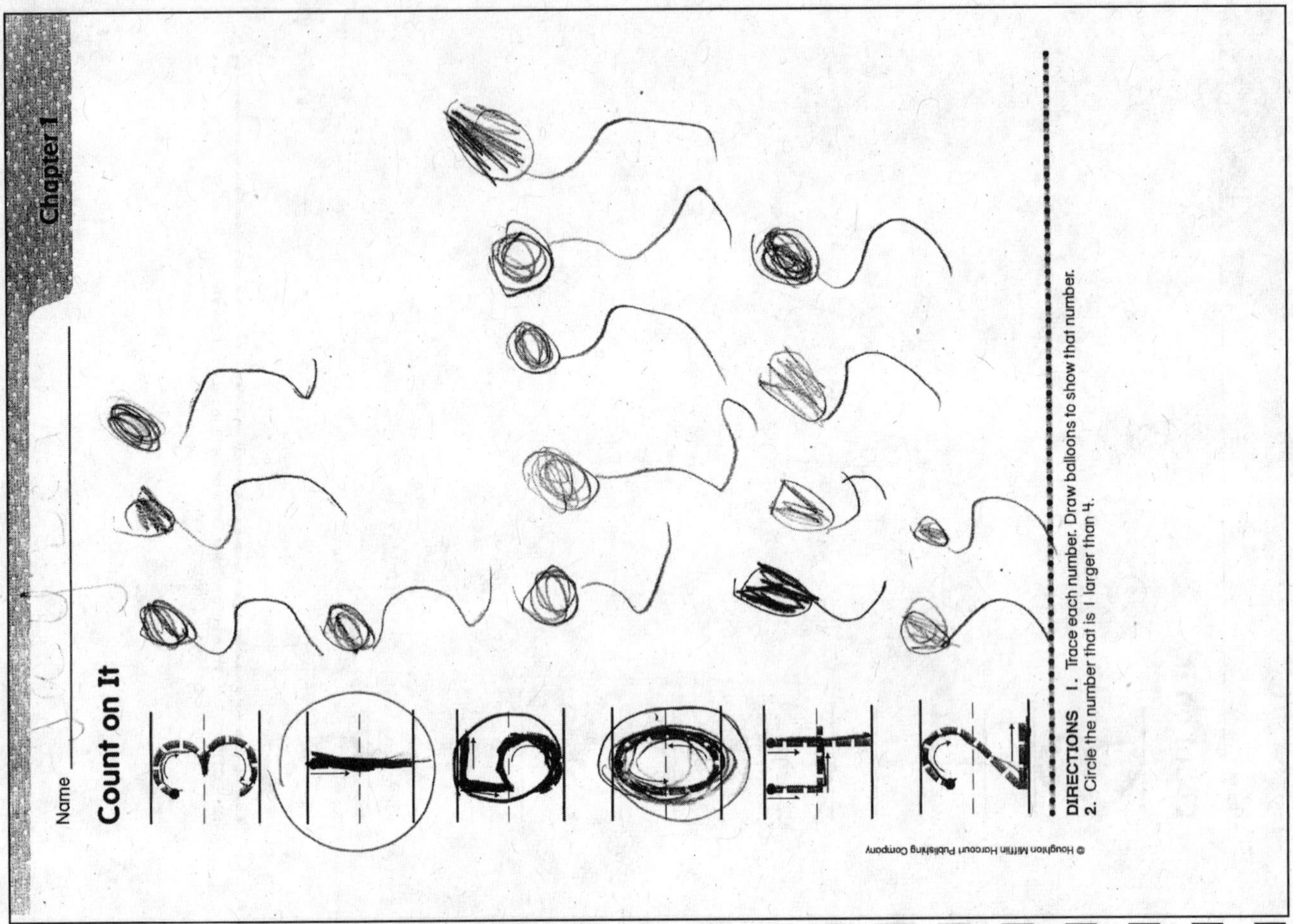

Chapter 1

Name

Count on It

3 1 5 0 4 2

DIRECTIONS **1.** Trace each number. Draw balloons to show that number. **2.** Circle the number that is 1 larger than 4.

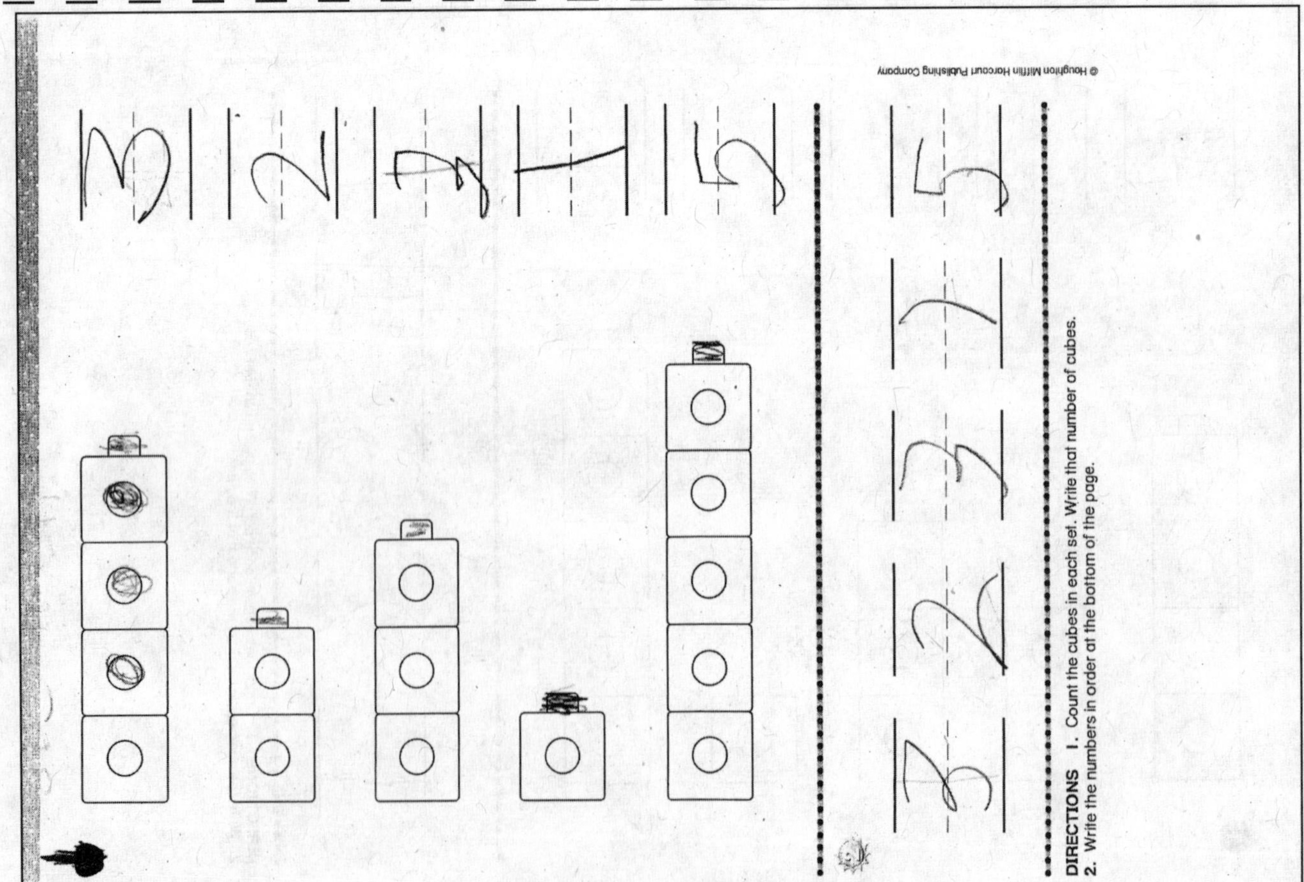

DIRECTIONS **1.** Count the cubes in each set. Write that number of cubes. **2.** Write the numbers in order at the bottom of the page.

Sample Level 1 Response

Chapter 1
Name
Count on It
3
1
5
0
4
2
DIRECTIONS 1. Trace each number. Draw balloons to show that number.
2. Circle the number that is 1 larger than 4.
© Houghton Mifflin Harcourt Publishing Company

1
DIRECTIONS 1. Count the cubes in each set. Write that number of cubes.
2. Write the numbers in order at the bottom of the page.
© Houghton Mifflin Harcourt Publishing Company

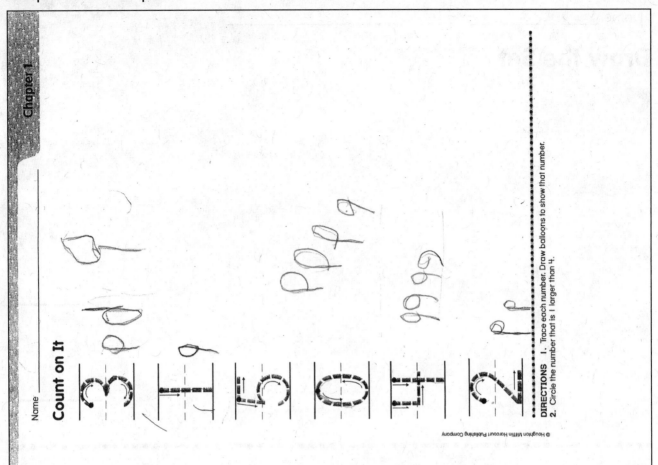

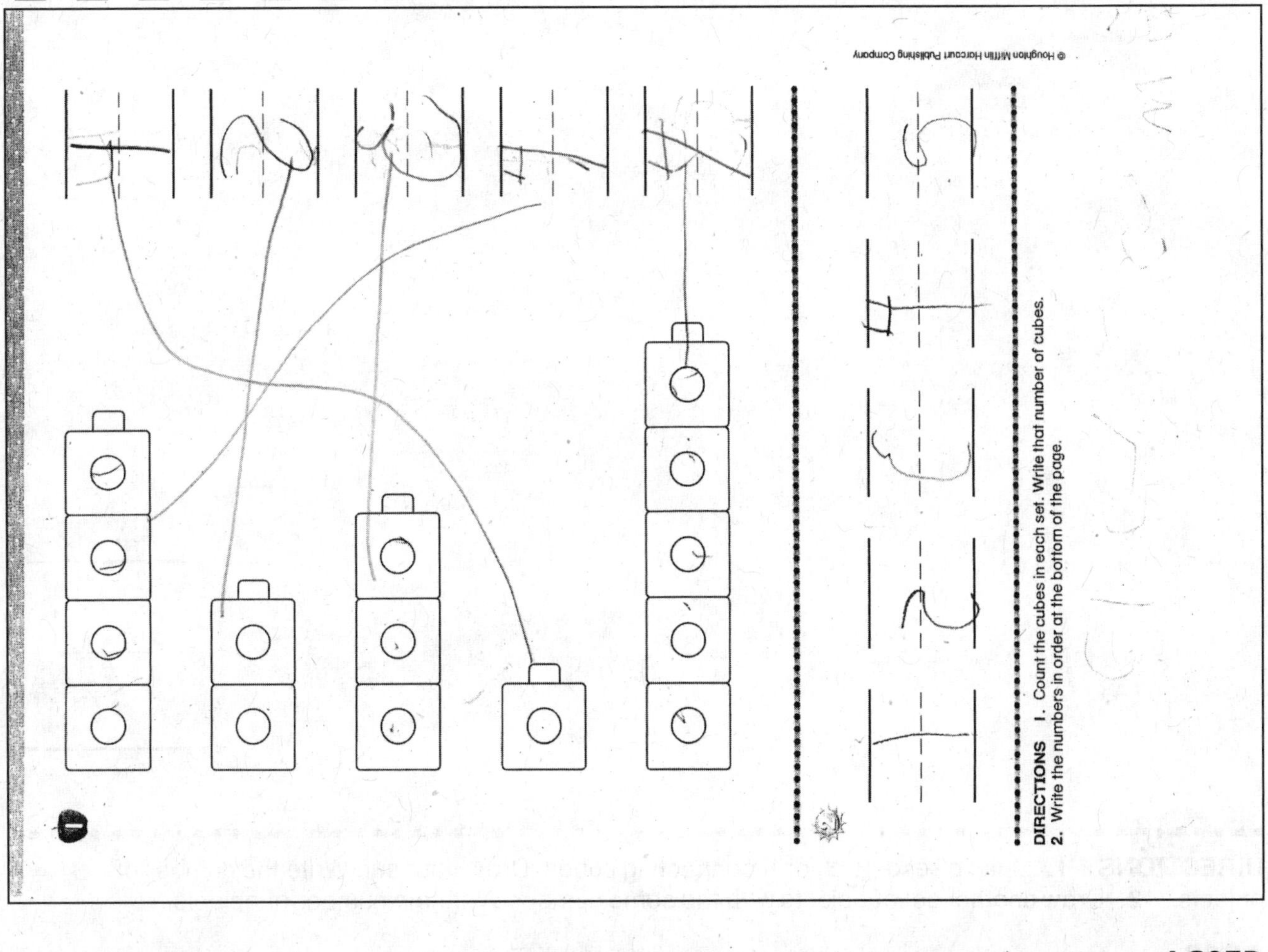

Name ______________________________

Draw the Set

DIRECTIONS 1. Make a set of 2, 3, or 4 connecting cubes. Draw your set. Write the number of objects. **2.** Draw another set of objects with the same number. Write the number of objects.

3 Nick

4 Matt

5 Jin

DIRECTIONS 3. Count Nick's crayons. Write the number. 4. Matt has a set of crayons that is greater than Nick's set. Draw a set that could be Matt's set. Write the number. 5. Jin has a set of crayons that is less than Nick's set. Draw a set that could be Jin's set. Write the number.

Compare Numbers to 5

Draw the Set

COMMON CORE STANDARDS

K.CC.6 Identify whether the number of objects in one group is greater than, less than, or equal to the number of objects in another group, e.g., by using matching and counting strategies.

PURPOSE

To assess the ability to count, model, write, and compare numbers

TIME

25–30 minutes

GROUPING

Individuals

MATERIALS

- Performance Task, paper, pencil
- Connecting cubes

PREPARATION HINTS

- Review modeling, counting, and writing numbers to 5 with children before assigning the task.
- Review strategies for comparing sets with children before assigning the task.
- Review vocabulary, including *greater*, *less*, *same number*, *sets*, *group*.

IMPLEMENTATION NOTES

- Read the task aloud to children and make sure that all children have a clear understanding of the task.
- Children may use manipulatives to complete the task.
- Allow children as much paper as they need to complete the task.
- Allow as much time as children need to complete the task.
- Children must complete the task individually, without collaboration.
- Collect all work when the task is complete.

TASK SUMMARY

Children use understanding of cardinality to model, count, and write numbers. They use strategies such as matching and counting to create sets that are greater than, less than, or equal to a given quantity.

REPRESENTATION

In this task teachers can…

- Provide options for comprehension by using cues to draw attention to critical features.
- Provide options for comprehension by highlighting the relationship between numeric and pictorial representations.

ACTION and EXPRESSION

In this task teachers can…

- Help children identify the end goal of each part of the assignment.
- Provide options for executive functions by reminding children to use strategies they have learned.

ENGAGEMENT

In this task teachers can…

- Provide options for self-assessment by offering strategies for checking work.
- Develop reflection by asking children to explain their process.

EXPECTED STUDENT OUTCOMES

- Complete the task within the time allowed
- Reflect engagement in a productive struggle
- Count, model, write, and compare numbers

SCORING

Use the associated Rubric to evaluate each child's work.

Performance Task Rubric

DRAW THE SET	
A level 3 response	• Indicates that the child has made sense of the task and persevered • Demonstrates an understanding of how to count and model sets of objects • Indicates an understanding of the relationship between numerals and quantities • Shows the ability to accurately apply counting or matching strategies to compare sets of objects
A level 2 response	• Indicates that the child has made sense of the task and persevered • Demonstrates an understanding of how to count and model sets of objects • Indicates an understanding of the relationship between numerals and quantities • Shows the ability to accurately apply counting or matching strategies to compare sets of objects • Addresses most or all aspects of the task, but there may be errors of omission
A level 1 response	• Shows that the child has made sense of at least some elements of the task • Shows evidence of understanding how to count and model sets of objects • Shows some understanding of the relationship between numerals and quantities • May not show the ability to accurately apply counting or matching strategies to compare sets of objects
A level 0 response	• Shows little evidence that the child has made sense of the problems of the task • Reflects a lack of understanding of how to count, model, compare, and write numbers • Shows little evidence of addressing the elements of the task

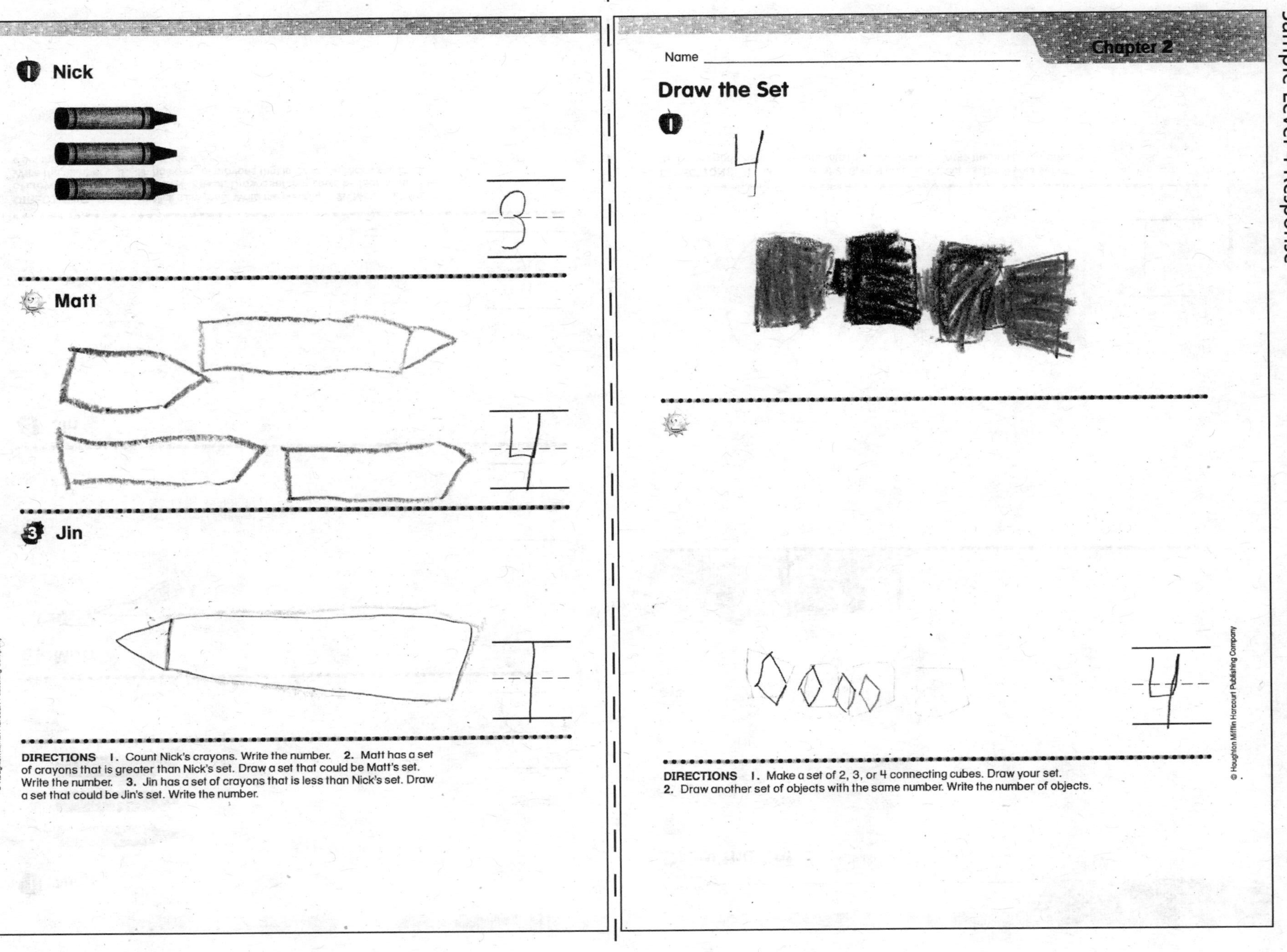

1 Nick

3

2 Matt

4

3 Jin

1

DIRECTIONS 1. Count Nick's crayons. Write the number. 2. Matt has a set of crayons that is greater than Nick's set. Draw a set that could be Matt's set. Write the number. 3. Jin has a set of crayons that is less than Nick's set. Draw a set that could be Jin's set. Write the number.

Name ______

Chapter 2

Draw the Set

1 4

2

4

DIRECTIONS 1. Make a set of 2, 3, or 4 connecting cubes. Draw your set. 2. Draw another set of objects with the same number. Write the number of objects.

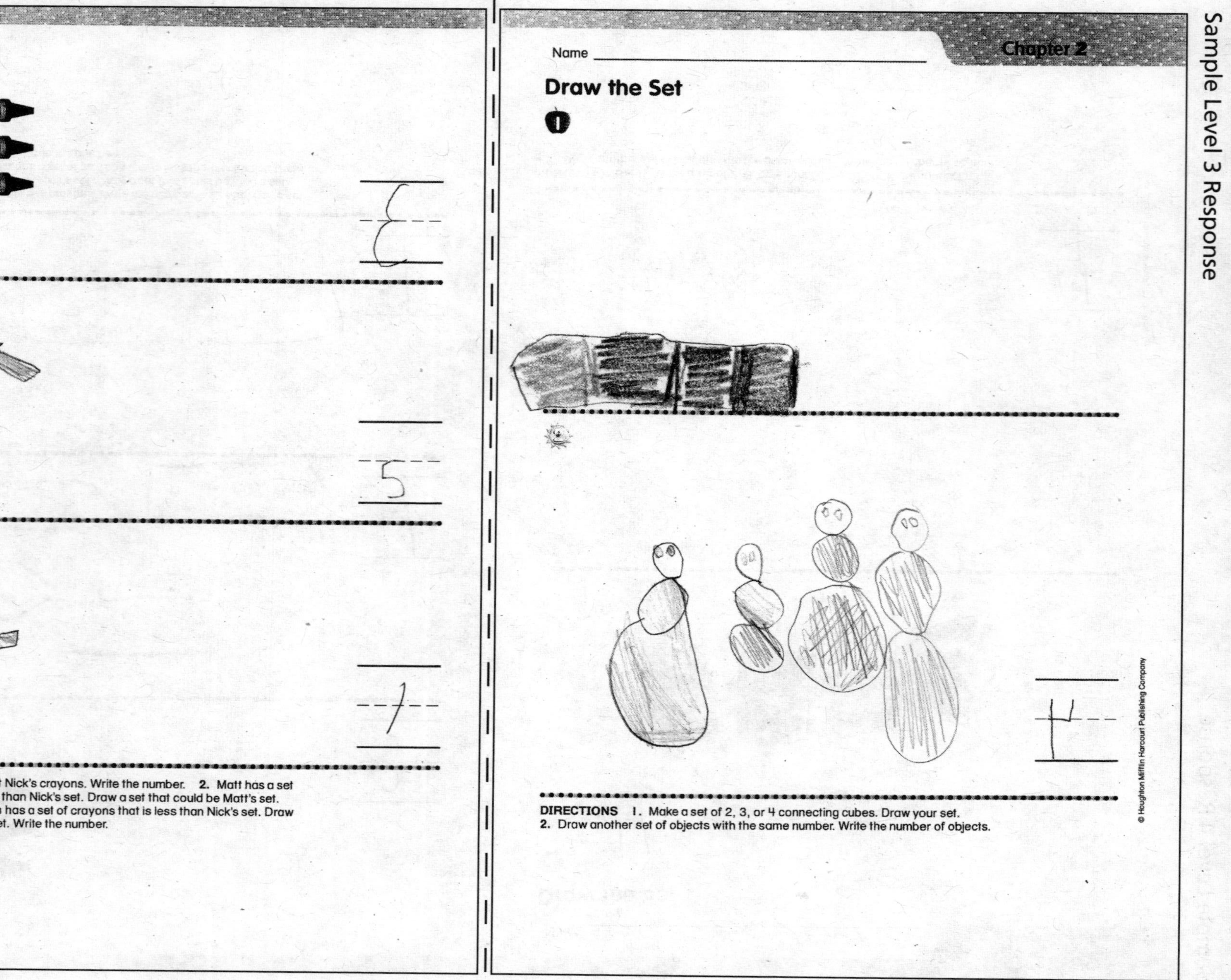

1 Nick

2 Matt

3 Jin

DIRECTIONS 1. Count Nick's crayons. Write the number. 2. Matt has a set of crayons that is greater than Nick's set. Draw a set that could be Matt's set. Write the number. 3. Jin has a set of crayons that is less than Nick's set. Draw a set that could be Jin's set. Write the number.

Name ____________________

Chapter 2

Draw the Set

1

2

DIRECTIONS 1. Make a set of 2, 3, or 4 connecting cubes. Draw your set. 2. Draw another set of objects with the same number. Write the number of objects.

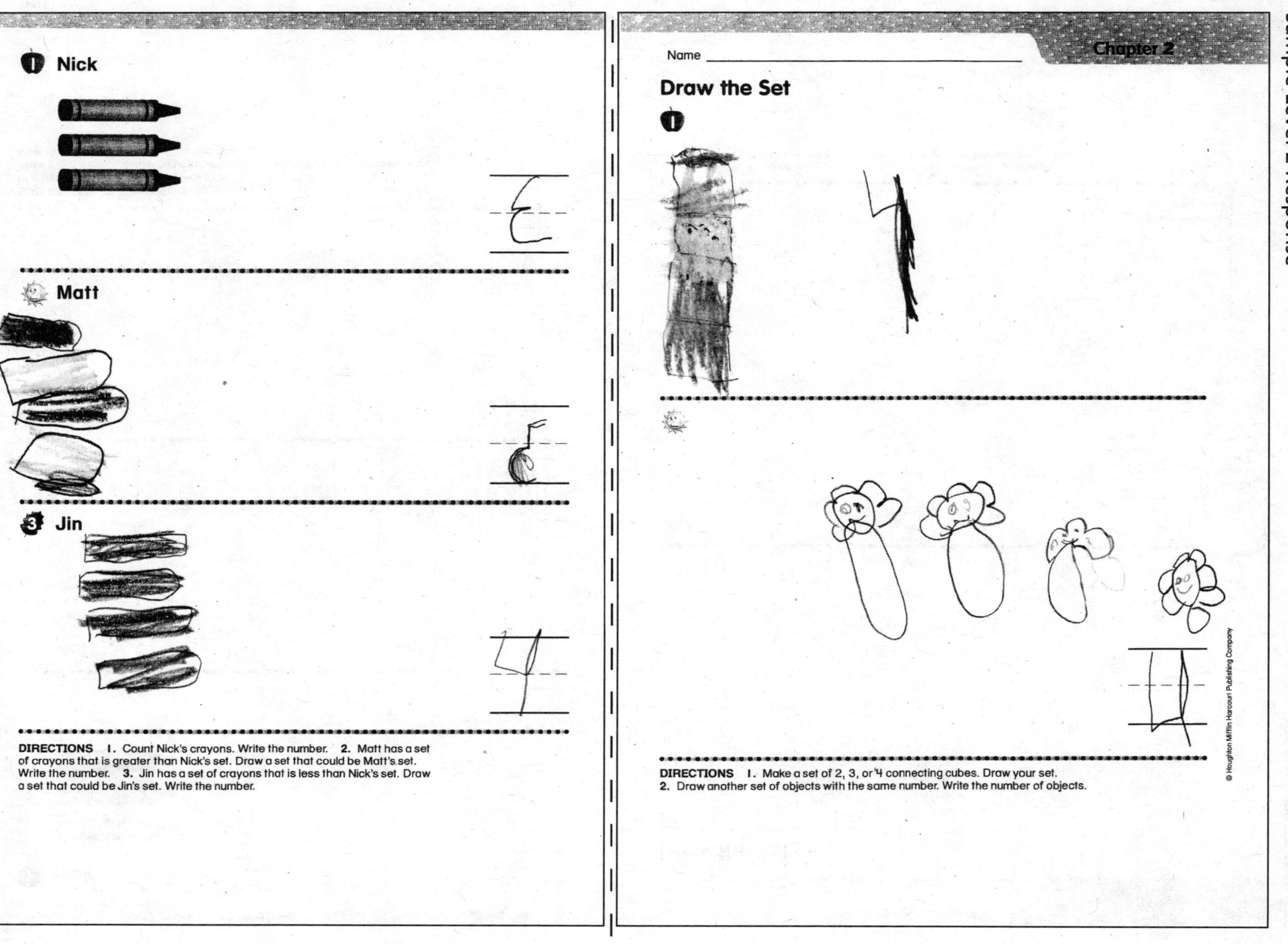
Nick
3
Matt
5
Jin
4
DIRECTIONS 1. Count Nick's crayons. Write the number. 2. Matt has a set of crayons that is greater than Nick's set. Draw a set that could be Matt's set. Write the number. 3. Jin has a set of crayons that is less than Nick's set. Draw a set that could be Jin's set. Write the number.
© Houghton Mifflin Harcourt Publishing Company
Name
Chapter 2
Draw the Set
DIRECTIONS 1. Make a set of 2, 3, or 4 connecting cubes. Draw your set. 2. Draw another set of objects with the same number. Write the number of objects.
© Houghton Mifflin Harcourt Publishing Company

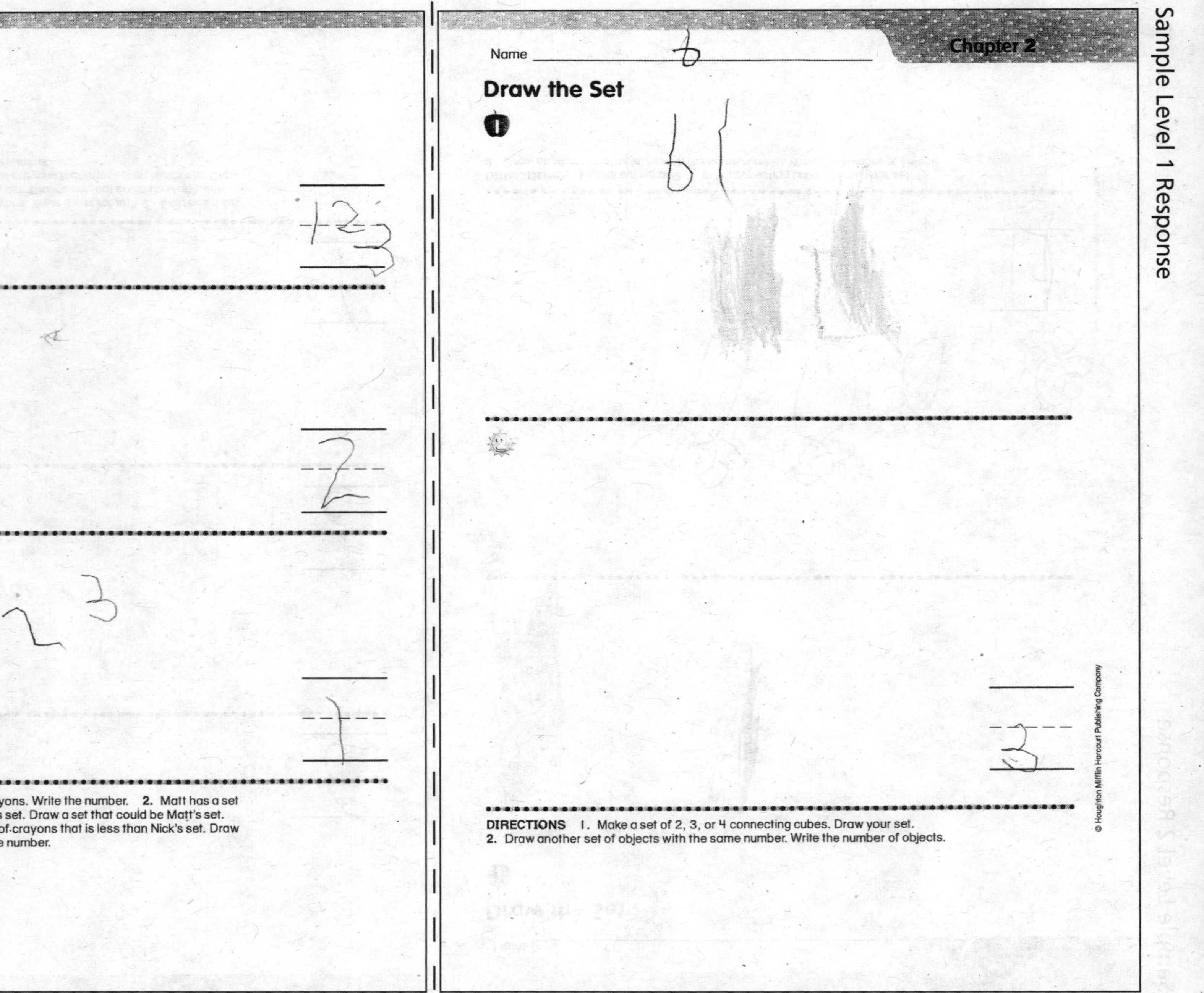

1 Nick

2 Matt

3 Jin

DIRECTIONS 1. Count Nick's crayons. Write the number. 2. Matt has a set of crayons that is greater than Nick's set. Draw a set that could be Matt's set. Write the number. 3. Jin has a set of crayons that is less than Nick's set. Draw a set that could be Jin's set. Write the number.

Chapter 2

Name

Draw the Set

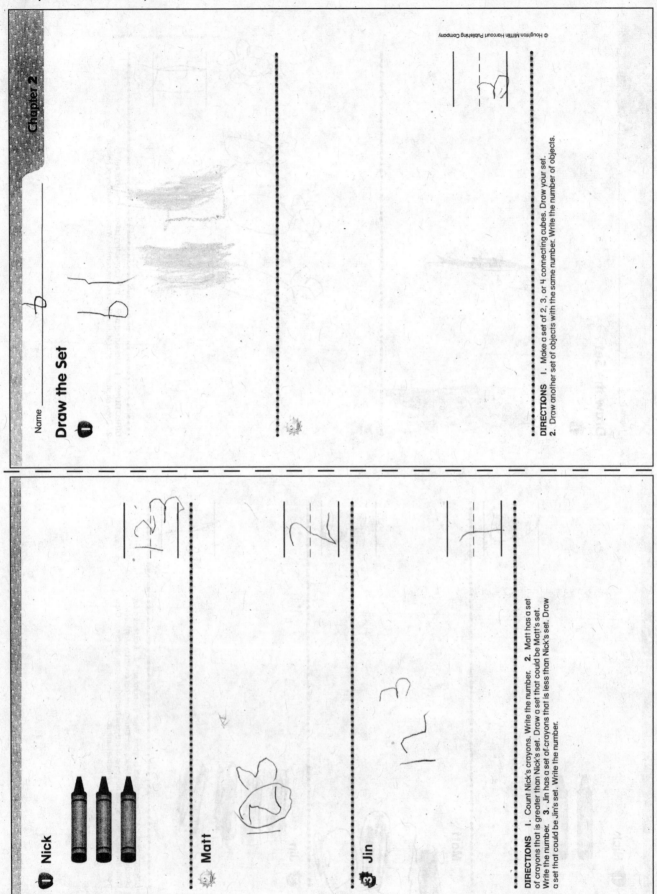

DIRECTIONS 1. Make a set of 2, 3, or 4 connecting cubes. Draw your set. 2. Draw another set of objects with the same number. Write the number of objects.

Name ____________________

Marco's Animals

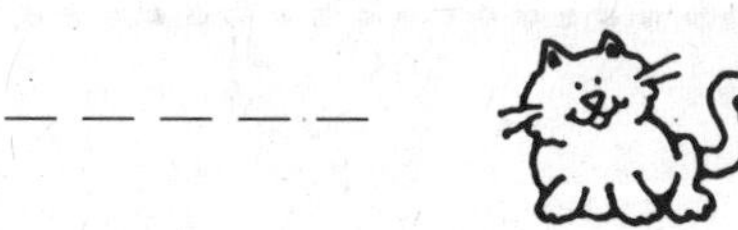

DIRECTIONS **1.** Marco puts all his toy cats in a line. He puts all his toy dogs in a circle. Look at the picture of Marco's toys. How many cats does Marco have? Write the number. How many dogs does Marco have? Write the number. **2.** Marco has toy mice, too. He wants to arrange a number of mice that is one greater than the number of dogs. Draw Marco's toy mice. Write the number of mice you drew.

3

4

5

DIRECTIONS **3.** Marco has a fish tank with red and blue fish. There are 5 red fish. The number of blue fish is 1 less than the number of red fish. Draw Marco's fish. **4.** Write the number of fish there are in the tank in all. **5.** Write the number word for that number.

Represent, Count, and Write Numbers 6 to 9

Marco's Animals

COMMON CORE STANDARDS

K.CC.3 Write numbers from 0 to 20. Represent a number of objects within a written numeral 0–20 (with 0 representing a count of no objects).

K.CC.5 Count to answer "how many?" questions about as many as 20 things arranged in a line, a rectangular array, or a circle, or as many as 10 things in a scattered configuration; given a number from 1 to 20 count out that many objects.

K.CC.6 Identify whether the number of objects in one group is greater than, less than, or equal to the number of objects in another group, e.g., by using matching and counting strategies.

PURPOSE

To assess the ability to count objects in a line and in a circle; count out a quantity of objects to match a given number; compare quantities of objects; and write numerals and number words to represent quantities

TIME

25–30 minutes

GROUPING

Individuals

MATERIALS

- Performance Task, paper, pencil
- Crayons (red and blue)

PREPARATION HINTS

- Review counting sets of objects with children before assigning the task.
- Review writing numerals and number words to 9 with children before assigning the task.
- Review vocabulary, including *six, seven, eight, nine, greater, less*.

IMPLEMENTATION NOTES

- Read the task aloud to children and make sure that all children have a clear understanding of the task.
- Children may use manipulatives to complete the task.
- Allow children as much paper as they need to complete the task.
- Allow as much time as children need to complete the task.
- Children must complete the task individually, without collaboration.
- Collect all work when the task is complete.

TASK SUMMARY

Children count objects in a line and in a circle and write numerals to represent the quantities. They count out a number of objects that is one greater or one less than a given number and then write the numeral and number word.

REPRESENTATION

In this task teachers can…

- Help children make connections between auditory and visual information.
- Guide children to notice critical details contained in pictures on the page.

ACTION and EXPRESSION

In this task teachers can…

- Help children approach the task methodically by marking or touching the page to show their progress.
- Help children monitor progress by keeping track of goals.

ENGAGEMENT

In this task teachers can…

- Provide options for self-regulation by encouraging children to go back and check that they completed every part of the task.

EXPECTED STUDENT OUTCOMES

- Complete the task within the time allowed
- Reflect engagement in a productive struggle
- Count and model sets of objects to 9
- Write numerals and number words to represent quantities of objects to 9

SCORING

Use the associated Rubric to evaluate each child's work.

Performance Task Rubric

MARCO'S ANIMALS	
A level 3 response	• Indicates that the child has made sense of the task and persevered • Demonstrates an understanding of counting and comparing sets of objects in various configurations • Indicates an understanding of the relationship between numerals, number words, and the quantities they represent • Shows the ability to accurately apply understanding of numbers to generate a specified quantity of objects
A level 2 response	• Indicates that the child has made sense of the task and persevered • Demonstrates an understanding of counting and comparing sets of objects in various configurations • Indicates an understanding of the relationship between numerals, number words, and the quantities they represent • Shows the ability to accurately apply understanding of numbers to generate a specified quantity of objects • Addresses most or all aspects of the task, but there may be errors of omission
A level 1 response	• Shows that the child has made sense of at least some elements of the task • Shows evidence of understanding of how to count and compare sets of objects in various configurations • Demonstrates some understanding of the relationship between numerals, number words, and quantities • May not show the ability to accurately count, write, or represent some numbers
A level 0 response	• Shows little evidence that the child has made sense of the problems of the task • Reflects a lack of understanding of how to count, model, compare, and represent numbers • Shows little evidence of addressing the elements of the task

Name ______________________

Ella's Art Projects

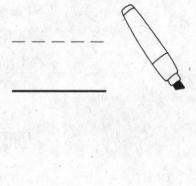

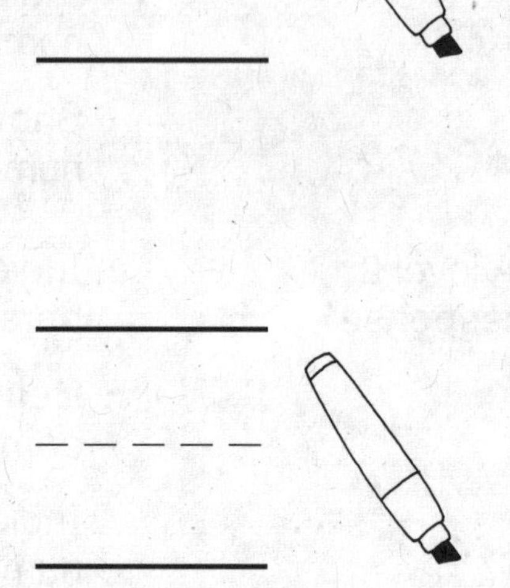

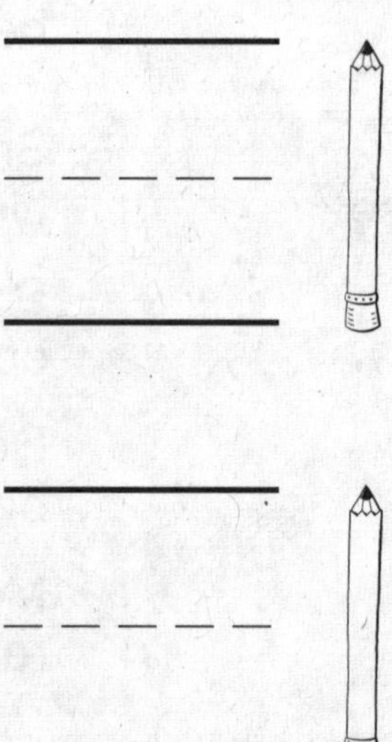

DIRECTIONS 1. Ella has 9 markers. She gives some of the markers to Ben. Now who has more markers, Ella or Ben? Use cube trains to model each child's markers. Draw the cube trains. Compare the cube trains. Write how many. Circle the number that is greater. **2.** Ben has 7 colored pencils. He gives some of the pencils to Ella. Use cube trains to model each child's pencils. Draw the cube trains. Compare the cube trains. Write how many. Circle the number that is less.

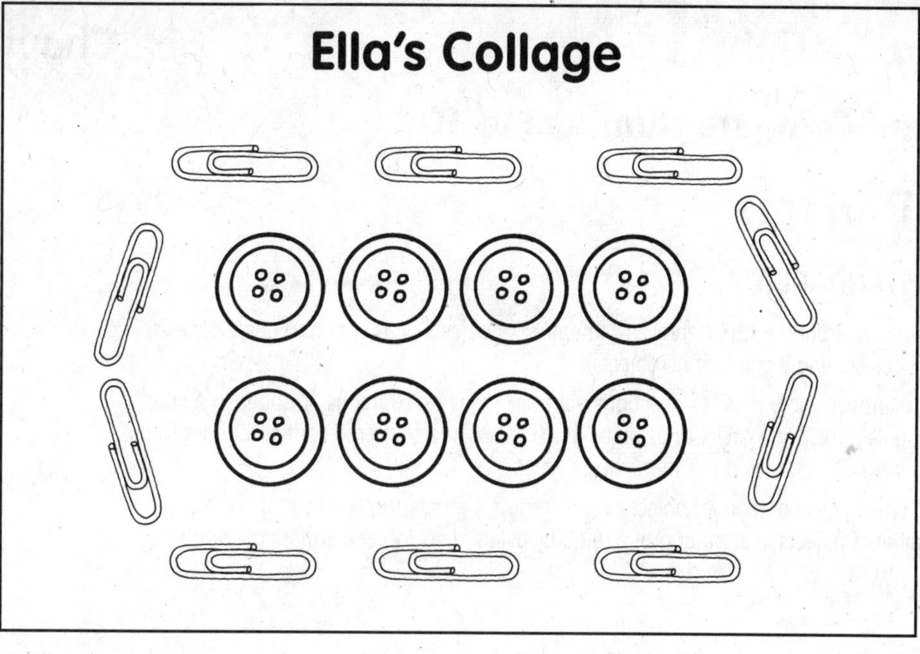

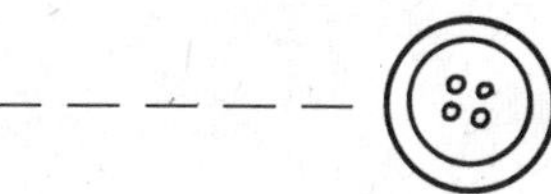

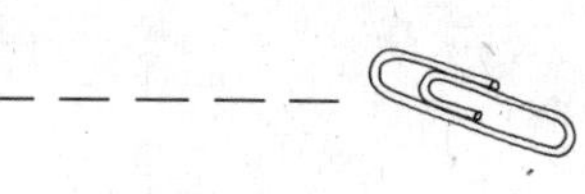

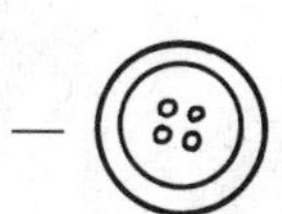

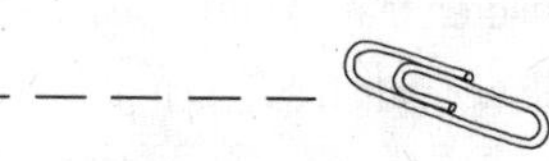

DIRECTIONS **3.** Ella makes a collage out of buttons and paperclips. Look at the picture of Ella's collage. How many buttons did Ella use? Write the number. How many paper clips did Ella use? Write the number. Compare the numbers. Circle the greater number. **4.** Think of a number less than 10. Draw that many buttons. Draw a number of paper clips that is 1 less than the number of buttons. Write the number of buttons and paper clips you drew. Compare the numbers. Circle the greater number.

Represent and Compare Numbers to 10

Ella's Art Projects

COMMON CORE STANDARDS

K.CC.3 Write numbers from 0 to 20. Represent a number of objects with a written numeral 0–20 (with 0 representing a count of no objects).

K.CC.5 Count to answer "how many?" questions about as many as 20 things arranged in a line, a rectangular array, or a circle, or as many as 10 things in a scattered configuration; given a number from 1–20, count out that many objects.

K.CC.6 Identify whether the number of objects in one group is greater than, less than, or equal to the number of objects in another group, e.g., by using matching and counting strategies.

PURPOSE

To assess the ability to count, model, write, and compare numbers to 10

TIME

25–30 minutes

GROUPING

Individuals

MATERIALS

- Performance Task, paper, pencil
- Connecting cubes

PREPARATION HINTS

- Review counting and writing numbers to 10 with children before assigning the task.
- Review comparing numbers by matching, counting, or ordering with children before assigning the task.
- Review vocabulary, including *greater*, *less*.

IMPLEMENTATION NOTES

- Read the task aloud to children and make sure that all children have a clear understanding of the task.
- Children may use manipulatives to complete the task.
- Allow children as much paper as they need to complete the task.
- Allow as much time as children need to complete the task.
- Children must complete the task individually, without collaboration.
- Collect all work when the task is complete.

TASK SUMMARY

Children count, write, and model numbers to 10. They use strategies such as matching, counting, and ordering to compare numbers to 10.

REPRESENTATION

In this task teachers can...

- Provide options for perception by offering alternative displays of information.
- Provide options for comprehension by using cues to draw attention to critical features.

ACTION and EXPRESSION

In this task teachers can...

- Provide options for physical action by offering connecting cubes to children while completing the task.

ENGAGEMENT

In this task teachers can...

- Provide options for self-assessment by offering strategies for checking work.
- Develop reflection by asking children to explain their process.

EXPECTED STUDENT OUTCOMES

- Complete the task within the time allowed
- Reflect engagement in a productive struggle
- Count, model, and write numbers to 10
- Compare quantities and represent quantities that are greater than or less than a given quantity

SCORING

Use the associated Rubric to evaluate each child's work.

Performance Task Rubric

ELLA'S ART PROJECTS	
A level 3 response	• Indicates that the child has made sense of the task and persevered • Demonstrates understanding of counting and modeling quantities to 10 • Demonstrates understanding of writing numerals to represent quantities to 10 • Shows the ability to accurately apply strategies such as counting, matching, or ordering to compare quantities
A level 2 response	• Indicates that the child has made sense of the task and persevered • Demonstrates understanding of counting and modeling quantities to 10 • Demonstrates understanding of writing numerals to represent quantities to 10 • Shows the ability to accurately apply strategies such as counting, matching, or ordering to compare quantities • Addresses most or all aspects of the task, but there may be errors of omission
A level 1 response	• Shows that the child has made sense of at least some elements of the task • Shows evidence of understanding of counting and modeling quantities to 10 • Indicates some understanding of writing numerals to represent quantities to 10 • May not show the ability to accurately apply strategies to compare quantities
A level 0 response	• Shows little evidence that the child has made sense of the problems of the task • Reflects a lack of understanding of counting, modeling, writing, and comparing numbers to 10 • Shows little evidence of addressing the elements of the task

Name ______________________

Bees and Flowers

9 = ___ + ___

DIRECTIONS **1.** Use counters to find a number pair for 9. Write the number pair to complete the addition sentence. **2.** Now use that number pair to draw or write an addition story about 9 bees.

3

DIRECTIONS 3. Molly has 10 flowers. She would like to put the flowers into two pots. Use counters to show four different ways Molly could put the flowers in the pots. Write the addition sentence for each way. Then circle one of your addition sentences. Draw flowers in the pot to match your addition sentence.

Addition

Bees and Flowers

COMMON CORE STANDARDS

K.OA.1 Represent addition and subtraction with objects, fingers, mental images, drawings, sounds (e.g., claps), acting out situations, verbal explanations, expressions, or equations.

K.OA.2 Solve addition and subtraction word problems, and add and subtract within 10, e.g., by using objects or drawings to represent the problem.

K.OA.3 Decompose numbers less than or equal to 10 into pairs in more than one way, e.g., by using objects or drawings, and record each decomposition by a drawing or equation (e.g., $5 = 2 + 3$ and $5 = 4 + 1$).

PURPOSE

To assess the ability to model and write addition sentences for number pairs for a specified sum

TIME

25–30 minutes

GROUPING

Individuals

MATERIALS

- Performance Task, paper, pencil
- Two-color counters

PREPARATION HINTS

- Review modeling number pairs for sums with children before assigning the task.
- Review writing addition sentences with children before assigning the task.
- Review vocabulary, including *nine, ten, pair*.

IMPLEMENTATION NOTES

- Read the task aloud to children and make sure that all children have a clear understanding of the task.
- Children may use manipulatives to complete the task.
- Allow children as much paper as they need to complete the task.
- Allow as much time as children need to complete the task.
- Children must complete the task individually, without collaboration.
- Collect all work when the task is complete.

TASK SUMMARY

Children model decomposing a number into pairs in more than one way. They write an addition sentence to record each decomposition. They draw or write a story to reflect the addition.

REPRESENTATION

In this task teachers can…

- Provide options for comprehension by having children use background knowledge to help them understand the task.
- Provide options for comprehension by using cues to draw attention to critical features.

ACTION and EXPRESSION

In this task teachers can…

- Provide options for expression and communication by allowing children to communicate their stories through multiple means.

ENGAGEMENT

In this task teachers can…

- Recruit interest by emphasizing uniqueness of children's interpretations.
- Recruit interest by engaging with children's stories.

EXPECTED STUDENT OUTCOMES

- Complete the task within the time allowed
- Reflect engagement in a productive struggle
- Decompose a number into pairs in more than one way and write a number sentence to represent the addition
- Present an addition story with the sum of 9

SCORING

Use the associated Rubric to evaluate each child's work.

Performance Task Rubric

BEES AND FLOWERS	
A level 3 response	• Indicates that the child has made sense of the task and persevered • Demonstrates an understanding of decomposing a number into pairs in more than one way • Indicates an understanding of using a number sentence to record addition • Shows the ability to apply understanding of decomposing numbers in a math story
A level 2 response	• Indicates that the child has made sense of the task and persevered • Demonstrates an understanding of decomposing a number into pairs in more than one way • Indicates an understanding of using a number sentence to record addition • Shows the ability to apply understanding of decomposing numbers in a math story • Addresses most or all aspects of the task, but there may be errors of omission
A level 1 response	• Shows that the child has made sense of at least some elements of the task • Shows evidence of understanding of decomposing numbers into pairs • Indicates some understanding of using a number sentence to record addition • May not show the ability to accurately model decomposition or record addition
A level 0 response	• Shows little evidence that the child has made sense of the problems of the task • Reflects a lack of understanding of decomposing numbers and using number sentences to record addition • Shows little evidence of addressing the elements of the task

Name ______________________________

Sharing Stickers

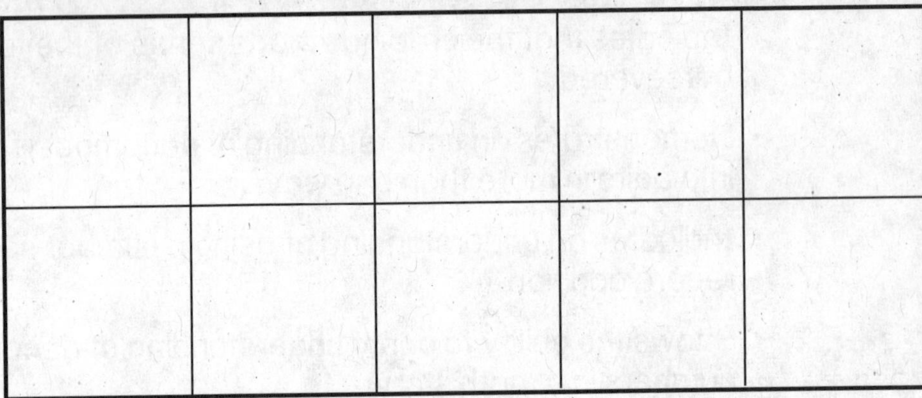

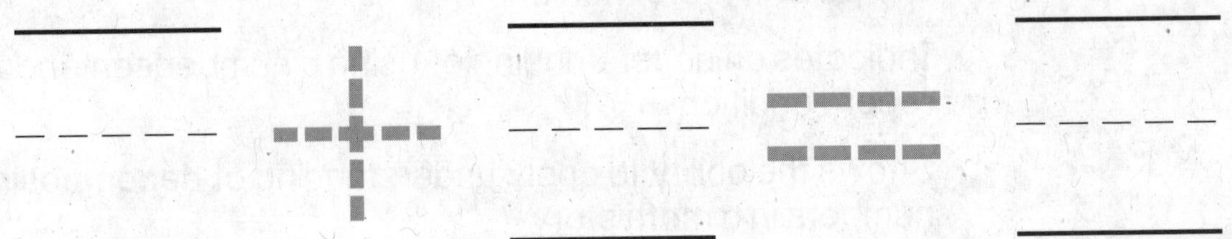

3

______ − ______ = ______

DIRECTIONS 1. Ana has 6 star stickers. Someone gives her 4 heart stickers. Put counters in the ten frame to show how many stickers Ana has in all. Draw the counters. 2. Write the number sentence that tells about the stickers. 3. Ana gives the 4 heart stickers to Paul. Cross out on your drawing to show the stickers Ana gives away. Write the number sentence that tells how many stickers Ana has left.

5

___ + ___ = ___

6

___ − ___ = ___

DIRECTIONS 4. Dylan has 9 stickers. Some are red and some are blue. Use cubes to show Dylan's stickers. Draw the cubes. 5. Write a number sentence that tells about Dylan's stickers. 6. What if Dylan gives his blue stickers away? Cross out on your drawing to show the stickers Dylan gives away. Write the number sentence that tells how many stickers Dylan has left.

Subtraction

Sharing Stickers

COMMON CORE STANDARDS

K.OA.1 Represent addition and subtraction with objects, fingers, mental images, drawings, sounds (e.g., claps), acting out situations, verbal explanations, expressions, or equations.

K.OA.2 Solve addition and subtraction word problems, and add and subtract within 10, e.g., by using objects or drawings to represent the problem.

K.OA.5 Fluently add and subtract within 5.

PURPOSE

To assess the ability to solve addition and subtraction word problems within 10 using models, drawings, and equations

TIME

25–30 minutes

GROUPING

Individuals

MATERIALS

- Performance Task, paper, pencil
- Two-color counters
- Connecting cubes
- Crayons or colored pencils

PREPARATION HINTS

- Review modeling addition as "putting together" and subtraction as "taking from" with children before assigning the task.
- Review writing addition and subtraction sentences with children before assigning the task.
- Review vocabulary, including *number sentence*.

IMPLEMENTATION NOTES

- Read the task aloud to children and make sure that all children have a clear understanding of the task.
- Children may use manipulatives to complete the task.
- Allow children as much paper as they need to complete the task.
- Allow as much time as children need to complete the task.
- Children must complete the task individually, without collaboration.
- Collect all work when the task is complete.

TASK SUMMARY

Children make models and draw pictures to solve addition and subtraction word problems within 10. They record the addition and subtraction using number sentences.

REPRESENTATION

In this task teachers can…

- Provide options for language, mathematical expressions and symbols by reviewing vocabulary and symbols in the context of children's prior knowledge.
- Provide options for comprehension by asking children to visualize scenarios in their mind.

ACTION and EXPRESSION

In this task teachers can…

- Provide options for physical action by offering manipulatives to children while completing the task.

ENGAGEMENT

In this task teachers can…

- Recruit interest by emphasizing the uniqueness of children's interpretations and engaging with children's stories.

EXPECTED STUDENT OUTCOMES

- Complete the task within the time allowed
- Reflect engagement in a productive struggle
- Model and use equations to solve addition and subtraction within 10

SCORING

Use the associated Rubric to evaluate each child's work.

Performance Task Rubric

SHARING STICKERS	
A level 3 response	• Indicates that the child has made sense of the task and persevered • Demonstrates an understanding of addition as "putting together" groups and subtraction as "taking from" a group • Indicates an understanding of the parts of addition and subtraction sentences • Shows an ability to model and solve addition and subtraction word problems within 10
A level 2 response	• Indicates that the child has made sense of the task and persevered • Demonstrates an understanding of addition as "putting together" groups and subtraction as "taking from" a group • Indicates an understanding of the parts of addition and subtraction sentences • Shows an ability to model and solve addition and subtraction word problems within 10 • Addresses most or all aspects of the task, but there may be errors of omission
A level 1 response	• Shows that the child has made sense of at least some elements of the task • Shows evidence of understanding of situations involving "putting together" groups and "taking from" a group • Indicates some understanding of the parts of addition and subtraction sentences • May not present accurate representations or solutions
A level 0 response	• Shows little evidence that the child has made sense of the problems of the task • Reflects a lack of understanding of addition as "putting together" groups and subtraction as "taking from" a group • Reflects a lack of understanding of the parts of addition and subtraction sentences • Shows little evidence of addressing the elements of the task

Name ____________________

Buttons and Flowers

2

DIRECTIONS **1–2.** For each set, circle 10 buttons, count how many in all, and write the number.

3

4

5

10 + ___ = ___

DIRECTIONS **3.** Yoshi and Neela are picking flowers. They pick more than 10 flowers but no more than 19 flowers. Write a number that could be the number of flowers they pick. **4.** Place counters in the ten frames to show that number. Draw the counters. **5.** Complete the number sentence to show how to make that number.

Represent, Count, and Write 11 to 19

Buttons and Flowers

COMMON CORE STANDARDS

K.CC.3 Write numbers from 0 to 20. Represent a number of objects with a written numeral 0–20 (with 0 representing a count of no objects).

2.NBT.1 Compose and decompose numbers from 11 to 19 into ten ones and some further ones, e.g., by using objects or drawings, and record each composition or decomposition by a drawing or equation (e.g., 18 = 10 + 8); understand that these numbers are composed of ten ones and one, two, three, four, five, six, seven, eight, or nine ones.

PURPOSE

To assess the ability to write numbers from 11 to 19 and decompose them into ten ones and some further ones using models and equations

TIME

25–30 minutes

GROUPING

Individuals

MATERIALS

- Performance Task, paper, pencil
- Crayons or colored pencils
- Two-color counters

PREPARATION HINTS

- Review numbers from 10 to 19 with children before assigning the task.
- Review decomposing numbers 11 to 19 into ten ones and some further ones with children before assigning the task.
- Review vocabulary, including *ten, more.*

IMPLEMENTATION NOTES

- Read the task aloud to children and make sure that all children have a clear understanding of the task.
- Children may use manipulatives to complete the task.
- Allow children as much paper as they need to complete the task.
- Allow as much time as children need to complete the task.
- Children must complete the task individually, without collaboration.
- Collect all work when the task is complete.

TASK SUMMARY

Children count and write numerals to represent quantities from 11 to 19. They decompose numbers from 11 to 19 into ten ones and some further ones using models and equations.

REPRESENTATION

In this task teachers can…

- Provide options for perception by offering alternative displays of visual information.
- Provide options for comprehension by making gestures to act out verbs contained in the directions.

ACTION and EXPRESSION

In this task teachers can…

- Provide options for physical action by allowing children to use counters to help them count.

ENGAGEMENT

In this task teachers can…

- Recruit interest by asking children to tell stories about their work.
- Encourage reflection by asking children to explain how they represented situations in story problems.

EXPECTED STUDENT OUTCOMES

- Complete the task within the time allowed
- Reflect engagement in a productive struggle
- Count, model, and write numbers from 11 to 19
- Decompose numbers from 11 to 19 into ten ones and some further ones

SCORING

Use the associated Rubric to evaluate each child's work.

Performance Task Rubric

BUTTONS AND FLOWERS	
A level 3 response	• Indicates that the child has made sense of the task and persevered • Shows the ability to accurately count and write numerals to represent quantities from 11 to 19 • Shows the ability to compose quantities from 11 to 19 as ten ones and some further ones using models and addition sentences
A level 2 response	• Indicates that the child has made sense of the task and persevered • Shows the ability to accurately count and write numerals to represent quantities from 11 to 19 • Shows the ability to compose quantities from 11 to 19 as ten ones and some further ones using models and addition sentences • Addresses most or all aspects of the task, but there may be errors of omission
A level 1 response	• Shows that the child has made sense of at least some elements of the task • Shows evidence of understanding of how to count, model, and write numbers from 11 to 19 • Indicates some understanding of quantities from 11 to 19 as composed of ten ones and some further ones • May not accurately represent quantities or their decomposition
A level 0 response	• Shows little evidence that the child has made sense of the problems of the task • Reflects a lack of understanding of how to count, model, and write numbers from 11 to 19 • Reflects a lack of understanding of quantities from 11 to 19 as composed of ten ones and some further ones • Shows little evidence of addressing the elements of the task

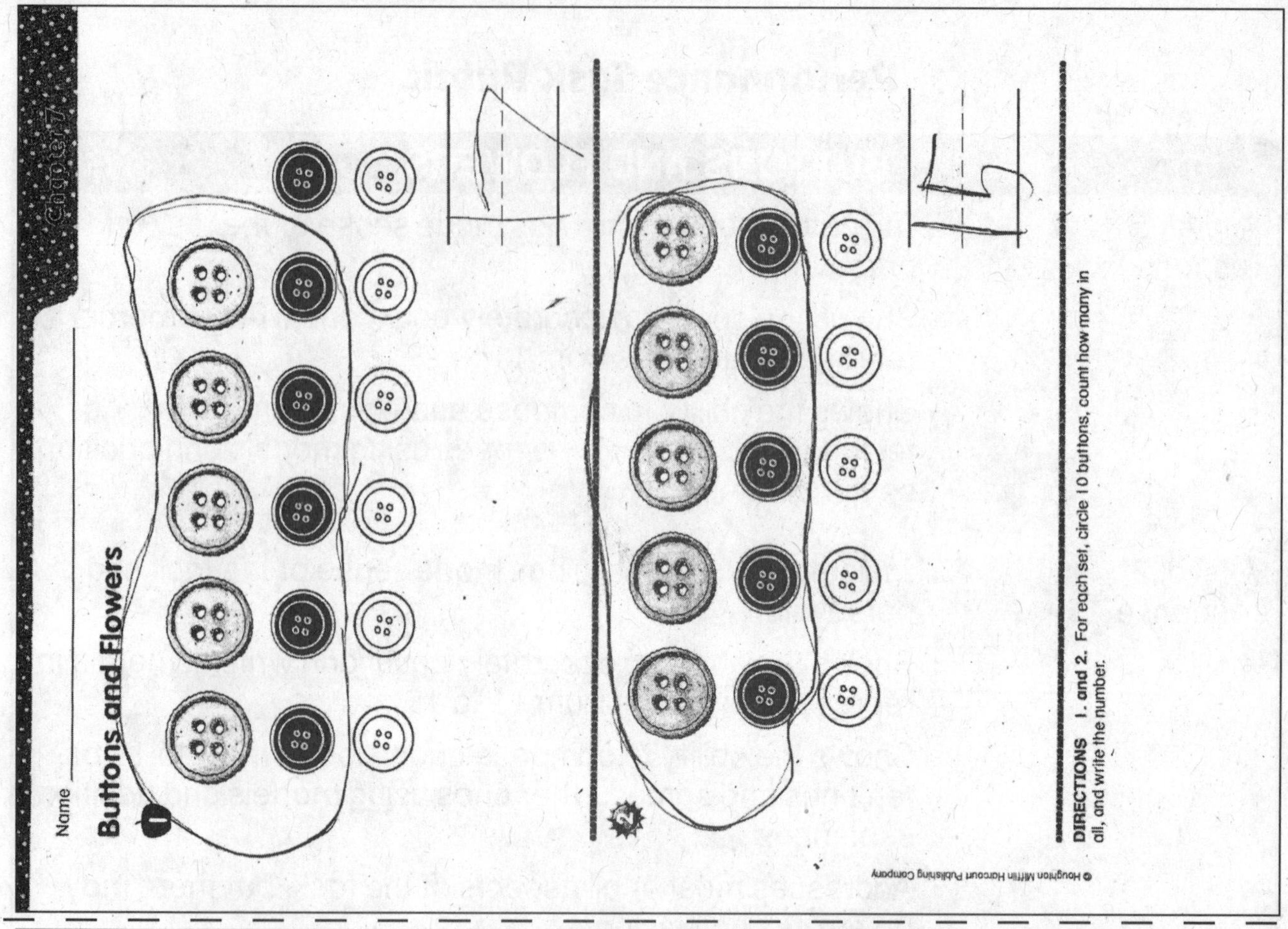

Chapter 7

Name ____________

Buttons and Flowers

1. 17

2. 15

DIRECTIONS 1. and 2. For each set, circle 10 buttons, count how many in all, and write the number.

3. 14

4.

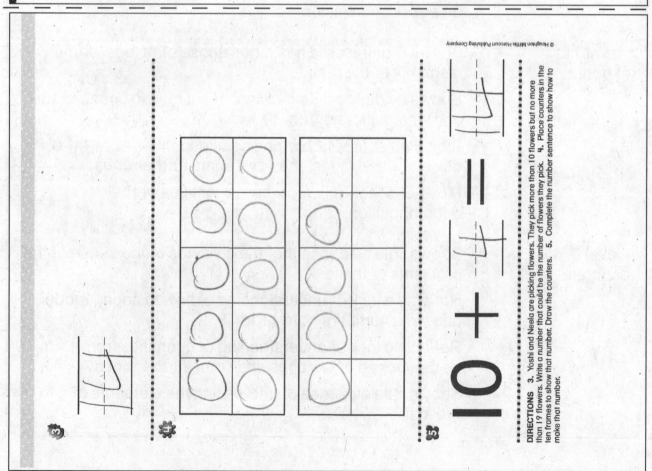

5. 10 + 4 = 14

DIRECTIONS 3. Yoshi and Neela are picking flowers. They pick more than 10 flowers but no more than 19 flowers. Write a number that could be the number of flowers they pick. 4. Place counters in the ten frames to show that number. Draw the counters. 5. Complete the number sentence to show how to make that number.

Chapter 7

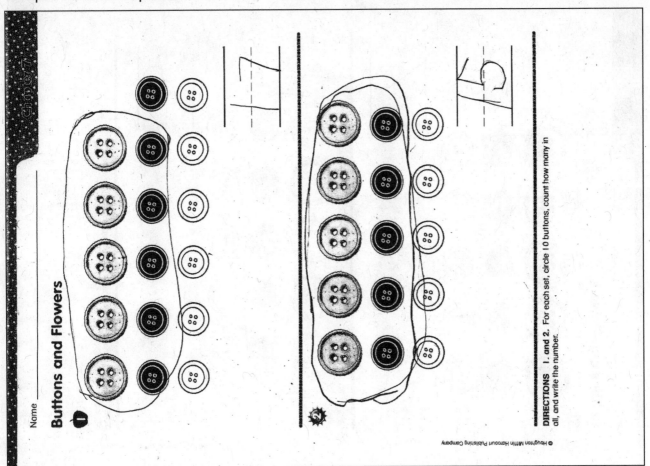

Name ______

Buttons and Flowers

1

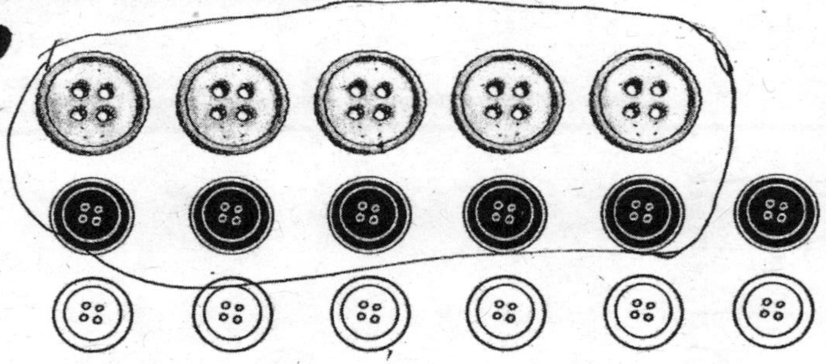

17

2

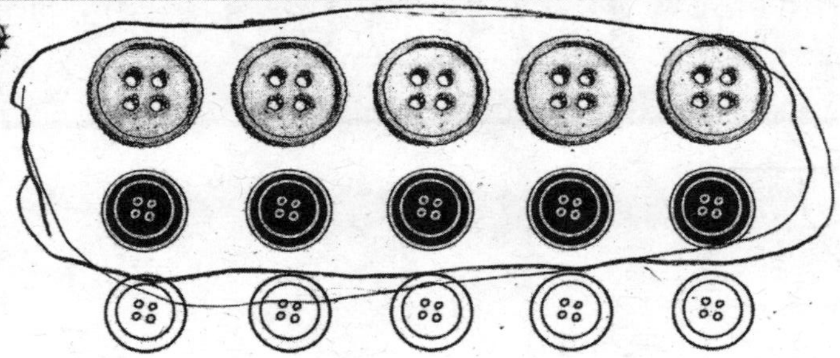

15

DIRECTIONS 1. and 2. For each set, circle 10 buttons, count how many in all, and write the number.

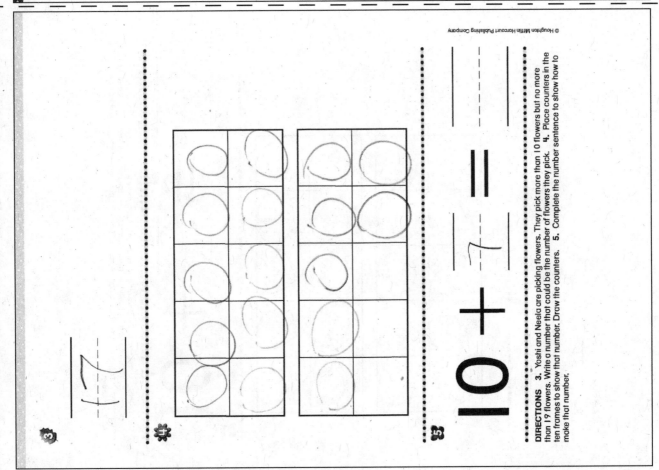

3

17

4

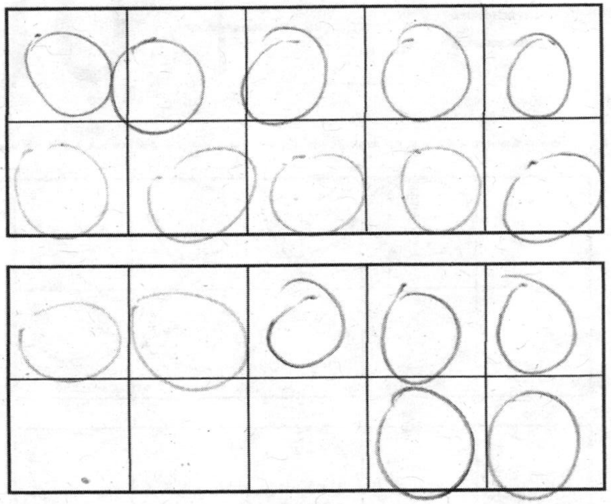

5

10 + 7 = ___

DIRECTIONS 3. Yoshi and Neela are picking flowers. They pick more than 10 flowers but no more than 19 flowers. Write a number that could be the number of flowers they pick. 4. Place counters in the ten frames to show that number. Draw the counters. 5. Complete the number sentence to show how to make that number.

Chapter 7

Name ____________

Buttons and Flowers

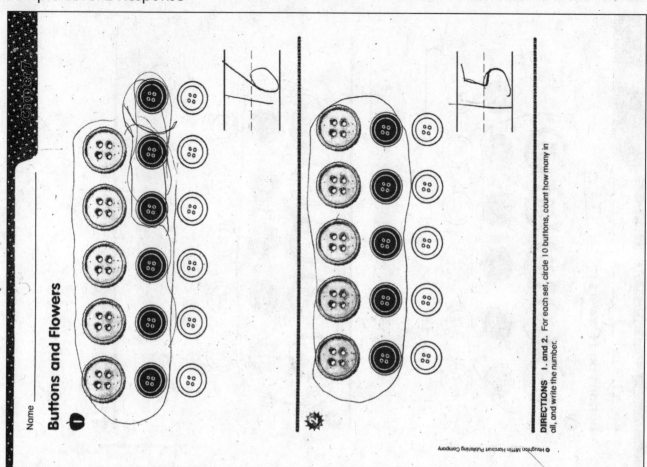

1. 16

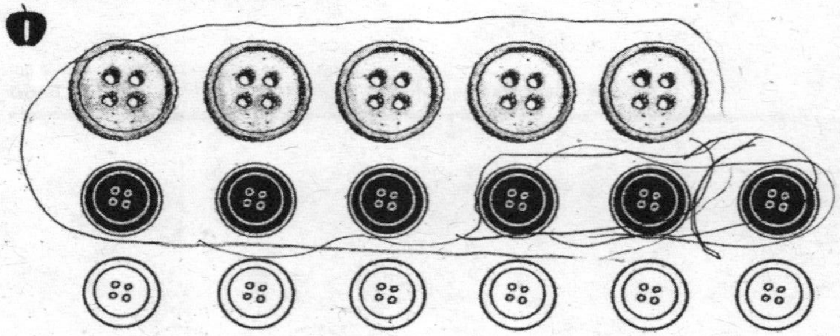

2. 15

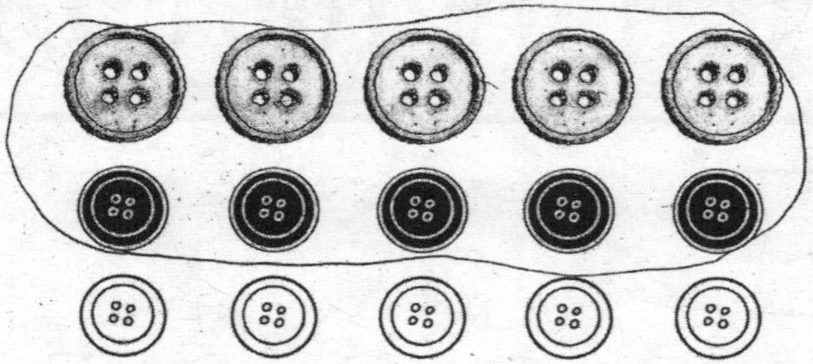

DIRECTIONS 1. and 2. For each set, circle 10 buttons, count how many in all, and write the number.

3. 18

4.

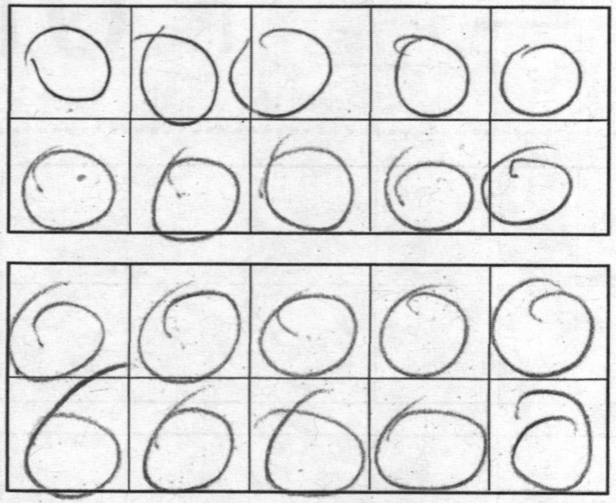

5. 10 + 8 = 18

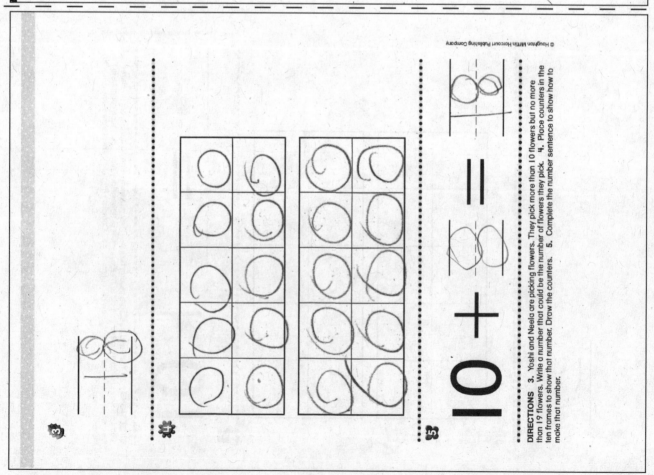

DIRECTIONS 3. Yoshi and Neela are picking flowers. They pick more than 10 flowers but no more than 19 flowers. Write a number that could be the number of flowers they pick. 4. Place counters in the ten frames to show that number. Draw the counters. 5. Complete the number sentence to show how to make that number.

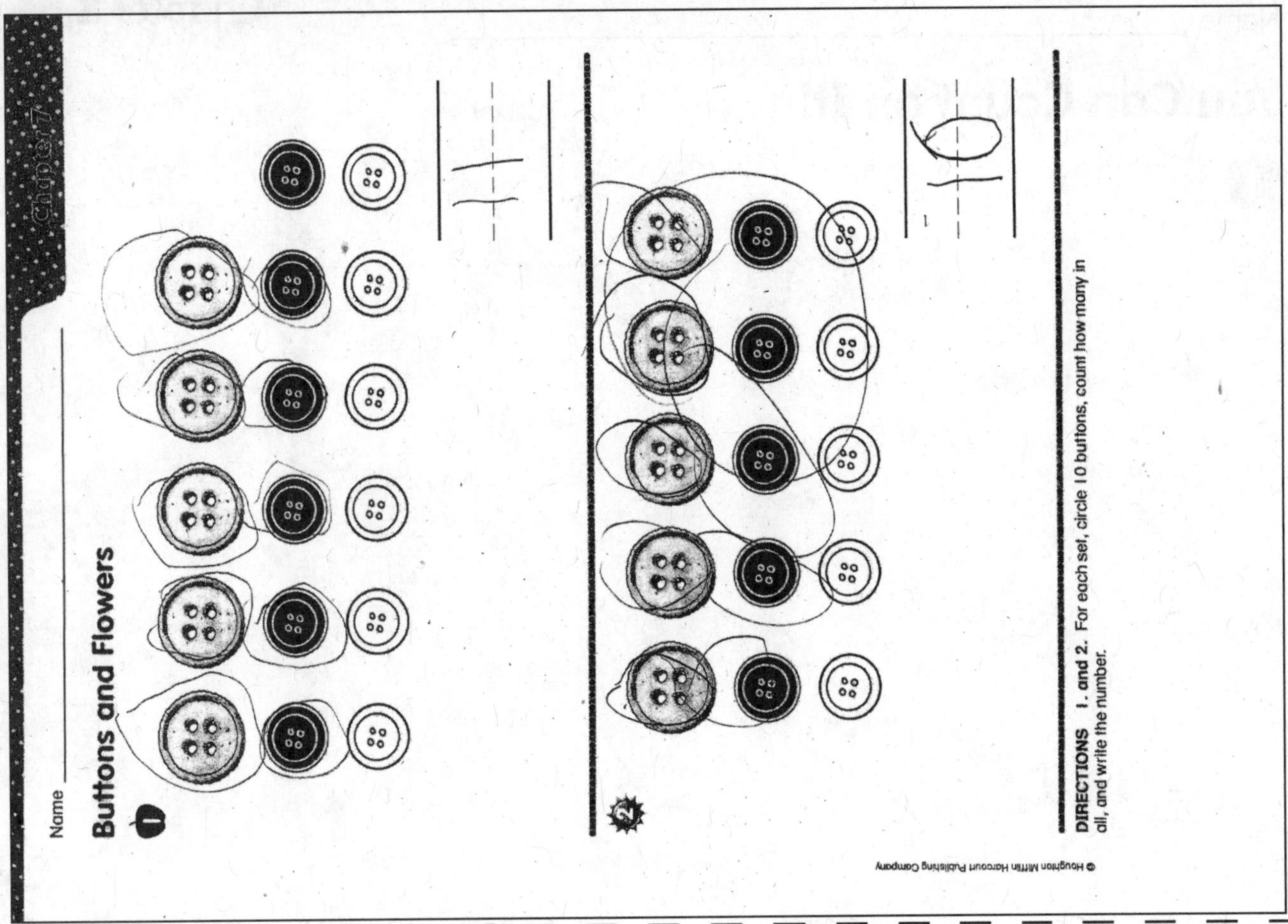

Chapter 7
Name
Buttons and Flowers
1
2
DIRECTIONS 1. and 2. For each set, circle 10 buttons, count how many in all, and write the number.
© Houghton Mifflin Harcourt Publishing Company

3
4
5
10 + ___ = ___
DIRECTIONS 3. Yoshi and Neela are picking flowers. They pick more than 10 flowers but no more than 19 flowers. Write a number that could be the number of flowers they pick. 4. Place counters in the ten frames to show that number. Draw the counters. 5. Complete the number sentence to show how to make that number.
© Houghton Mifflin Harcourt Publishing Company

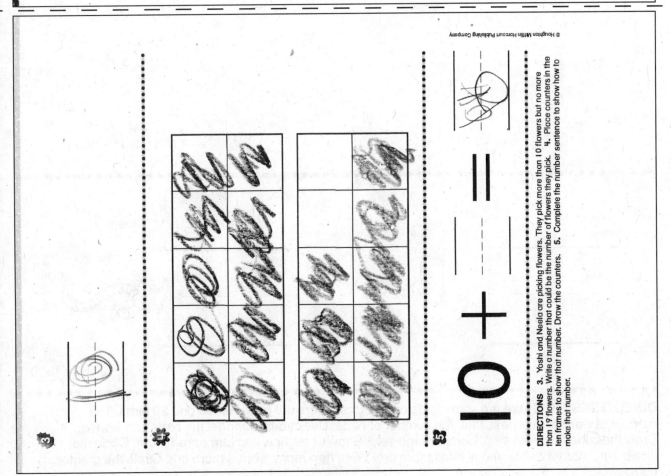

Name ____________________

You Can Count on It!

2

____ ____

DIRECTIONS **1.** There are some birds and worms. There are between 15 and 20 birds. The number of worms is two less than the number of birds. Use cubes to model the birds and worms. Draw the cubes for both sets. Compare the sets. Show or tell how you compared them. Circle the larger set. **2.** Write how many birds there are. Write how many worms there are. Circle the greater number.

3

51	52	53	54	55		57	58	59	60
61	62		64	65	66	67	68	69	70
71	72	73	74			77	78	79	
	82	83	84	85	86		88	89	90
91	92	93		95	96	97	98	99	100

4

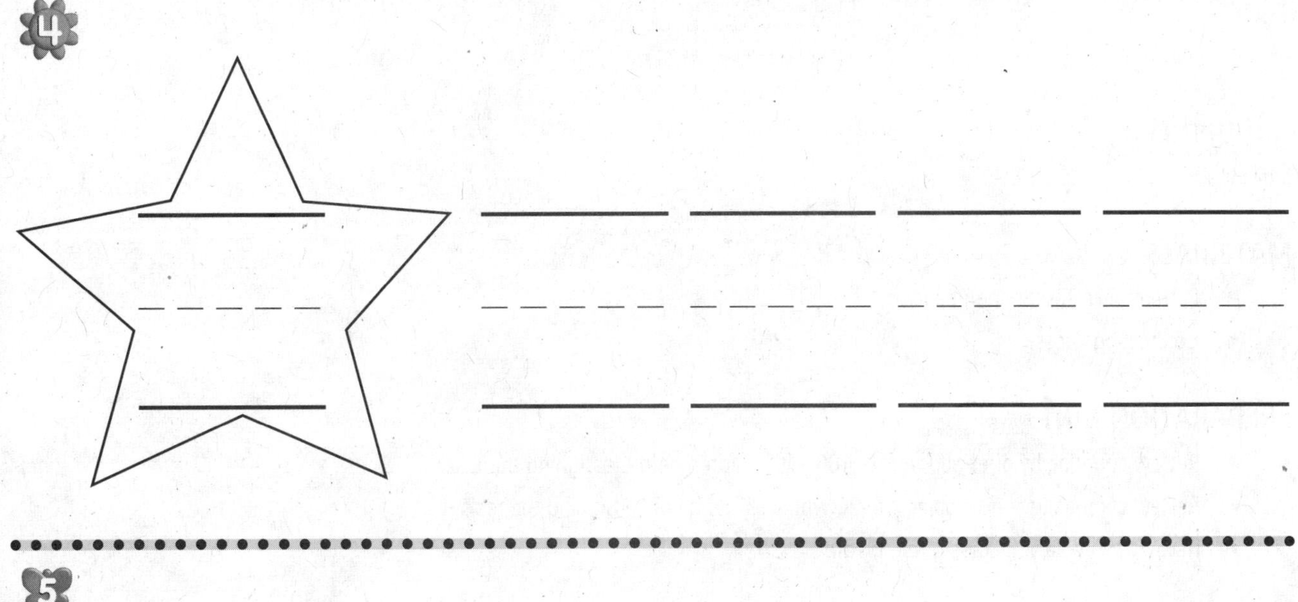

5

60

DIRECTIONS **3.** Complete the number chart. **4.** Circle one of the new numbers you wrote on the chart. Write that number in the star. Count forward from that number. Use the chart to help. Write the numbers you count. **5.** Start at 60. Count by tens to 100. Write the numbers you count. On the chart, circle the numbers that you counted.

Represent, Count, and Write 20 and Beyond

You Can Count on It!

COMMON CORE STANDARDS

K.CC.1 Count to 100 by ones and tens.

K.CC.2 Count forward beginning from a given number within the known sequence (instead of having to begin at 1).

K.CC.3 Write numbers from 0 to 20. Represent a number of objects with a written numeral 0 to 20 (with 0 representing a count of no objects).

K.CC.6 Identify whether the number of objects in one group is greater than, less than, or equal to the number of objects in another group, e.g., by using matching and counting strategies.

Also K.CC.5

PURPOSE

To assess the ability to model, count, and compare numbers to 20; to count to 100 by ones and tens; and to count forward from a given number

TIME

25–30 minutes

GROUPING

Individuals

MATERIALS

- Performance Task, paper, pencil
- Connecting cubes

PREPARATION HINTS

- Review counting by ones and tens to 100 with children before assigning the task.
- Review comparing sets of objects to 20 with children before assigning the task.
- Review vocabulary, including *ten, greater, less.*

IMPLEMENTATION NOTES

- Read the task aloud to children and make sure that all children have a clear understanding of the task.
- Children may use manipulatives to complete the task.
- Allow children as much paper as they need to complete the task.
- Allow as much time as children need to complete the task.
- Children must complete the task individually, without collaboration.
- Collect all work when the task is complete.

TASK SUMMARY

Children model, compare, and write numbers to represent quantities to 20. They count by ones and tens to 100 and count forward from a given number.

REPRESENTATION

In this task teachers can…

- Provide options for language, mathematical expressions and symbols by reviewing vocabulary and symbols in the context of children's prior knowledge.
- Provide options for comprehension by using cues to draw attention to critical features.

ACTION and EXPRESSION

In this task teachers can…

- Provide options for physical action by encouraging children to tap or make marks on their hundred chart to help them count.

ENGAGEMENT

In this task teachers can…

- Sustain effort and persistence by providing specific feedback.
- Develop reflection by asking children to explain their process.

EXPECTED STUDENT OUTCOMES

- Complete the task within the time allowed
- Reflect engagement in a productive struggle
- Model, count, compare, and write numbers to 20
- Count to 100 by ones and tens

SCORING

Use the associated Rubric to evaluate each child's work.

Performance Task Rubric

YOU CAN COUNT ON IT!	
A level 3 response	• Indicates that the child has made sense of the task and persevered • Demonstrates an understanding of how to model, count, write, and compare numbers to 20 • Demonstrates an understanding of the count sequence to 100 • Shows the ability to accurately apply base ten concepts to count by tens to 100
A level 2 response	• Indicates that the child has made sense of the task and persevered • Demonstrates an understanding of how to model, count, write, and compare numbers to 20 • Demonstrates an understanding of the count sequence to 100 • Shows the ability to accurately apply base ten concepts to count by tens to 100 • Addresses most or all aspects of the task, but there may be errors of omission
A level 1 response	• Shows that the child has made sense of at least some elements of the task • Gives evidence of understanding the count sequence to 100 • Shows some ability to count, model, and represent numbers to 20 • May not accurately compare numbers or count by tens
A level 0 response	• Shows little evidence that the child has made sense of the problems of the task • Reflects a lack of understanding of modeling, counting, writing, and comparing numbers to 20 • Reflects a lack of understanding of the count sequence to 100 and counting by tens • Shows little evidence of addressing the elements of the task

Name ______________________

CRITICAL AREA Number and Operations

How Many Marbles?

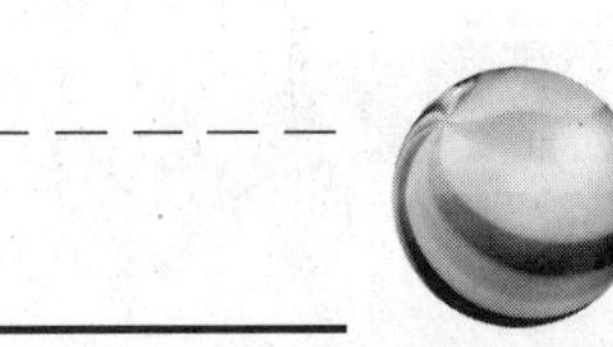

2

______ — ______ = ______

DIRECTIONS 1. Draw 8 marbles. Write the number of marbles you drew. 2. Cross out 3 or 4 marbles. Write an equation to show how many marbles are left.

3

$$10 = \underline{\quad} + \underline{\quad}$$

$$10 = \underline{\quad} + \underline{\quad}$$

DIRECTIONS Use counters. **3.** Bo has 7 blue marbles. Then he gets some red marbles. Now he has 10 marbles in all. Draw Bo's marbles. Write an equation to tell about Bo's marbles. **4.** Mia has 10 marbles. Four of her marbles are yellow and the rest are green. Draw Mia's marbles. Write an equation to tell about Mia's marbles.

Name ______________________________

5 ____________

6

7

10 + ______ = ______

DIRECTIONS 5. Rory has 16, 17, or 18 marbles. Write a number that could be Rory's marbles. 6. Place counters in the ten frames to show that number. Draw the counters. 7. Complete the equation to show how to make that number.

9

DIRECTIONS **8.** There are 6 bags of marbles on the table. Each bag has 10 marbles. Draw the bags of marbles. Count by tens to show how many marbles in all. Write the number. **9.** Sam has 14 marbles. Liam has 2 more marbles than Sam. Draw both sets of marbles. Circle the set that has a greater number of marbles.

Critical Area: Number and Operations

How Many Marbles?

COMMON CORE STANDARDS

K.CC.1 Count to 100 by ones and tens.

K.CC.6 Identify whether the number of objects in one group is greater than, less than, or equal to the number of objects in another group, e.g., by using matching and counting strategies.

K.OA.2 Solve addition and subtraction word problems, and add and subtract within 10, e.g., by using objects or drawings to represent the problem.

K.OA.3 Decompose numbers less than or equal to 10 into pairs in more than one way, e.g., by using objects or drawings, and record each decomposition by a drawing or equation.

K.NBT.1 Compose and decompose numbers from 11 to 19 into ten ones and some further ones, e.g., by using objects or drawings, and record each composition or decomposition by a drawing or equation (e.g., $18 = 10 + 8$); understand that these numbers are composed of ten ones and one, two, three, four, five, six, seven, eight, or nine ones.

Also K.CC.3, K.CC.4c, K.OA.1

PURPOSE

To assess the ability to represent and solve addition and subtraction within 10; to decompose numbers within 19 into pairs of addends; to count to 100 by tens; and to use strategies to compare quantities of objects

TIME

40–45 minutes

GROUPING

Individuals

MATERIALS

- Performance Task, paper, pencil
- Two-color counters
- Crayons or colored pencils
- Ten frames (optional)

PREPARATION HINTS

- Review writing addition and subtraction sentences with children before assigning the task.
- Review decomposing numbers to 19 into pairs of addends with children before assigning the task.
- Review counting to 100 by tens with children before assigning the task.
- Review comparing quantities of objects with children before assigning the task.
- Review vocabulary, including *equation, tens, greater, less*.

IMPLEMENTATION NOTES

- Read the task aloud to children and make sure that all children have a clear understanding of the task.

- Children may use manipulatives to complete the task.
- Allow children as much paper as they need to complete the task.
- Allow as much time as children need to complete the task.
- Children must complete the task individually, without collaboration.
- Collect all work when the task is complete.

TASK SUMMARY

Children model and write number sentences to represent and solve addition and subtraction problems within 10. They decompose numbers to 19 into pairs of addends. They count within 100 by tens and use strategies to compare numbers.

REPRESENTATION

In this task teachers can…

- Provide options for language, mathematical expressions and symbols by reviewing vocabulary and symbols in the context of children's prior knowledge.
- Provide options for comprehension by using cues to draw attention to critical features.

ACTION and EXPRESSION

In this task teachers can…

- Provide options for physical action by offering counters and ten frames to children while completing the task.

ENGAGEMENT

In this task teachers can…

- Provide options for self-assessment by reviewing the goals for each part of the task.
- Develop reflection by asking children to explain their process.

EXPECTED STUDENT OUTCOMES

- Complete the task within the time allowed
- Reflect engagement in a productive struggle
- Model and write equations to solve addition and subtraction problems within 10 and to decompose numbers to 19 into pairs of addends
- Count to 100 by tens
- Use strategies to compare quantities of objects

SCORING

Use the associated Rubric to evaluate each child's work.

Performance Task Rubric

HOW MANY MARBLES?	
A level 3 response	• Indicates that the child has made sense of the task and persevered • Demonstrates an understanding of using models and equations to represent addition and subtraction and to decompose numbers • Shows the ability to accurately count by tens within 100 and compare numbers
A level 2 response	• Indicates that the child has made sense of the task and persevered • Demonstrates an understanding of using models and equations to represent addition and subtraction and to decompose numbers • Shows the ability to accurately count by tens within 100 and compare numbers • Addresses most or all aspects of the task, but there may be errors of omission
A level 1 response	• Shows that the child has made sense of at least some elements of the task • Shows evidence of understanding of using models and equations to add, subtract, and decompose numbers • Shows some ability to count by tens within 100 and compare numbers • May represent some numbers inaccurately
A level 0 response	• Shows little evidence that the child has made sense of the problems of the task • Reflects a lack of understanding of modeling and representing addition, subtraction, and decomposition • Reflects a lack of understanding of counting by tens and comparing numbers • Shows little evidence of addressing the elements of the task

Name ______________________________

Shape Pictures

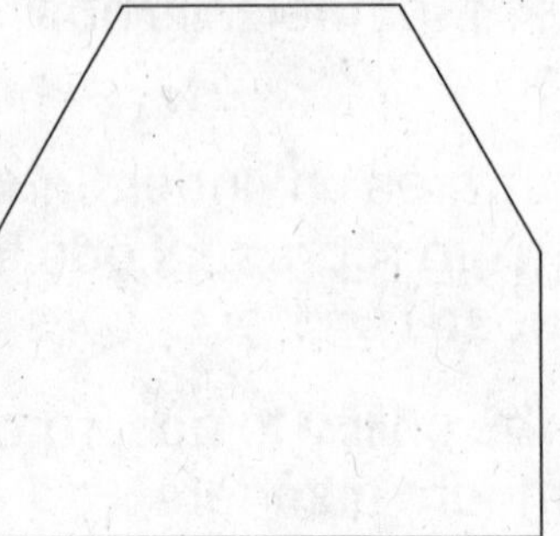

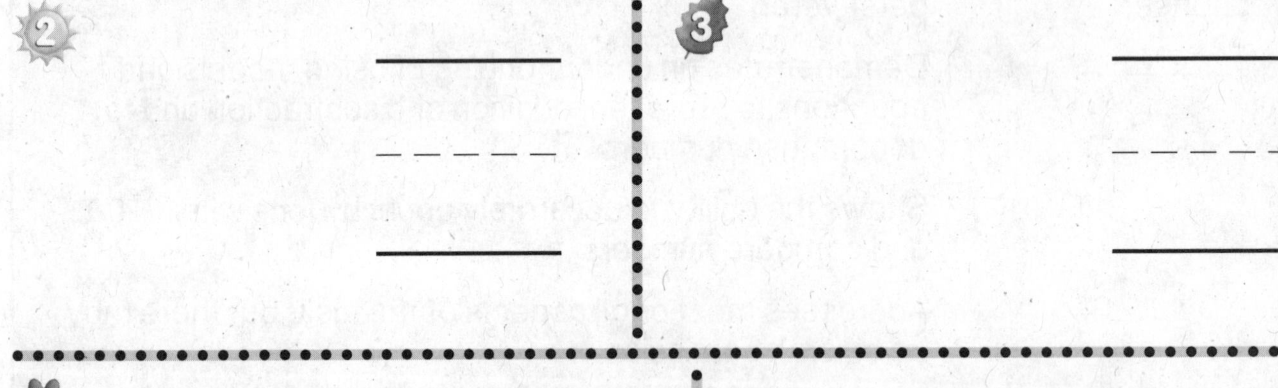

4

______ sides

______ vertices

______ sides

______ vertices

DIRECTIONS 1. Use your shapes. Put shapes together to make the big shape. Draw to show how you put the shapes together. **2.** Draw one of the shapes you used. Write how many of that shape you used. **3.** Draw a different shape you used. Write how many of that shape you used. **4.** Name the kinds of shapes you used. Tell how many sides and vertices each shape has.

5

6

alike	different

DIRECTIONS Use your shapes. **5.** Draw or trace a shape with 3 sides and 3 vertices. Draw or trace a shape with 4 sides and 4 vertices. Draw or trace a curved shape. Draw or trace a shape with sides of equal length. Draw or trace some more shapes of your choice. **6.** Think about a way to sort the shapes. Draw what you did. Explain how you sorted the shapes.

Identify and Describe Two-Dimensional Shapes

Shape Pictures

COMMON CORE STANDARDS

K.G.2 Correctly name shapes regardless of their orientations or overall size.

K.G.4 Analyze and compare two- and three-dimensional shapes, in different sizes and orientations, using informal language to describe their similarities, differences, parts (e.g., number of sides and vertices/"corners") and other attributes (e.g., having sides of equal length).

K.G.6 Compose simple shapes to form larger shapes.

PURPOSE

To assess the ability to identify, analyze, draw, and compose two-dimensional shapes

TIME

25–30 minutes

GROUPING

Individuals

MATERIALS

- Performance Task, paper, pencil
- Two-dimensional shapes (squares, triangles, circles, rectangles)

PREPARATION HINTS

- Review identifying and describing two-dimensional shapes with children before assigning the task.
- Review joining shapes with children before assigning the task.
- Review vocabulary, including *triangle, square, sides, vertices, curved*.

IMPLEMENTATION NOTES

- Read the task aloud to children and make sure that all children have a clear understanding of the task.
- Children may use manipulatives to complete the task.
- Allow children as much paper as they need to complete the task.
- Allow as much time as children need to complete the task.
- Children must complete the task individually, without collaboration.
- Collect all work when the task is complete.

TASK SUMMARY

Children identify two-dimensional shapes. They model composing simple shapes to form larger shapes. They recognize attributes of two-dimensional shapes including number of sides and vertices. They compare and sort shapes based on attributes.

REPRESENTATION

In this task teachers can…

- Provide options for comprehension by setting guidelines for use of manipulatives and helping children make connections between objects and pictures.

ACTION and EXPRESSION

In this task teachers can…

- Provide options for physical action by modeling strategies for accurate drawing.
- Provide options for executive functions by promoting a trial-and-error approach to problem solving.

ENGAGEMENT

In this task teachers can…

- Sustain effort and persistence by emphasizing problem solving as a challenging process with a clear end goal.
- Enhance motivation by noticing and valuing improvement.

EXPECTED STUDENT OUTCOMES

- Complete the task within the time allowed
- Reflect engagement in a productive struggle
- Identify and recognize attributes of two-dimensional shapes
- Model composing simple shapes into larger shapes
- Compare and sort shapes based on attributes

SCORING

Use the associated Rubric to evaluate each child's work.

Performance Task Rubric

SHAPE PICTURES	
A level 3 response	• Indicates that the child has made sense of the task and persevered • Shows ability to apply understanding of two-dimensional shapes to identify and draw shapes • Shows ability to compose simple shapes into larger shapes • Demonstrates an understanding of specific attributes of two-dimensional shapes
A level 2 response	• Indicates that the child has made sense of the task and persevered • Shows ability to apply understanding of two-dimensional shapes to identify and draw shapes • Shows ability to compose simple shapes into larger shapes • Demonstrates an understanding of specific attributes of two-dimensional shapes • Addresses most or all aspects of the task, but there may be errors of omission
A level 1 response	• Shows that the child has made sense of at least some elements of the task • Shows some ability to identify, draw, and compose shapes • Shows evidence of understanding of specific attributes of two-dimensional shapes • May not accurately represent some shapes
A level 0 response	• Shows little evidence that the child has made sense of the problems of the task • Reflects a lack of understanding of basic two-dimensional shapes and their attributes • Does not accurately represent and compose shapes • Shows little evidence of addressing the elements of the task

Name ______________________________

Shape Safari

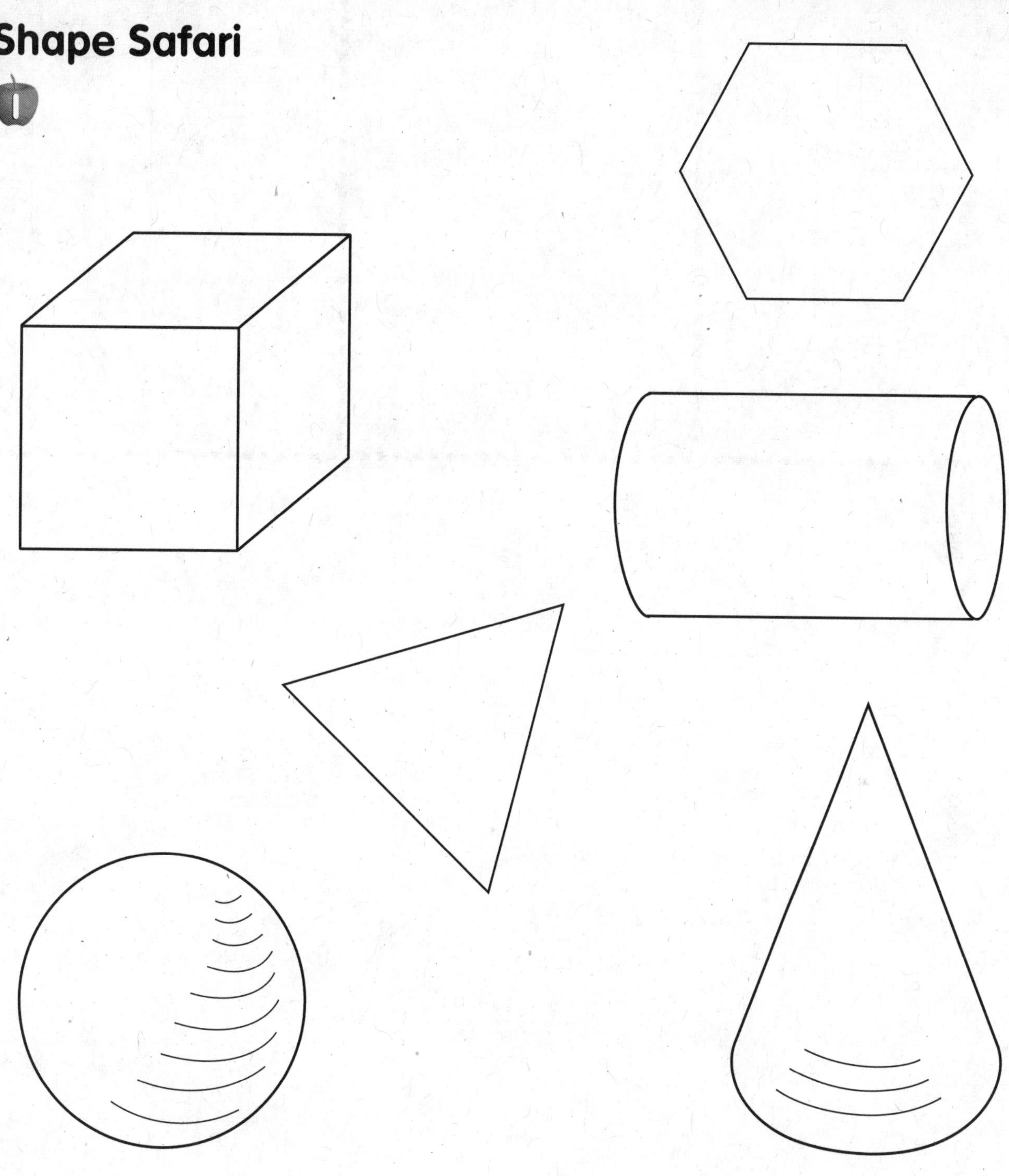

DIRECTIONS **1.** If it has one flat surface and can roll, color it blue. If it has six flat surfaces and can stack, color it yellow. If it has three sides and three vertices, color it orange. If it has no flat surfaces and can roll, color it green. If it has six sides and six vertices, color it purple. If it has two flat surfaces and can roll, color it red. Write the name of each shape you colored. Circle the shapes that are three-dimensional. Cross out the shapes that are two-dimensional. Choose two of the three-dimensional shapes. Tell or write about how they are alike and different.

2

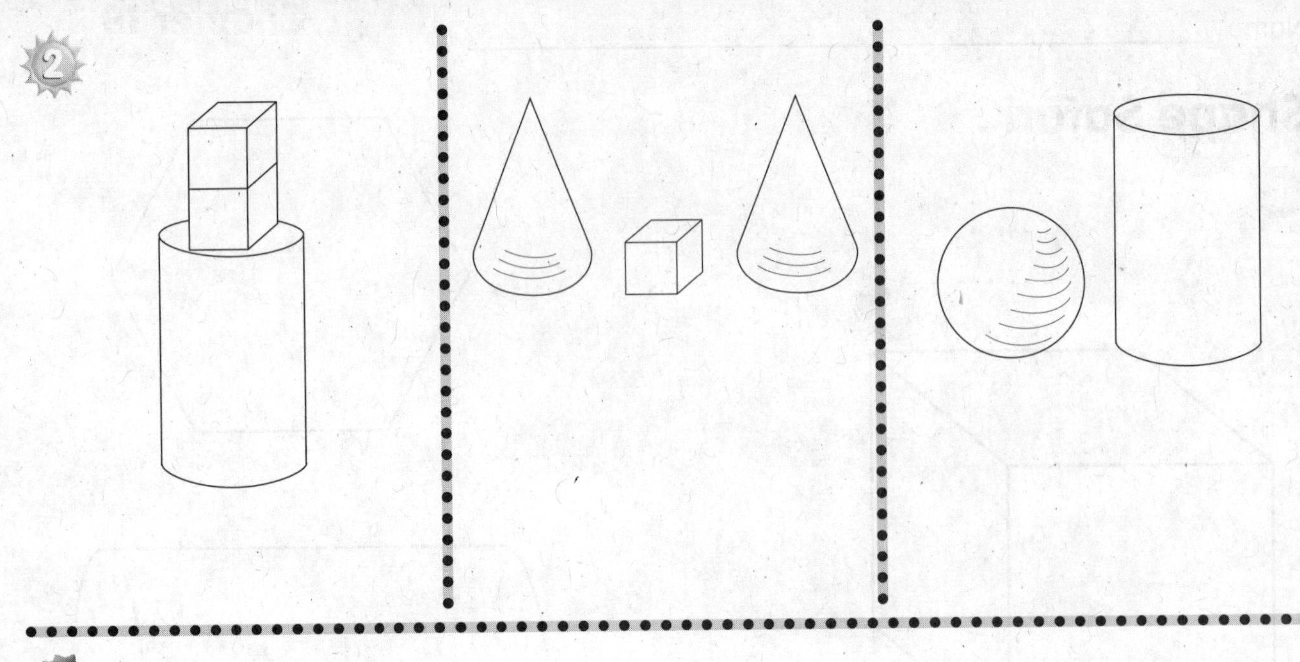

3

DIRECTIONS **2.** Circle the set that shows a cube between two cones. Put a line under the set that shows a sphere next to a cylinder. Put an X on the set that shows 2 cubes above a cylinder. **3.** Draw a sphere with a cube below it. Draw a cone beside your sphere. Tell or write about where you placed your shapes.

Identify and Describe Three-Dimensional Shapes

Shape Safari

COMMON CORE STANDARDS

K.G.1 Describe objects in the environment using names of shapes, and describe the relative positions of these objects using terms such as *above, below, beside, in front of, behind,* and *next to.*

K.G.2 Correctly name shapes regardless of their orientations or overall size.

K.G.3 Identify shapes as two-dimensional (lying in a plane, "flat") or three-dimensional ("solid").

K.G.4 Analyze and compare two- and three-dimensional shapes, in different sizes and orientations, using informal language to describe their similarities, differences, parts (e.g., number of sides and vertices / "corners") and other attributes (e.g., having sides of equal length).

PURPOSE

To assess the ability to identify two- and three-dimensional shapes and their attributes; to distinguish between two- and three-dimensional shapes; and to describe the position of objects in the environment

TIME

25–30 minutes

GROUPING

Individuals

MATERIALS

- Performance Task, paper, pencil
- Crayons or colored pencils
- Three-dimensional shapes (optional)

PREPARATION HINTS

- Review names and attributes of two- and three-dimensional shapes with children before assigning the task.
- Review describing the position of shapes in the environment with children before assigning the task.
- Review vocabulary, including *flat surface, roll, stack, sphere, cube, cylinder, cone, sides, vertices, square, triangle, rectangle, hexagon, circle.*

IMPLEMENTATION NOTES

- Read the task aloud to children and make sure that all children have a clear understanding of the task.
- Children may use manipulatives to complete the task.
- Allow children as much paper as they need to complete the task.
- Allow as much time as children need to complete the task.
- Children must complete the task individually, without collaboration.
- Collect all work when the task is complete.

TASK SUMMARY

Children analyze three-dimensional shapes based on attributes such as number of flat surfaces and whether they can stack and roll. They analyze two-dimensional shapes based on number of sides and vertices. Children identify two- and three-dimensional shapes by name. They describe the position of objects in the environment.

REPRESENTATION

In this task teachers can…

- Offer alternatives for visual information by displaying models of three-dimensional shapes.
- Provide options for comprehension by reviewing real-world examples of vocabulary terms.

ACTION and EXPRESSION

In this task teachers can…

- Provide options for physical action by allowing children to use three-dimensional shape models while completing the task.

ENGAGEMENT

In this task teachers can…

- Recruit interest by modeling the shapes and configurations depicted in the task using three-dimensional models after children have turned in work.
- Sustain effort and persistence by breaking goals into small steps.

EXPECTED STUDENT OUTCOMES

- Complete the task within the time allowed
- Reflect engagement in a productive struggle
- Identify two- and three-dimensional shapes and their attributes
- Describe location of objects in the environment

SCORING

Use the associated Rubric to evaluate each child's work.

Performance Task Rubric

SHAPE SAFARI	
A level 3 response	• Indicates that the child has made sense of the task and persevered • Demonstrates understanding of attributes of two- and three-dimensional shapes • Demonstrates understanding of words used to describe locations of objects in environment • Shows ability to name and identify shapes
A level 2 response	• Indicates that the child has made sense of the task and persevered • Demonstrates understanding of attributes of two- and three-dimensional shapes • Demonstrates understanding of words used to describe locations of objects in environment • Shows ability to name and identify shapes • Addresses most or all aspects of the task, but there may be errors of omission
A level 1 response	• Shows that the child has made sense of at least some elements of the task • Shows evidence of understanding of some attributes of two- and three-dimensional shapes • Shows understanding of words used to describe locations of objects in environment • May not accurately name and identify some shapes
A level 0 response	• Shows little evidence that the child has made sense of the problems of the task • Reflects a lack of understanding of names or attributes of two- and three-dimensional shapes • Reflects a lack of understanding of words used to describe locations of objects in environment • Shows little evidence of addressing the elements of the task

Name ______________________ CRITICAL AREA Geometry and Positions

Shapes, Shapes, Shapes!

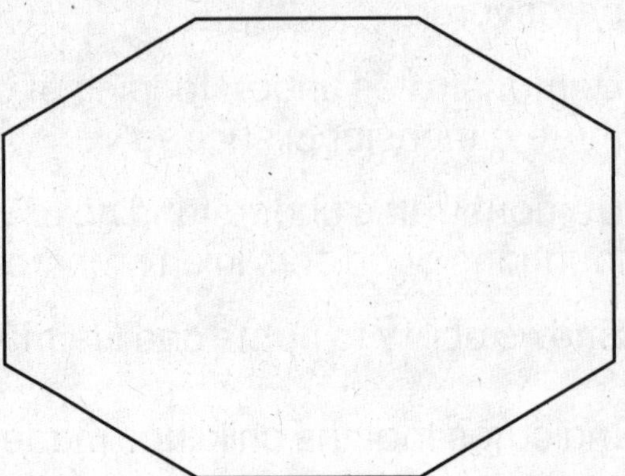

2

3

DIRECTIONS **1.** Use triangles and squares to create the big shape. Draw the shapes you used. **2.** How many triangles did you draw? Write the number. **3.** How many squares did you draw? Write the number.

DIRECTIONS Use your shapes. **4.** Trace the rectangle. Color it green. Above the green shape, draw a shape with no sides and no vertices. Color this shape yellow. Under the green shape, draw a shape that has 3 sides and 3 vertices. Color this shape blue. Next to the blue shape, draw a shape that has 6 sides and 6 vertices. Color this shape red. Put an X on any shape that has more than 3 sides.

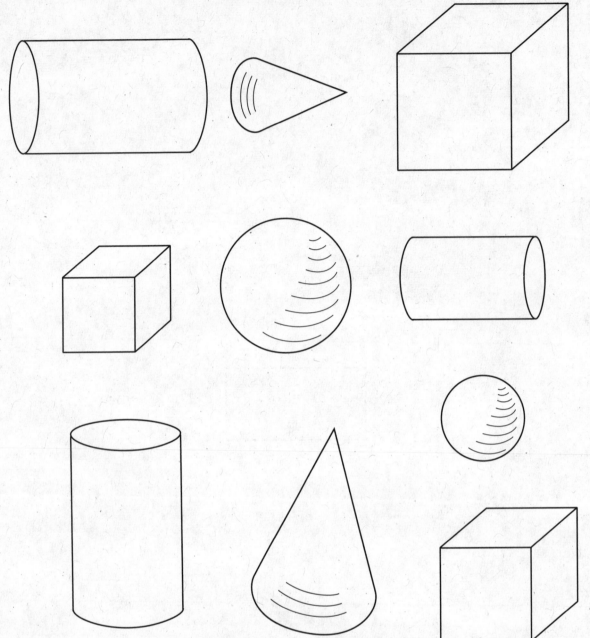

DIRECTIONS 5. Find all the shapes that have no flat surfaces and can roll. Color them red. Find all the shapes that have six flat surfaces and can stack. Color them blue. Find all the shapes that have one flat surface and can roll. Color them green. Find all the shapes that have two flat surfaces and can roll. Color them yellow.

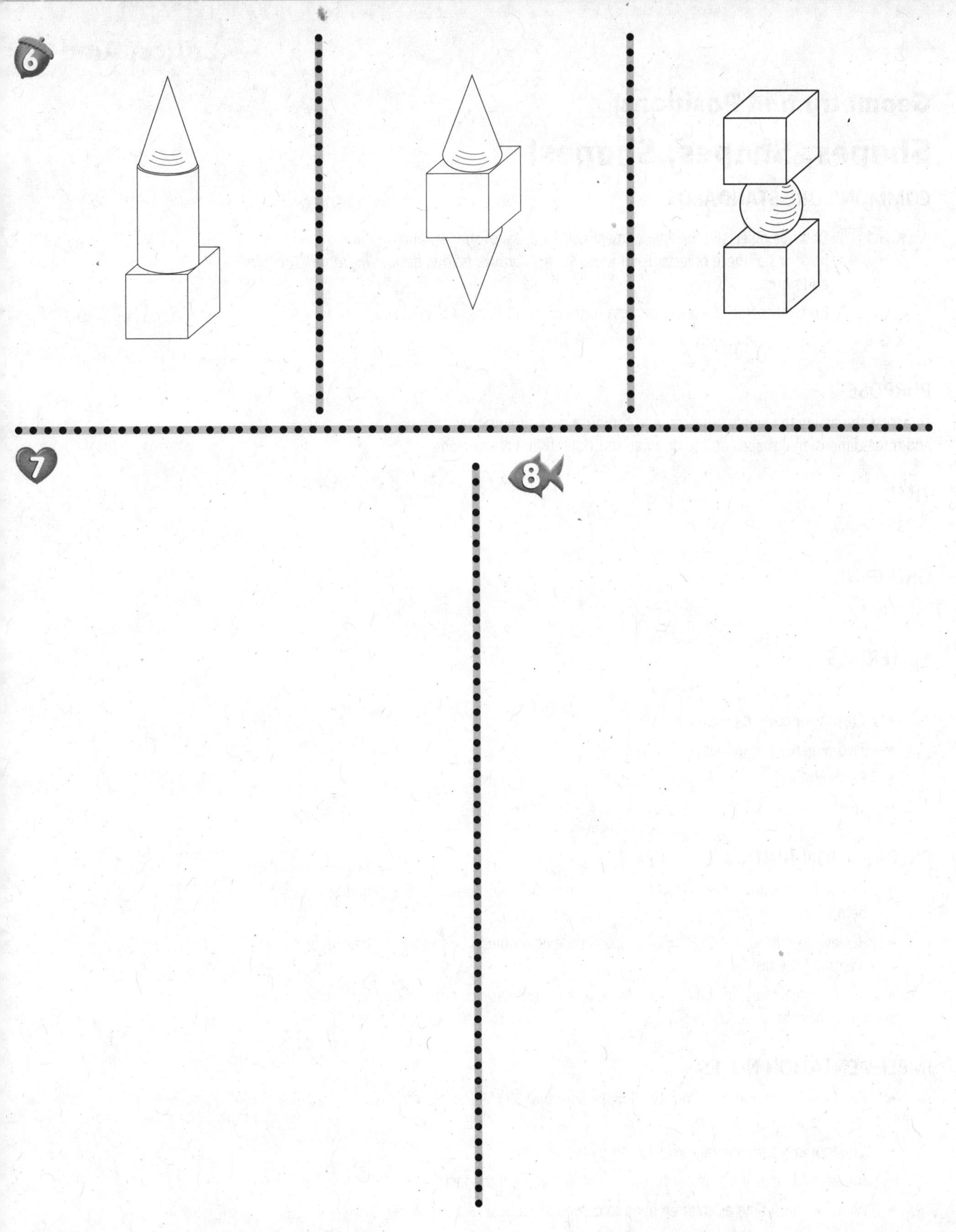

DIRECTIONS 6. John is moving to a new house. He wants to stack items on a moving truck. Circle the picture that shows a way John could stack his items. Then find a picture with cubes that are above and below a sphere. Color that picture. 7. Draw a way that John could stack a cube and a cone. Tell or write how you stacked the shapes. 8. Draw a shape that can roll next to a shape that cannot roll. Write the names of the shapes you drew.

Geometry and Positions

Shapes, Shapes, Shapes!

COMMON CORE STANDARDS

K.G.1 Describe objects in the environment using names of shapes, and describe the relative positions of these objects using terms such as *above, below, beside, in front of, behind,* and *next to*.

K.G.2 Correctly name shapes regardless of their orientations or overall size.

K.G.6 Compose simple shapes to form larger shapes.

PURPOSE

To assess the ability to identify, analyze, and compose two-dimensional and three-dimensional shapes and to describe shapes in their environment

TIME

25–30 minutes

GROUPING

Individuals

MATERIALS

- Performance Task, paper, pencil
- Crayons or colored pencils
- Two-dimensional shapes
- Pattern blocks
- Three-dimensional shapes (optional)

PREPARATION HINTS

- Review names and attributes of two- and three-dimensional shapes with children before assigning the task.
- Review describing the position of shapes in the environment with children before assigning the task.
- Review vocabulary, including *triangle, square, sides, vertices, flat surface, roll, stack, sphere, cube, cylinder, cone.*

IMPLEMENTATION NOTES

- Read the task aloud to children and make sure that all children have a clear understanding of the task.
- Children may use manipulatives to complete the task.
- Allow children as much paper as they need to complete the task.
- Allow as much time as children need to complete the task.
- Children must complete the task individually, without collaboration.
- Collect all work when the task is complete.

TASK SUMMARY

Children identify, analyze, and draw two- and three-dimensional shapes based on their attributes. They compose simple shapes into larger shapes and use words that describe positions of shapes in the environment.

REPRESENTATION

In this task teachers can…

- Offer alternatives for visual information by displaying models of three-dimensional shapes.
- Provide options for comprehension by reviewing two-dimensional representations of three-dimensional shapes.

ACTION and EXPRESSION

In this task teachers can…

- Provide options for physical action by allowing children to use three-dimensional shape models while completing the task.

ENGAGEMENT

In this task teachers can…

- Recruit interest by modeling the shapes and configurations depicted in the task using three-dimensional models after children have turned in work.
- Develop reflection by asking children to describe their drawings.

EXPECTED STUDENT OUTCOMES

- Complete the task within the time allowed
- Reflect engagement in a productive struggle
- Identify two- and three-dimensional shapes and their attributes
- Compose two- and three-dimensional shapes
- Describe location of objects in the environment

SCORING

Use the associated Rubric to evaluate each child's work.

Performance Task Rubric

SHAPES, SHAPES, SHAPES!	
A level 3 response	• Indicates that the child has made sense of the task and persevered • Demonstrates understanding of attributes of two- and three-dimensional shapes • Shows ability to name, identify, and compose shapes and locate them in the environment
A level 2 response	• Indicates that the child has made sense of the task and persevered • Demonstrates understanding of attributes of two- and three-dimensional shapes • Shows ability to name, identify, and compose shapes and locate them in the environment • Addresses most or all aspects of the task, but there may be errors of omission
A level 1 response	• Shows that the child has made sense of at least some elements of the task • Shows evidence of understanding of attributes of two- and three-dimensional shapes • Shows evidence of understanding of words used to describe locations of objects in environment • May not include accurate names, identifications, drawings, or compositions of shapes
A level 0 response	• Shows little evidence that the child has made sense of the problems of the task • Reflects a lack of understanding of how to name, analyze, or compose shapes • Reflects a lack of understanding of words used to describe locations of objects in environment • Shows little evidence of addressing the elements of the task

Name ______________________________

Weight, Length, and Height

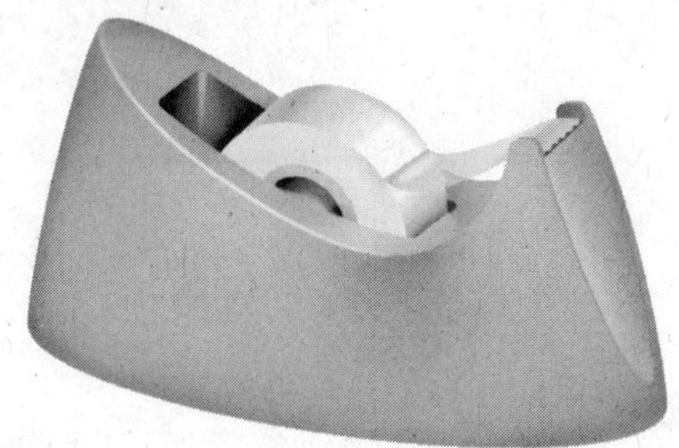

lighter

heavier

DIRECTIONS 1. Hold the classroom object pictured above in your hand. Find an object in the classroom that is heavier. Draw the object. Draw a picture of a classroom object that is lighter. Draw lines to match the words to the objects you drew.

2 

longer

shorter

taller

shorter

DIRECTIONS **2.** Draw a pencil that is shorter or longer than the crayon. Draw lines to match the words to the objects. **3.** Draw a plant that is taller or shorter than the first plant. Draw lines to match the words to the objects.

Measurement

Weight, Length, and Height

COMMON CORE STANDARDS

K.MD.1 Describe measurable attributes of objects, such as length or weight. Describe several measurable attributes of a single object.

K.MD.2 Directly compare two objects with a measurable attribute in common, to see which object has "more of"/"less of" the attribute, and describe the difference.

PURPOSE

To assess the ability to compare weights, lengths, and heights of objects using words such as *lighter, heavier, longer, shorter,* and *taller*

TIME

25–30 minutes

GROUPING

Individuals

MATERIALS

- Performance Task, paper, pencil
- Tape dispenser and assortment of classroom objects of varying weights

PREPARATION HINTS

- Review comparing lengths, heights, and weights with children before assigning the task.
- Review vocabulary, including *lighter, heavier, longer, shorter, taller.*

IMPLEMENTATION NOTES

- Read the task aloud to children and make sure that all children have a clear understanding of the task.
- Children may use manipulatives to complete the task.
- Allow children as much paper as they need to complete the task.
- Allow as much time as children need to complete the task.
- Children must complete the task individually, without collaboration.
- Collect all work when the task is complete.

TASK SUMMARY

Children compare weights, lengths, and heights of objects and pictures. They use words such as *lighter, heavier, longer, shorter,* and *taller* to describe the comparison.

REPRESENTATION

In this task teachers can…

- Provide options for language by using gestures to act out adjectives contained in the task.

ACTION and EXPRESSION

In this task teachers can…

- Provide options for physical action by allowing children to hold two objects at the same time to compare them.
- Provide options for expression and communication by allowing children to explain their drawings.

ENGAGEMENT

In this task teachers can…

- Optimize individual choice by encouraging children to choose different objects than their classmates.
- Foster collaboration and community by inviting children to share their ideas after the assignment has been turned in.

EXPECTED STUDENT OUTCOMES

- Complete the task within the time allowed
- Reflect engagement in a productive struggle
- Compare weights, lengths, and heights of objects and accurately describe the comparison

SCORING

Use the associated Rubric to evaluate each child's work.

Performance Task Rubric

WEIGHT, LENGTH, AND HEIGHT	
A level 3 response	• Indicates that the child has made sense of the task and persevered • Demonstrates an understanding of weight, length, and height • Indicates an understanding of how to compare weights, lengths, and heights • Accurately represents comparisons of length, width, and height using adjectives
A level 2 response	• Indicates that the child has made sense of the task and persevered • Demonstrates an understanding of weight, length, and height • Indicates an understanding of how to compare weights, lengths, and heights • Accurately represents comparisons of length, width, and height using adjectives • Addresses most or all aspects of the task, but there may be errors of omission
A level 1 response	• Shows that the child has made sense of at least some elements of the task • Shows evidence of understanding of weight, length, and height and how to compare them • May not accurately describe comparisons of weights, lengths, and heights using adjectives
A level 0 response	• Shows little evidence that the child has made sense of the problems of the task • Reflects a lack of understanding of weight, length, and height and how to compare them • Shows little evidence of addressing the elements of the task

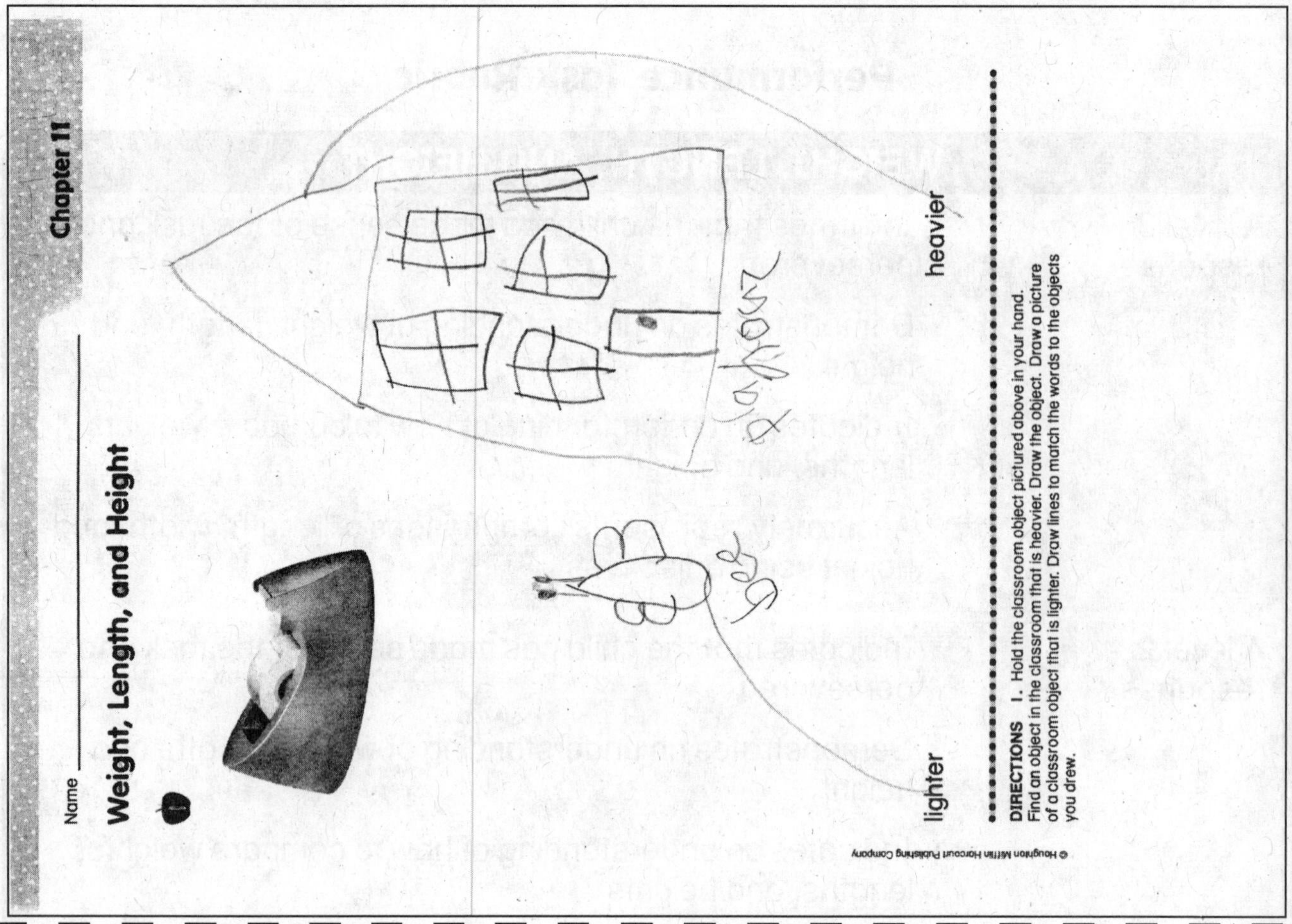

Chapter 11

Name ________

Weight, Length, and Height

lighter

heavier

DIRECTIONS **1.** Hold the classroom object pictured above in your hand. Find an object in the classroom that is heavier. Draw the object. Draw a picture of a classroom object that is lighter. Draw lines to match the words to the objects you drew.

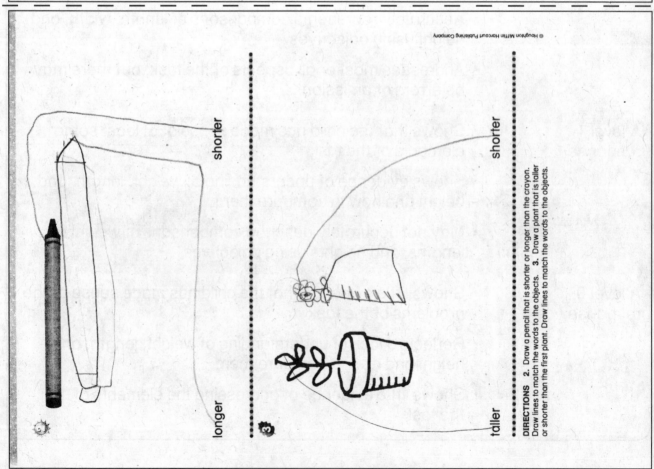

longer

shorter

taller

shorter

DIRECTIONS **2.** Draw a pencil that is shorter or longer than the crayon. Draw lines to match the words to the objects. **3.** Draw a plant that is taller or shorter than the first plant. Draw lines to match the words to the objects.

Sample Level 3 Response

Name ____________________

Weight, Length, and Height

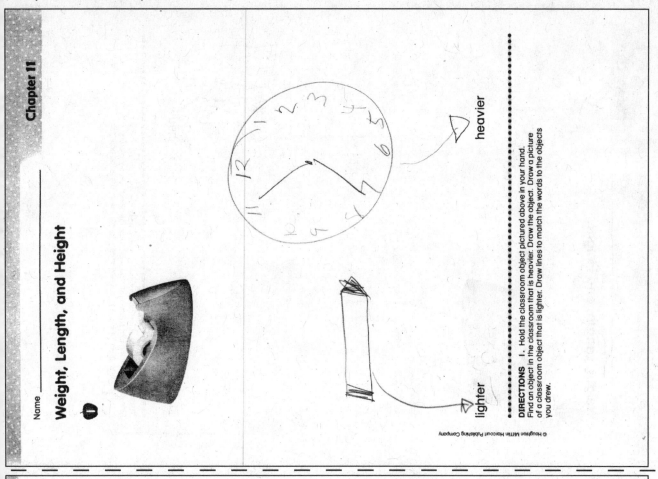

1

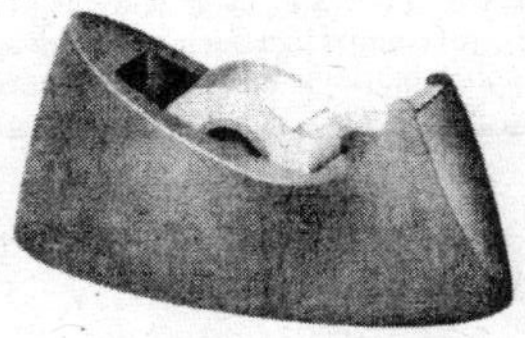

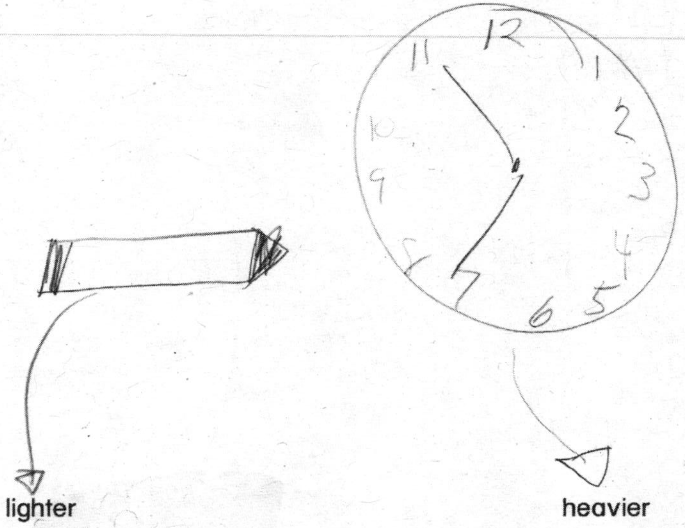

lighter

heavier

DIRECTIONS 1. Hold the classroom object pictured above in your hand. Find an object in the classroom that is heavier. Draw the object. Draw a picture of a classroom object that is lighter. Draw lines to match the words to the objects you drew.

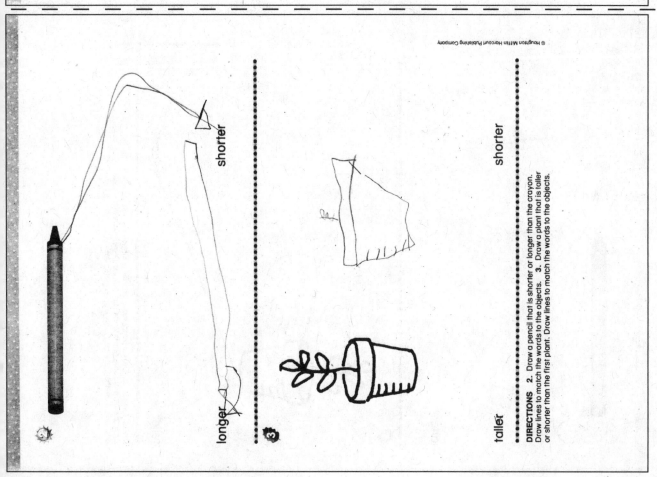

2

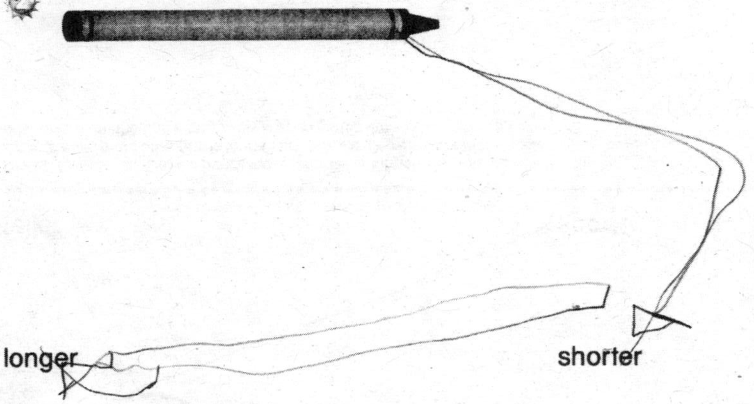

longer

shorter

3

taller

shorter

DIRECTIONS 2. Draw a pencil that is shorter or longer than the crayon. Draw lines to match the words to the objects. 3. Draw a plant that is taller or shorter than the first plant. Draw lines to match the words to the objects.

Chapter 11

Name

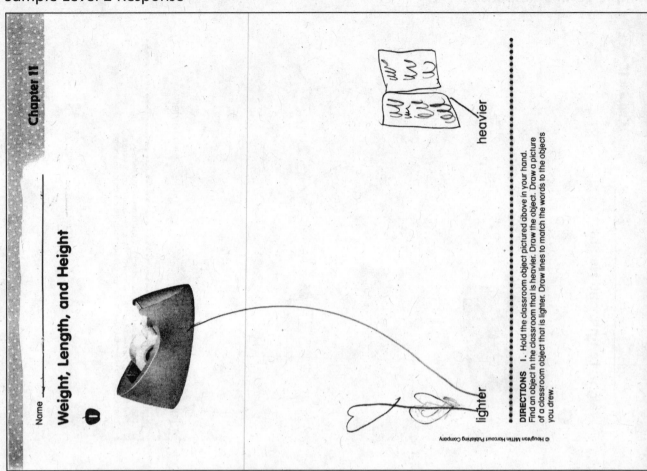

Weight, Length, and Height

1

lighter

heavier

DIRECTIONS 1. Hold the classroom object pictured above in your hand. Find an object in the classroom that is heavier. Draw the object. Draw a picture of a classroom object that is lighter. Draw lines to match the words to the objects you drew.

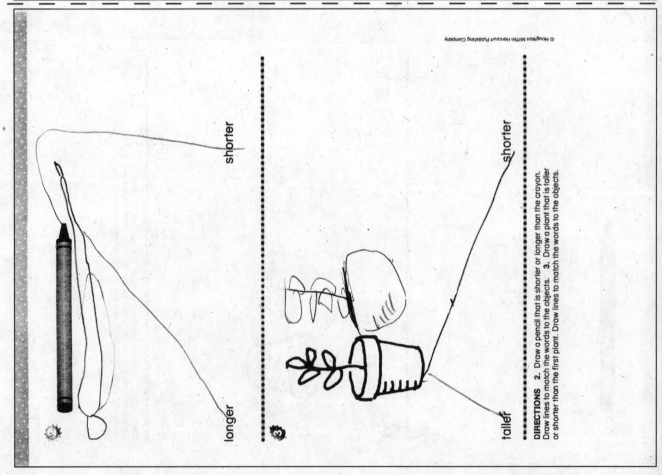

2

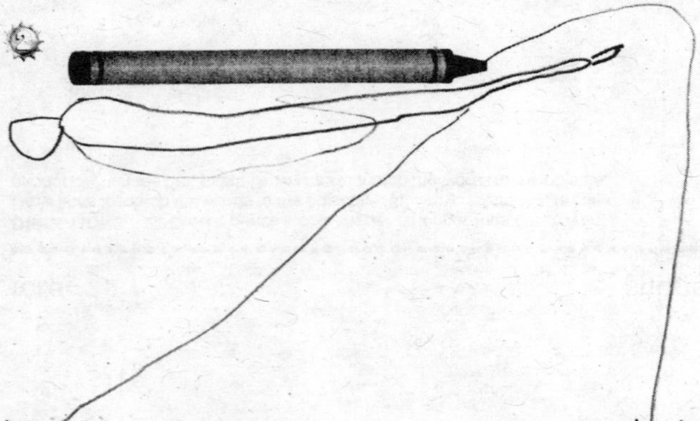

longer

shorter

3

taller

shorter

DIRECTIONS 2. Draw a pencil that is shorter or longer than the crayon. Draw lines to match the words to the objects. 3. Draw a plant that is taller or shorter than the first plant. Draw lines to match the words to the objects.

Sample Level 1 Response

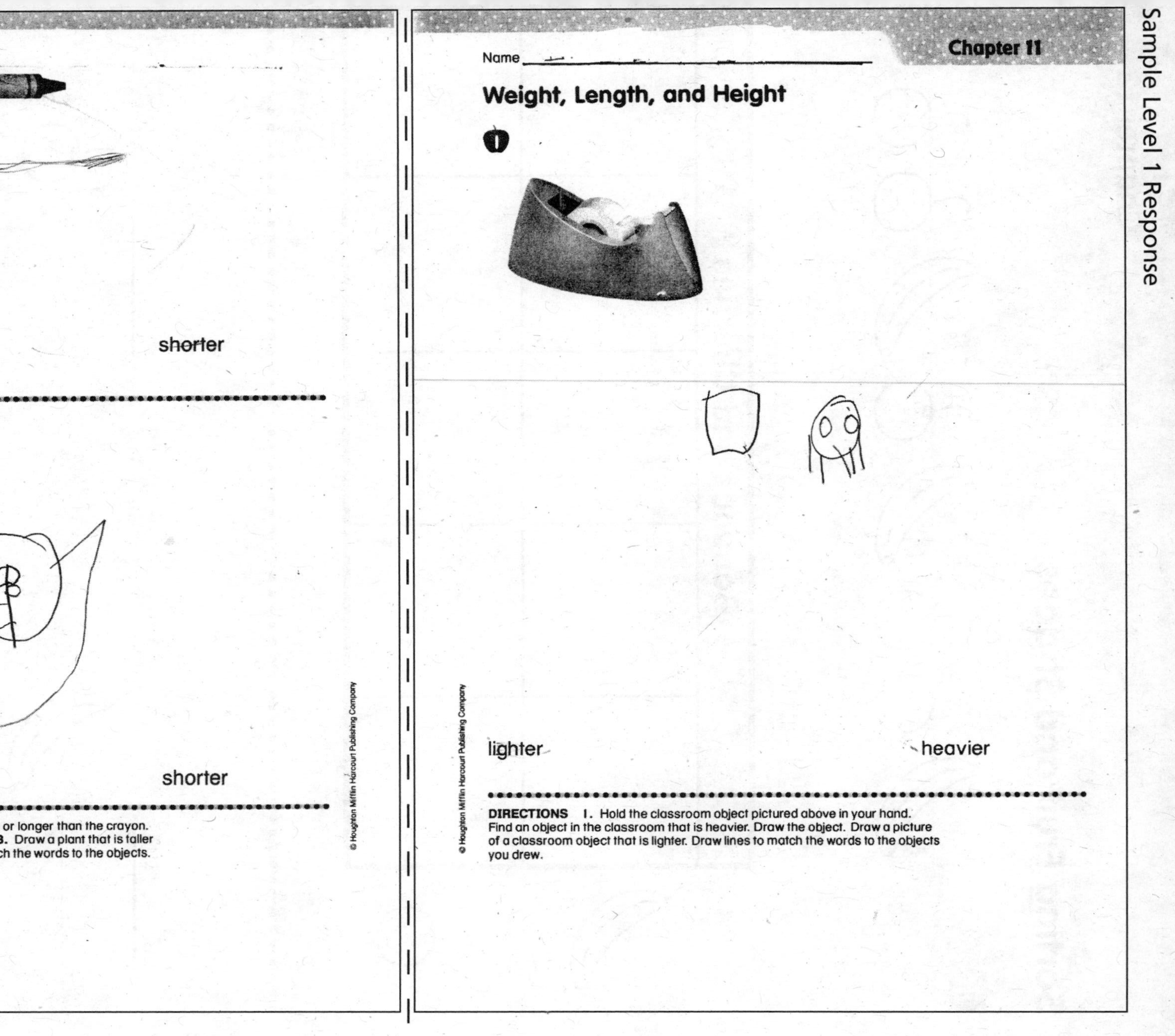

Chapter 11

Name

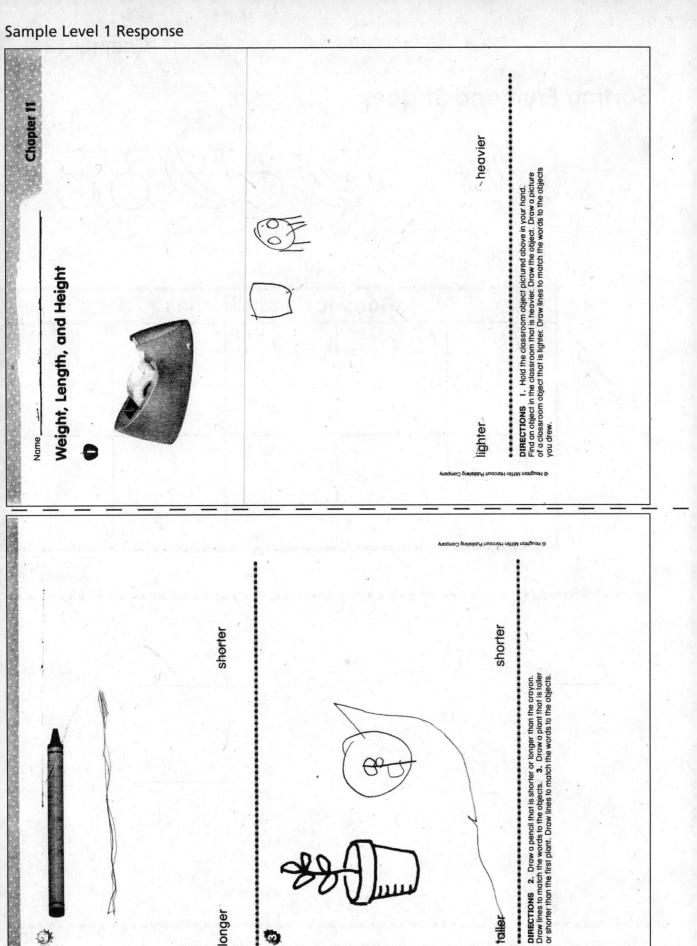

Weight, Length, and Height

1

lighter

heavier

DIRECTIONS 1. Hold the classroom object pictured above in your hand. Find an object in the classroom that is heavier. Draw the object. Draw a picture of a classroom object that is lighter. Draw lines to match the words to the objects you drew.

2

longer

shorter

3

taller

shorter

DIRECTIONS 2. Draw a pencil that is shorter or longer than the crayon. Draw lines to match the words to the objects. 3. Draw a plant that is taller or shorter than the first plant. Draw lines to match the words to the objects.

Sorting Fruit and Shapes

Bananas and Cherries				

2

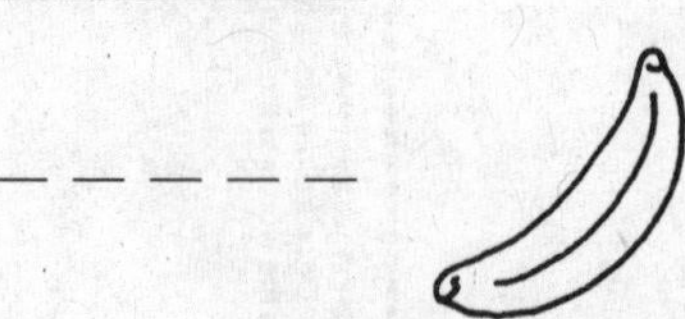

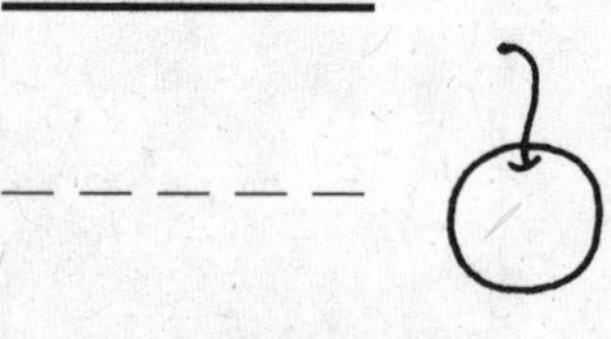

DIRECTIONS 1. Look at the bananas and cherries. Sort the fruit to complete the graph. **2.** Write how many of each.

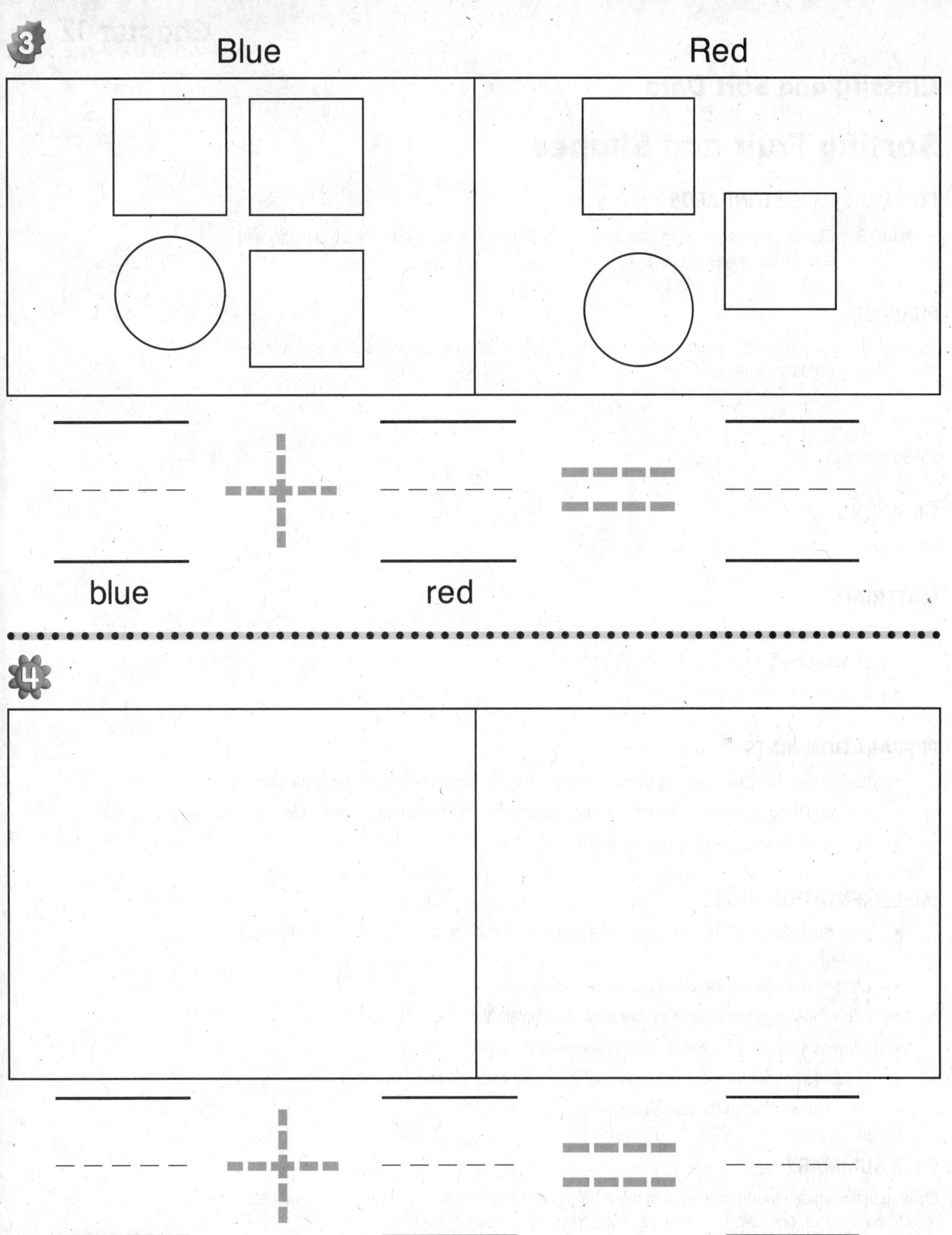

DIRECTIONS **3.** Color the shapes in the first box blue. Color the shapes in the second box red. How are the shapes sorted? Write the number sentence. **4.** Sort the shapes a different way. Draw and color them into the empty boxes. Write the number sentence.

Classify and Sort Data

Sorting Fruit and Shapes

COMMON CORE STANDARDS

K.MD.3 Classify objects into given categories; count the number of objects in each category and sort the categories by count.

PURPOSE

To assess the ability to make a graph to count objects, classify objects by color and shape, and represent counts using an addition sentence

TIME

25–30 minutes

GROUPING

Individuals

MATERIALS

- Performance Task, paper, pencil
- Crayons or colored pencils
- 2-color counters (optional)

PREPARATION HINTS

- Review classifying and counting by color and shape with children before assigning the task.
- Review making and reading graphs to count objects with children before assigning the task.
- Review vocabulary, including *classify, graph*.

IMPLEMENTATION NOTES

- Read the task aloud to children and make sure that all children have a clear understanding of the task.
- Children may use manipulatives to complete the task.
- Allow children as much paper as they need to complete the task.
- Allow as much time as children need to complete the task.
- Children must complete the task individually, without collaboration.
- Collect all work when the task is complete.

TASK SUMMARY

Children make a graph to sort, classify, and count objects by type. They draw pictures to sort and classify objects in more than one way. They write addition sentences to record these counts.

REPRESENTATION

In this task teachers can…

- Provide options for perception by explaining what pictures represent.
- Guide information processing by asking children to restate the instructions in their own words.

ACTION and EXPRESSION

In this task teachers can…

- Provide options for physical action by allowing children to use counters to help them count objects.
- Provide options for expression and communication by asking children to explain the content of their drawings.

ENGAGEMENT

In this task teachers can…

- Sustain effort and persistence by encouraging children to be thorough in completing each part of the task.
- Provide options for self-regulation by offering strategies for checking work.

EXPECTED STUDENT OUTCOMES

- Complete the task within the time allowed
- Reflect engagement in a productive struggle
- Make a graph to sort, classify, and count objects
- Sort and classify objects in more than one way and represent counts using an addition sentence

SCORING

Use the associated Rubric to evaluate each child's work.

Performance Task Rubric

SORTING FRUIT AND SHAPES	
A level 3 response	• Indicates that the child has made sense of the task and persevered • Demonstrates an understanding of sorting, classifying, and counting objects by category • Accurately represents data on a graph • Accurately represents sorting, classifying, and counting of objects through drawings and equations
A level 2 response	• Indicates that the child has made sense of the task and persevered • Demonstrates an understanding of sorting, classifying, and counting objects by category • Accurately represents data on a graph • Accurately represents sorting, classifying, and counting of objects through drawings and equations • Addresses most or all aspects of the task, but there may be errors of omission
A level 1 response	• Shows that the child has made sense of at least some elements of the task • Demonstrates evidence of understanding of sorting, classifying, and counting objects by category • May not accurately represent sorting, classifying, and counting objects with a graph, drawings, or equations
A level 0 response	• Shows little evidence that the child has made sense of the problems of the task • Reflects a lack of understanding of sorting, classifying, and counting objects by category • Reflects a lack of understanding of how to represent sorting, classifying, and counting using graphs, drawings, and equations • Shows little evidence of addressing the elements of the task

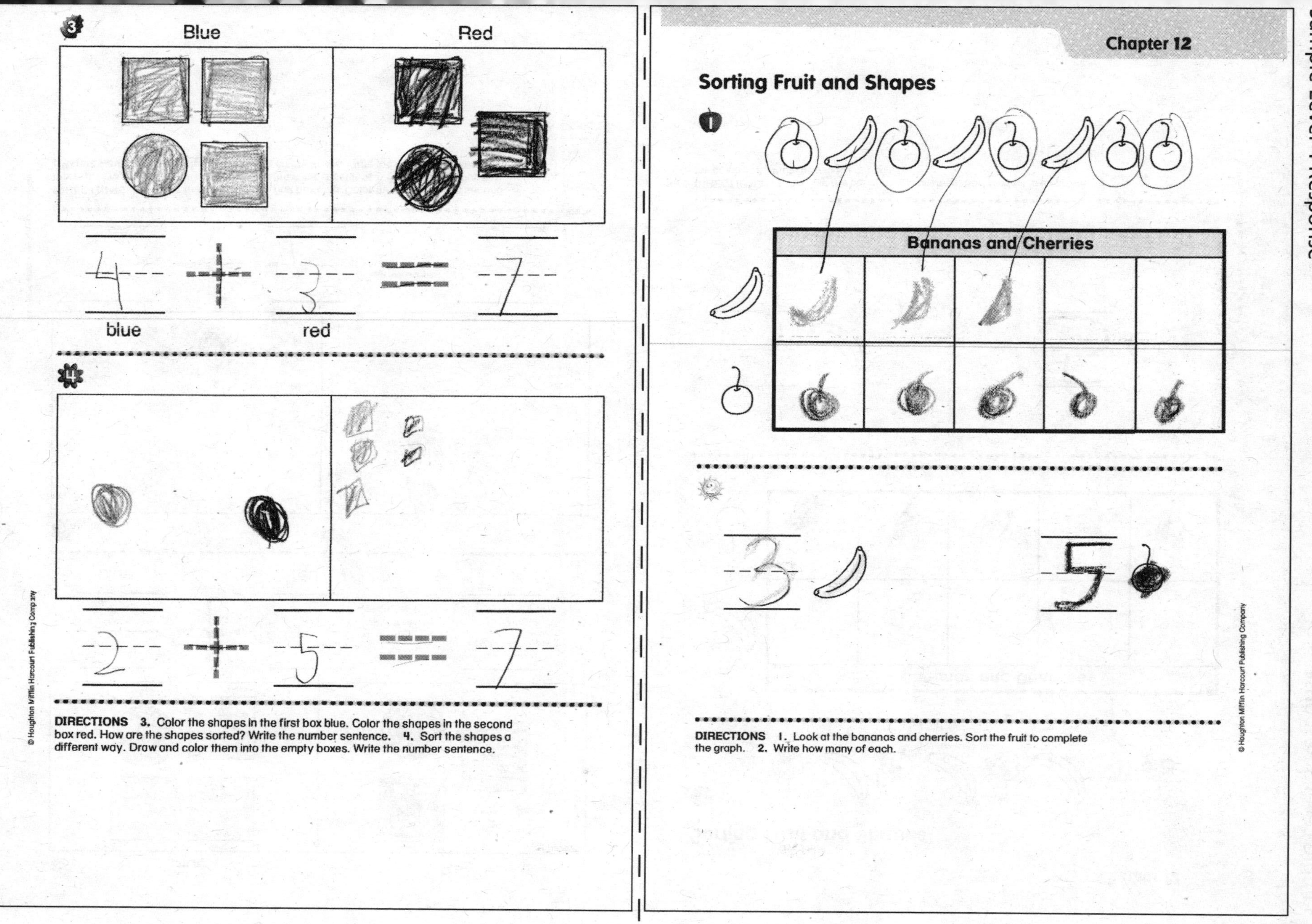
3
Blue
Red
4 + 3 = 7
blue
red
4
2 + 5 = 7
DIRECTIONS 3. Color the shapes in the first box blue. Color the shapes in the second box red. How are the shapes sorted? Write the number sentence. 4. Sort the shapes a different way. Draw and color them into the empty boxes. Write the number sentence.
© Houghton Mifflin Harcourt Publishing Company
Chapter 12
Sorting Fruit and Shapes
1
Bananas and Cherries
2
3
5
DIRECTIONS 1. Look at the bananas and cherries. Sort the fruit to complete the graph. 2. Write how many of each.
© Houghton Mifflin Harcourt Publishing Company

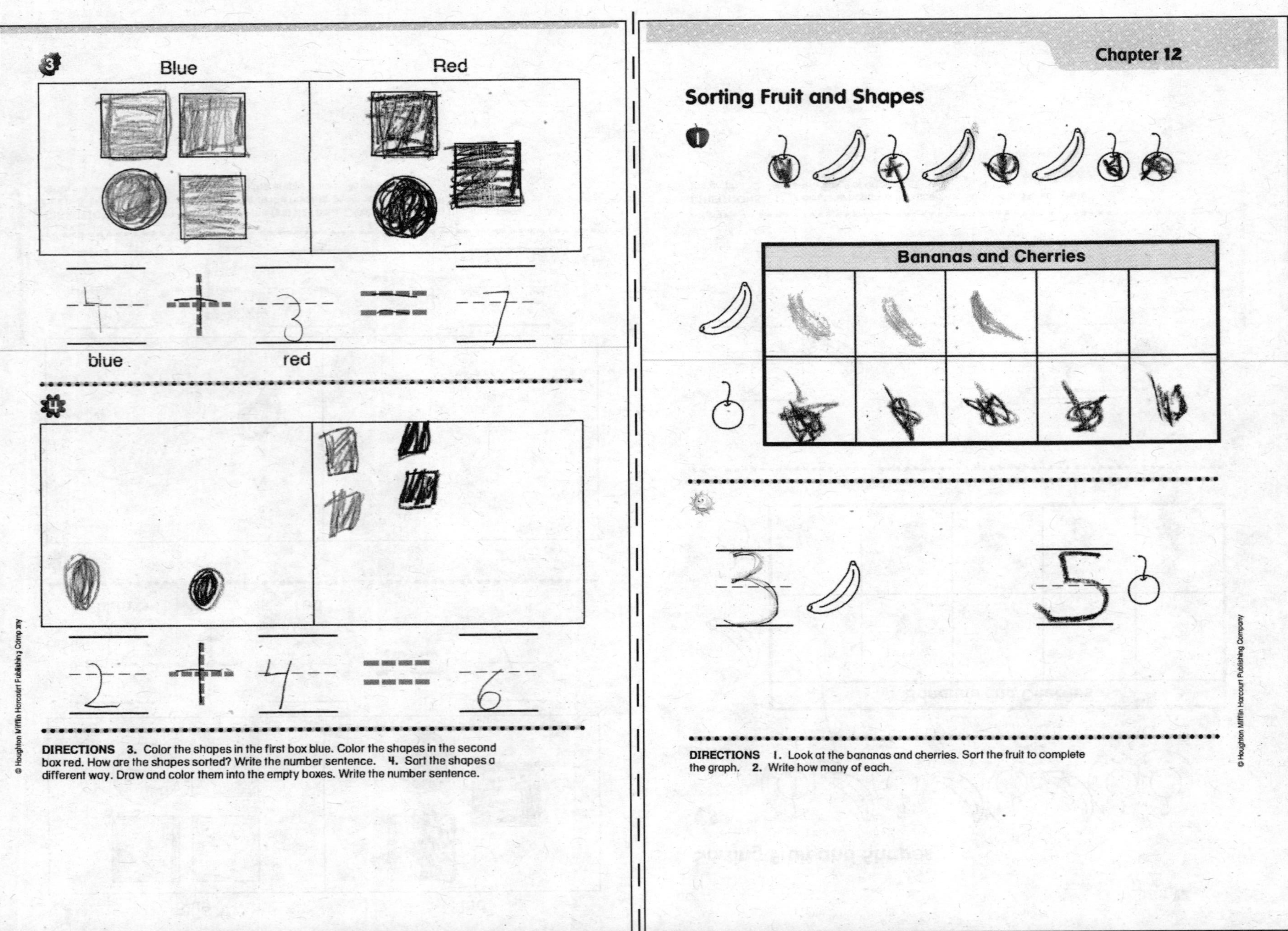

3

Blue

Red

4 + 3 = 7

blue red

4

2 + 4 = 6

DIRECTIONS 3. Color the shapes in the first box blue. Color the shapes in the second box red. How are the shapes sorted? Write the number sentence. 4. Sort the shapes a different way. Draw and color them into the empty boxes. Write the number sentence.

Chapter 12

Sorting Fruit and Shapes

1

Bananas and Cherries

2

3 5

DIRECTIONS 1. Look at the bananas and cherries. Sort the fruit to complete the graph. 2. Write how many of each.

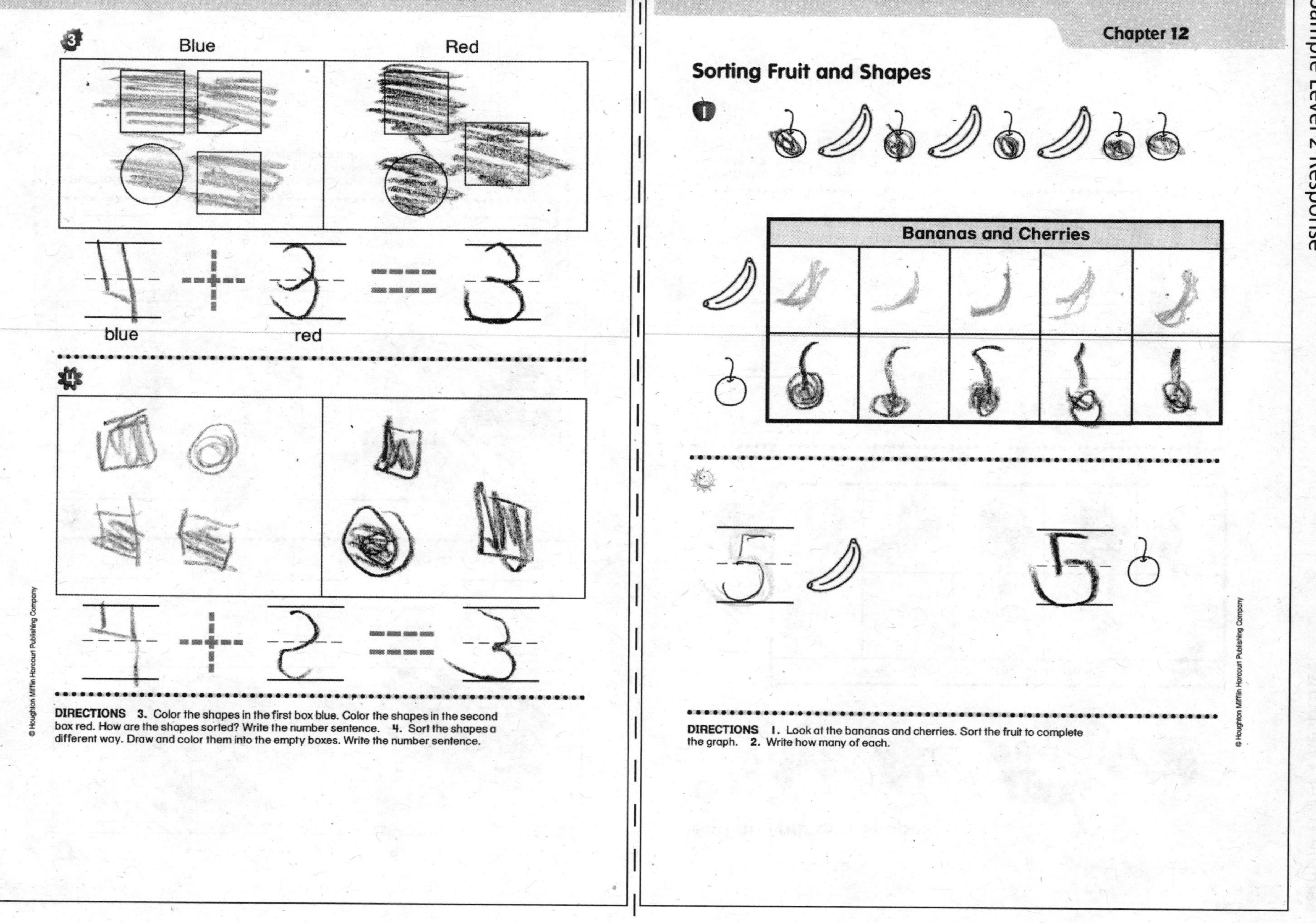

3

Blue

Red

blue

red

4

DIRECTIONS 3. Color the shapes in the first box blue. Color the shapes in the second box red. How are the shapes sorted? Write the number sentence. 4. Sort the shapes a different way. Draw and color them into the empty boxes. Write the number sentence.

Chapter 12

Sorting Fruit and Shapes

1

Bananas and Cherries

2

DIRECTIONS 1. Look at the bananas and cherries. Sort the fruit to complete the graph. 2. Write how many of each.

Sorting Fruit and Shapes

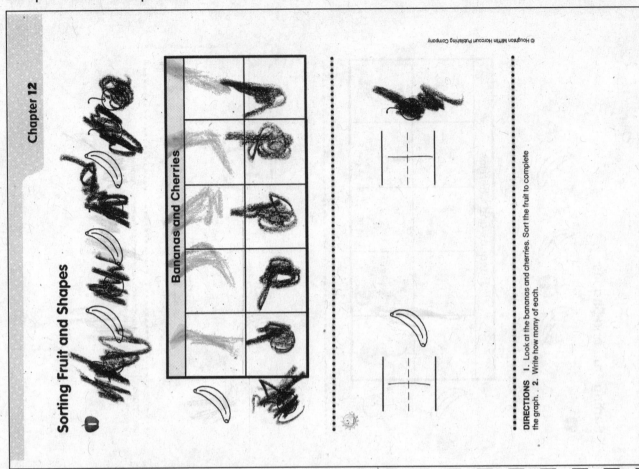

1

Bananas and Cherries					

2

1   1

DIRECTIONS 1. Look at the bananas and cherries. Sort the fruit to complete the graph. 2. Write how many of each.

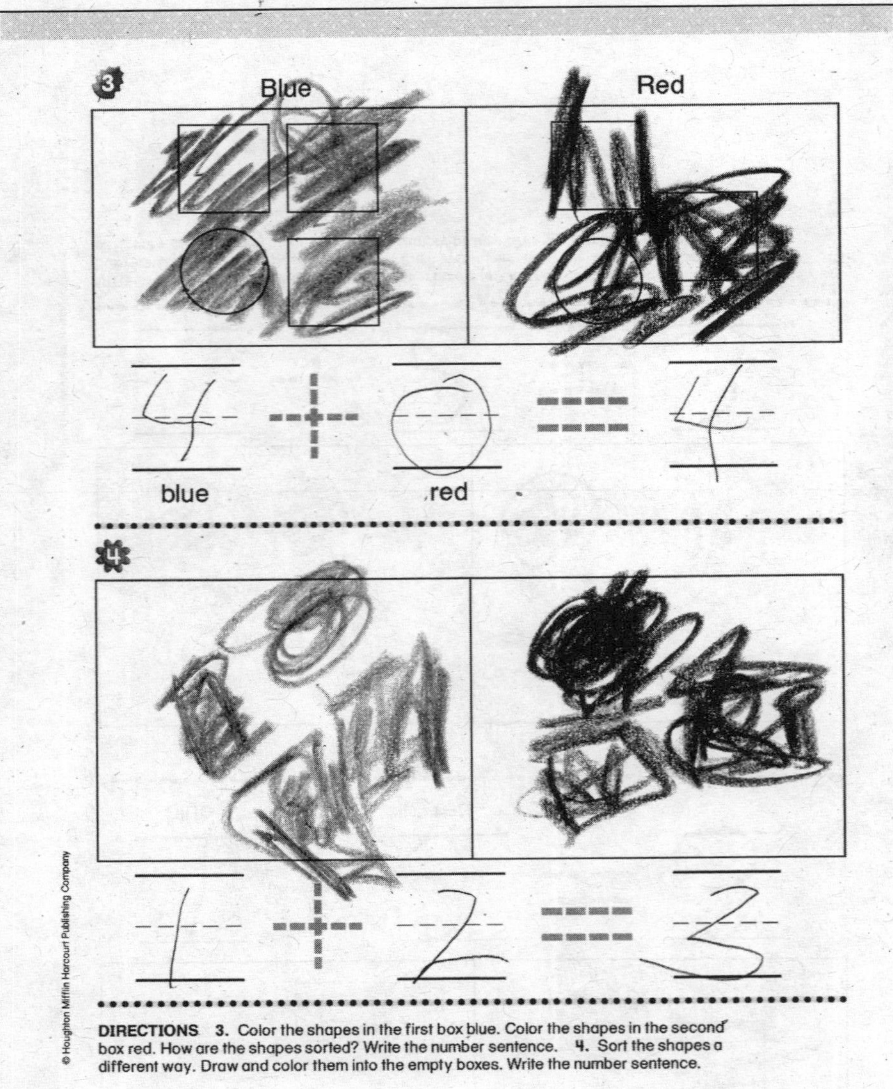

DIRECTIONS 3. Color the shapes in the first box blue. Color the shapes in the second box red. How are the shapes sorted? Write the number sentence. 4. Sort the shapes a different way. Draw and color them into the empty boxes. Write the number sentence.

Name ____________________ CRITICAL AREA Measurement and Data

Comparing and Sorting

Felipe's Marbles

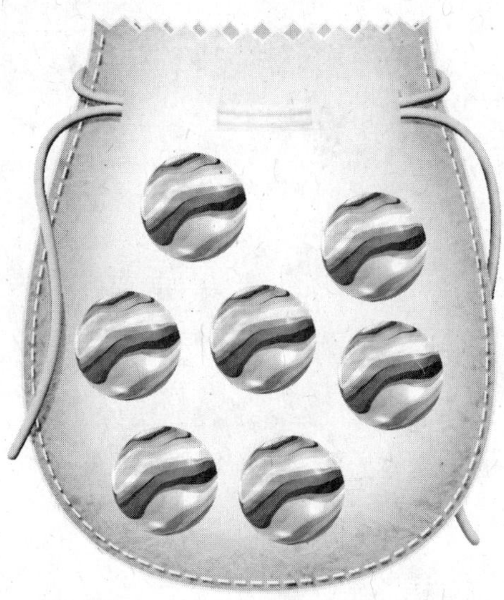

1 lighter

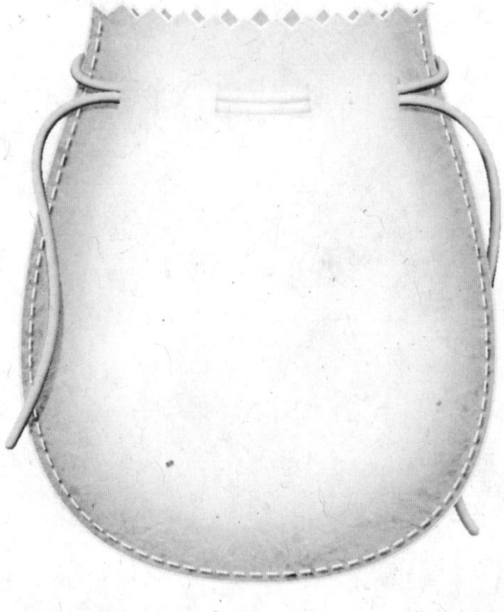

2 heavier

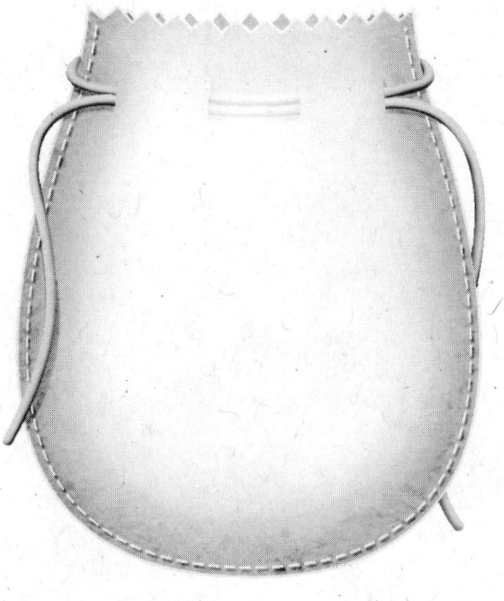

DIRECTIONS **1.** Felipe has a bag of marbles. Draw marbles in the first bag to make a bag that is lighter than Felipe's bag. **2.** Draw marbles in the second bag to make a bag that is heavier than Felipe's bag.

3

4

DIRECTIONS 3. Draw two worms. Make one longer than the other. Circle the worm that is shorter. 4. Draw two trees. Make one tree shorter than the other. Circle the tree that is taller.

5

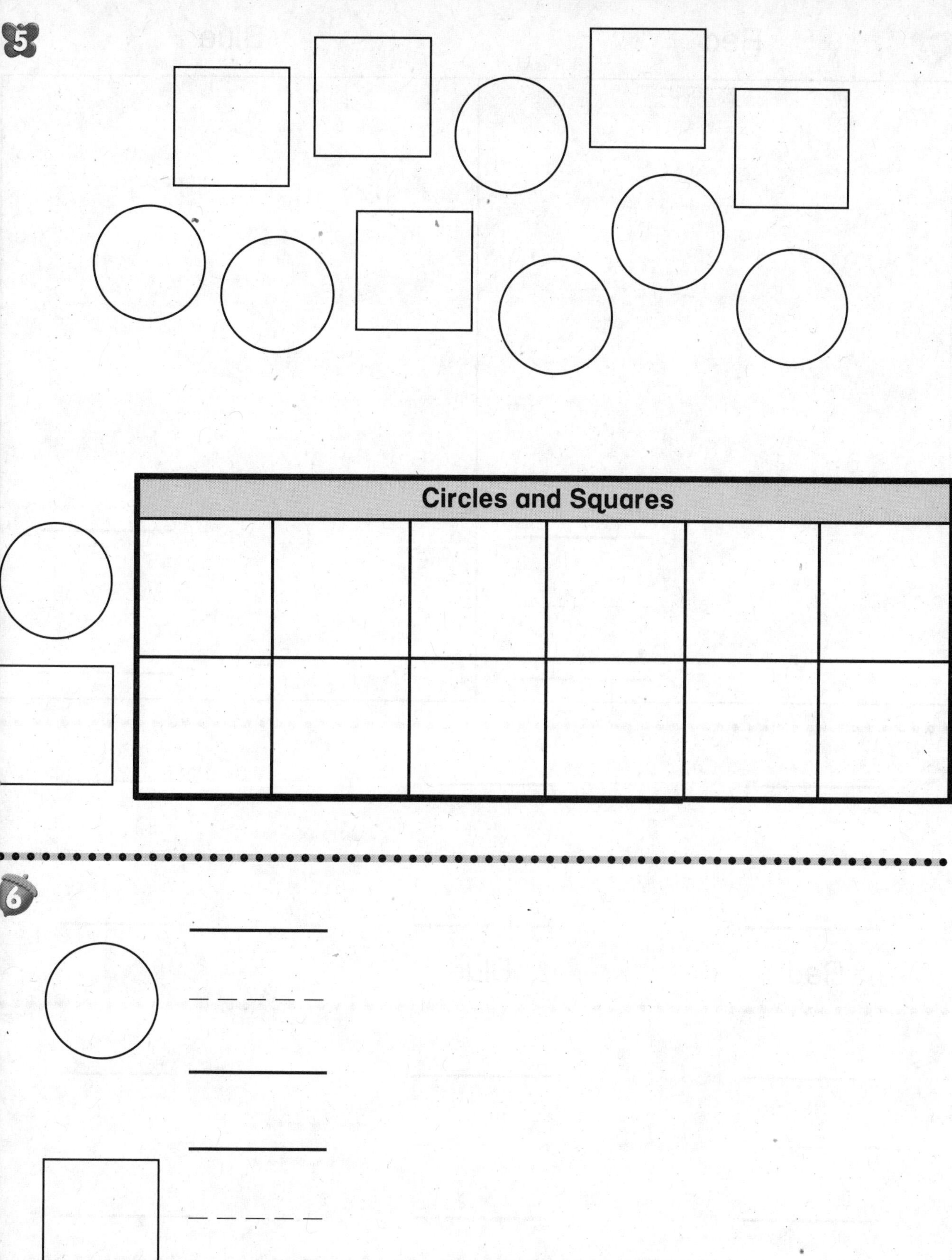

6

DIRECTIONS 5. Look at the circles and squares. Sort the shapes to complete the graph. Use your shape blocks to help you. 6. Write how many of each.

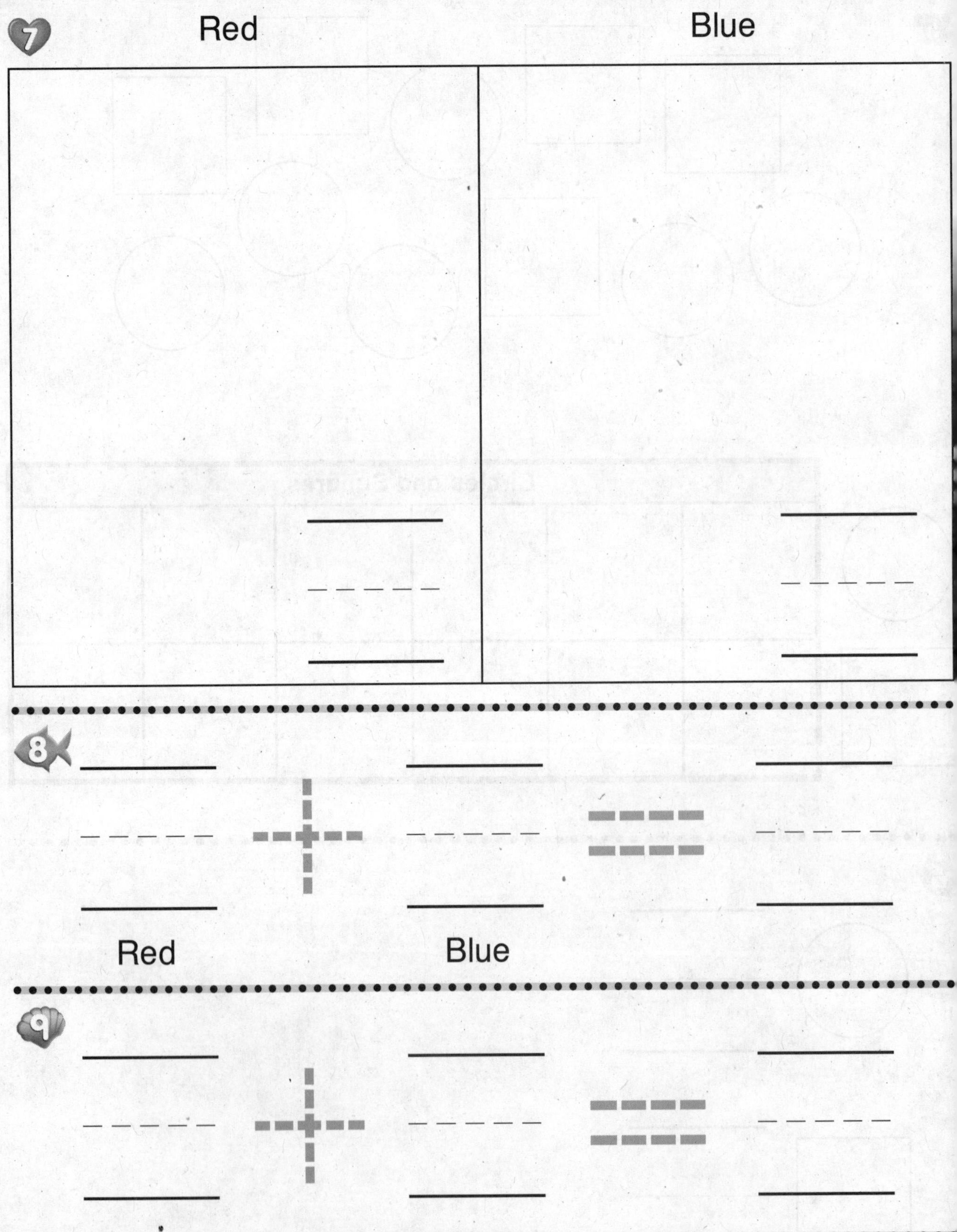

DIRECTIONS **7.** Draw 1, 2, or 3 red shapes in the first box. Write the number of red shapes you drew. Draw 4, 5, or 6 blue shapes in the second box. Write the number of blue shapes you drew. **8.** Write the number sentence for the number of shapes in all. **9.** Write the number sentence a different way.

Measurement and Data

Comparing and Sorting

COMMON CORE STANDARDS

K.MD.1 Describe measurable attributes of objects, such as length or weight. Describe several measurable attributes of a single object.

K.MD.2 Directly compare two objects with a measurable attribute in common, to see which object has "more of"/"less of" the attribute, and describe the difference.

K.MD.3 Classify objects into given categories; count the number of objects in each category and sort the categories by count.

PURPOSE

To assess the ability to compare measurable attributes and to sort, classify, and count objects using graphs, drawings, and equations

TIME

25–30 minutes

GROUPING

Individuals

MATERIALS

- Performance Task, paper, pencil
- Two-color counters or connecting cubes (optional)

PREPARATION HINTS

- Review comparing weights, lengths, and heights with children before assigning the task.
- Review sorting, classifying, and representing data with children before assigning the task.
- Review vocabulary, including *lighter, heavier, longer, shorter, taller, circle, square, classify, graph.*

IMPLEMENTATION NOTES

- Read the task aloud to children and make sure that all children have a clear understanding of the task.
- Children may use manipulatives to complete the task.
- Allow children as much paper as they need to complete the task.
- Allow as much time as children need to complete the task.
- Children must complete the task individually, without collaboration.
- Collect all work when the task is complete.

TASK SUMMARY

Children compare measurable attributes of pictures they draw using words such as *lighter*, *heavier*, *longer*, *shorter*, and *taller*. They sort, classify, count, and represent categories of objects using graphs, drawings, and equations.

REPRESENTATION

In this task teachers can…

- Provide options for perception by clarifying meaning of pictures.
- Guide information processing by connecting parts of the instructions to specific areas on the page.

ACTION and EXPRESSION

In this task teachers can…

- Provide options for physical action by allowing children to use counters or cubes in place of drawings to model their answers.
- Provide options for expression and communication by asking children to explain the content of their drawings.

ENGAGEMENT

In this task teachers can…

- Foster collaboration and community by inviting children to share their ideas after the assignment has been turned in.
- Sustain effort and persistence by providing specific feedback.

EXPECTED STUDENT OUTCOMES

- Complete the task within the time allowed
- Reflect engagement in a productive struggle
- Compare weights, lengths, and heights of objects in drawings
- Sort, classify, count, and represent data using graphs, drawings, and equations

SCORING

Use the associated Rubric to evaluate each child's work.

Performance Task Rubric

COMPARING AND SORTING	
A level 3 response	• Indicates that the child has made sense of the task and persevered • Demonstrates understanding of measurable attributes • Demonstrates understanding of comparing weights, lengths, and heights • Demonstrates an understanding of sorting, classifying, and counting objects by category
A level 2 response	• Indicates that the child has made sense of the task and persevered • Demonstrates understanding of measurable attributes • Demonstrates understanding of comparing weights, lengths, and heights • Demonstrates an understanding of sorting, classifying, and counting objects by category • Addresses most or all aspects of the task, but there may be errors of omission
A level 1 response	• Shows that the child has made sense of at least some elements of the task • Gives evidence of understanding of measurable attributes and how to compare them • Demonstrates an understanding of sorting, classifying, and counting objects by category • May not accurately represent sorting, classifying, and counting of objects with graphs, drawings, and equations
A level 0 response	• Shows little evidence that the child has made sense of the problems of the task • Reflects a lack of understanding of weight, length, and height and how to compare them • Reflects a lack of understanding of sorting, classifying, and counting objects by category and representing data • Shows little evidence of addressing the elements of the task

Name ____________

CRITICAL AREA Measurement and Data

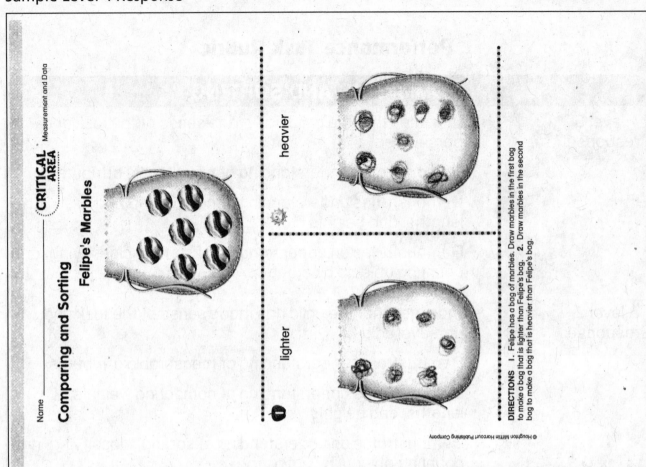

Comparing and Sorting

Felipe's Marbles

1 lighter

2 heavier

DIRECTIONS 1. Felipe has a bag of marbles. Draw marbles in the first bag to make a bag that is lighter than Felipe's bag. 2. Draw marbles in the second bag to make a bag that is heavier than Felipe's bag.

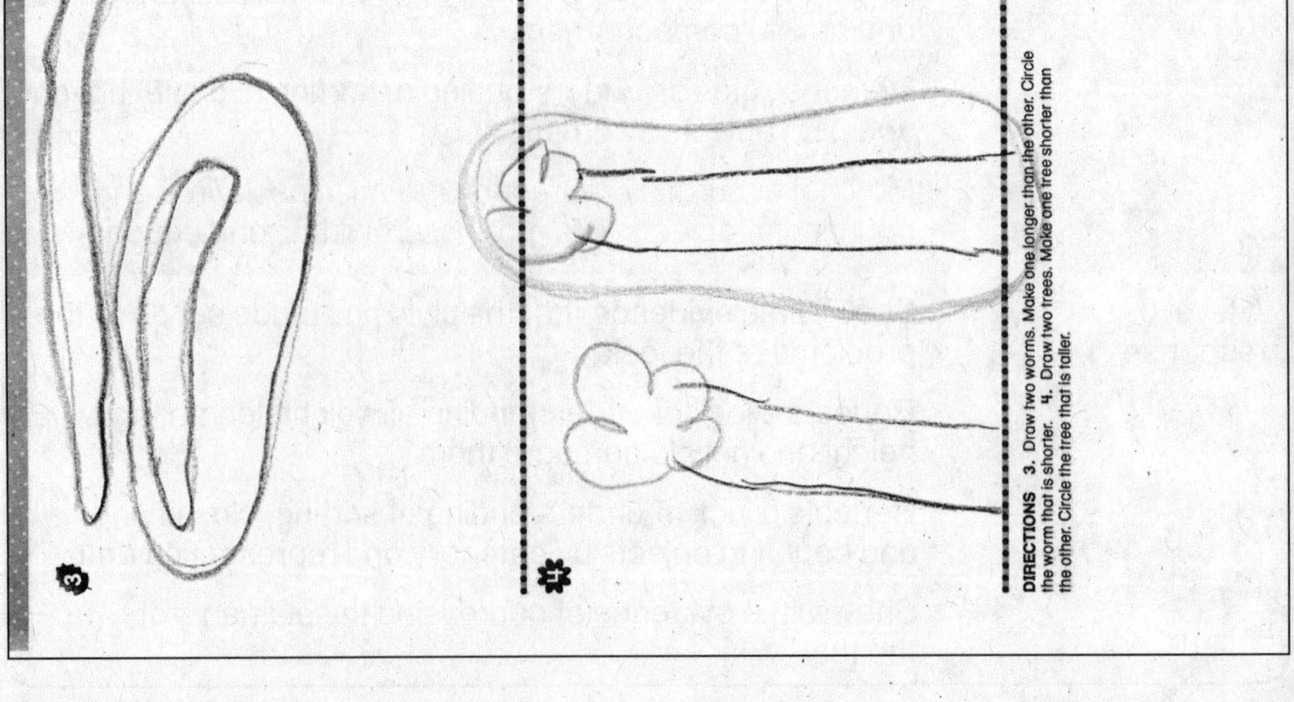

3

4

DIRECTIONS 3. Draw two worms. Make one longer than the other. Circle the worm that is shorter. 4. Draw two trees. Make one tree shorter than the other. Circle the tree that is taller.

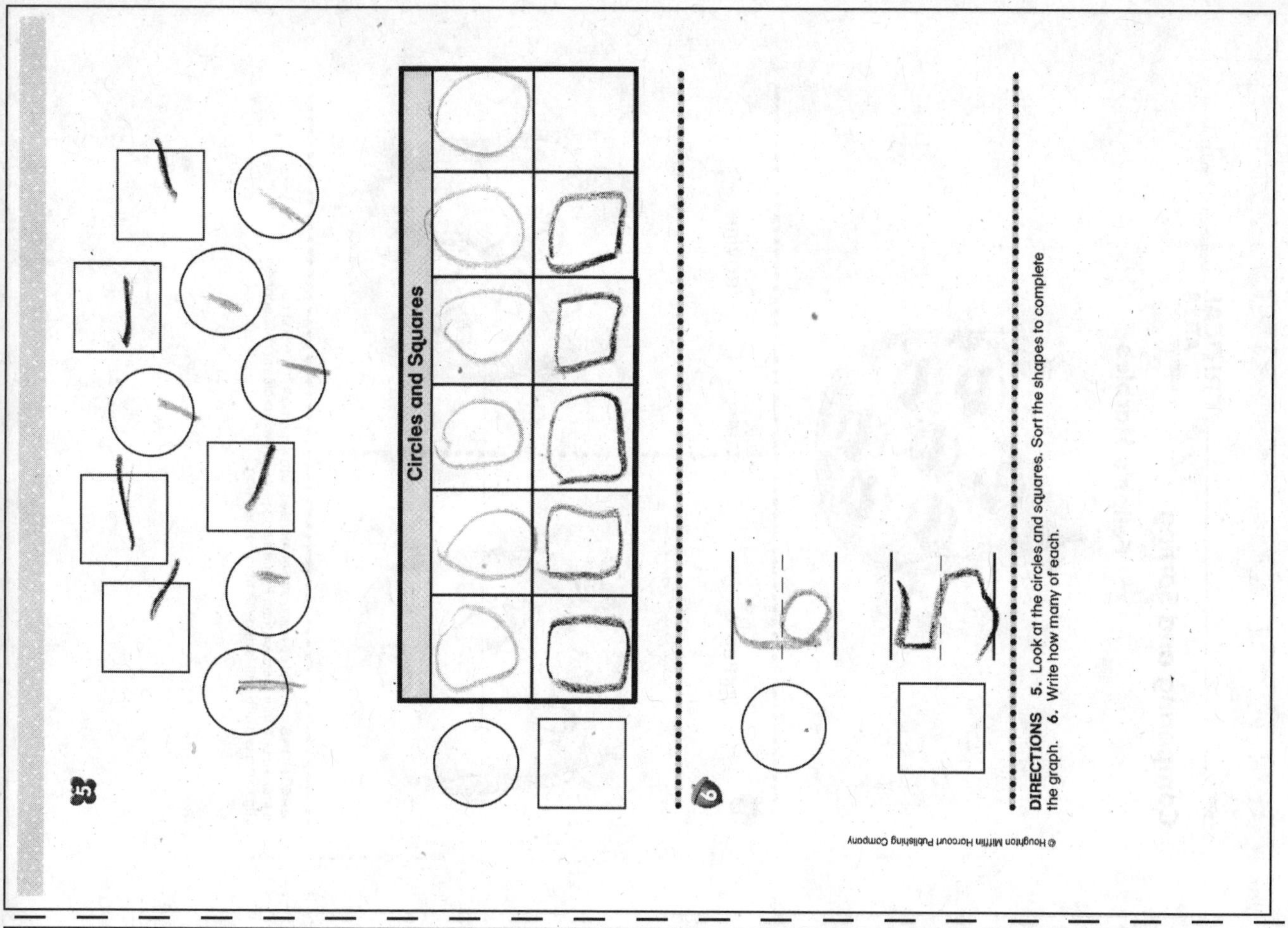

Sample Level 4 Response

5

Circles and Squares

6

DIRECTIONS 5. Look at the circles and squares. Sort the shapes to complete the graph. 6. Write how many of each.

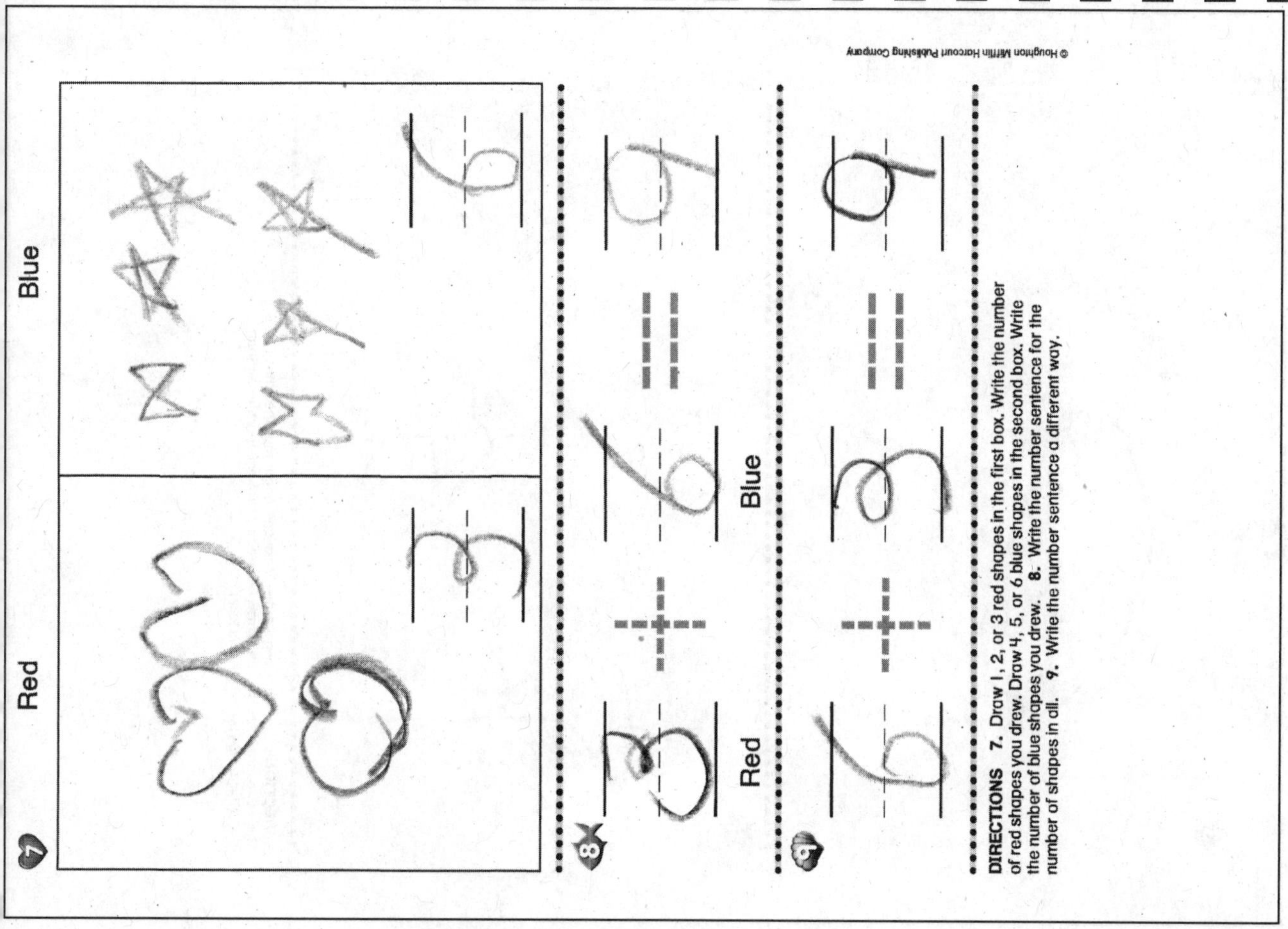

7

Red

Blue

8

Red

Blue

9

DIRECTIONS 7. Draw 1, 2, or 3 red shapes in the first box. Write the number of red shapes you drew. Draw 4, 5, or 6 blue shapes in the second box. Write the number of blue shapes you drew. 8. Write the number sentence for the number of shapes in all. 9. Write the number sentence a different way.

Name ______________ **CRITICAL AREA** Measurement and Data

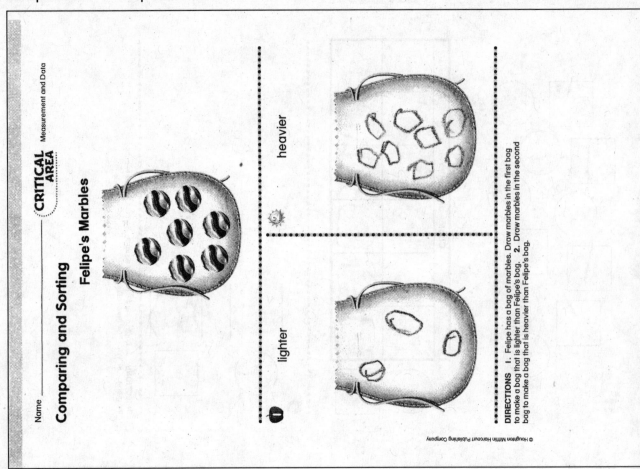

Comparing and Sorting

Felipe's Marbles

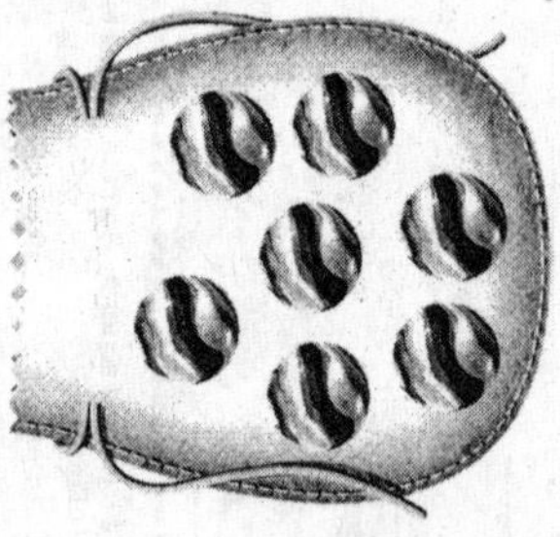

1 lighter

2 heavier

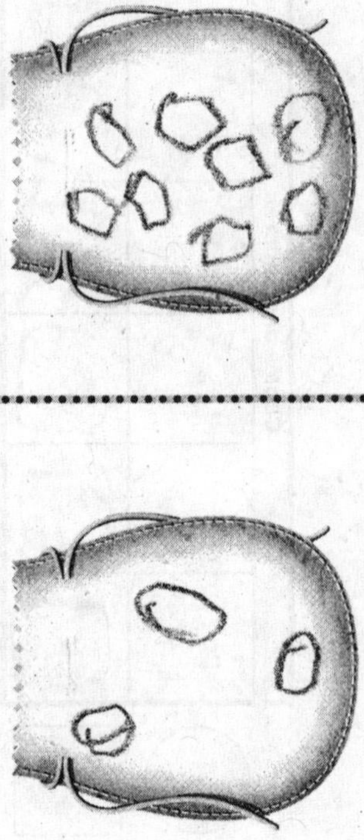

DIRECTIONS **1.** Felipe has a bag of marbles. Draw marbles in the first bag to make a bag that is lighter than Felipe's bag. **2.** Draw marbles in the second bag to make a bag that is heavier than Felipe's bag.

3

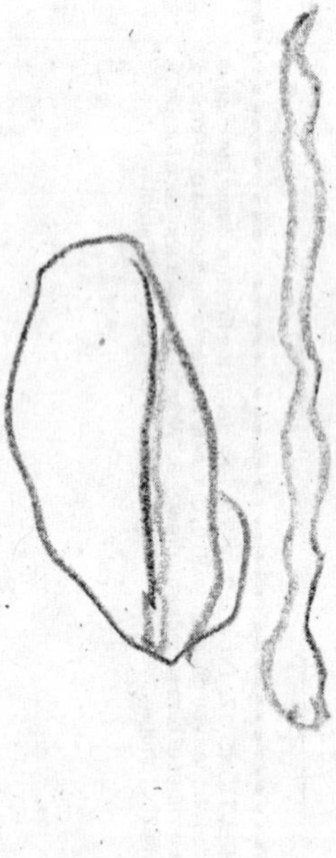

4

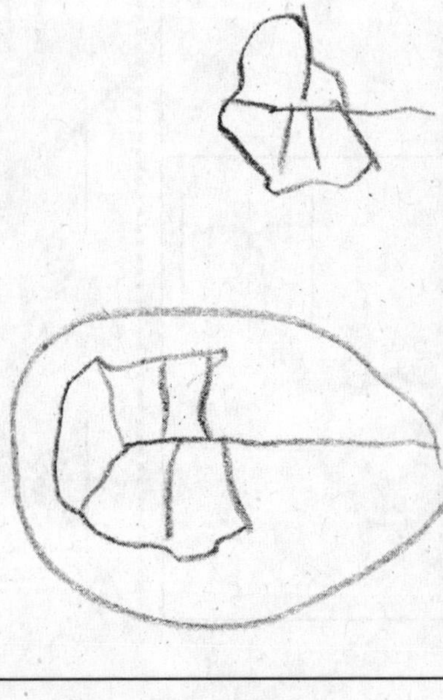

DIRECTIONS **3.** Draw two worms. Make one longer than the other. Circle the worm that is shorter. **4.** Draw two trees. Make one tree shorter than the other. Circle the tree that is taller.

© Houghton Mifflin Harcourt Publishing Company

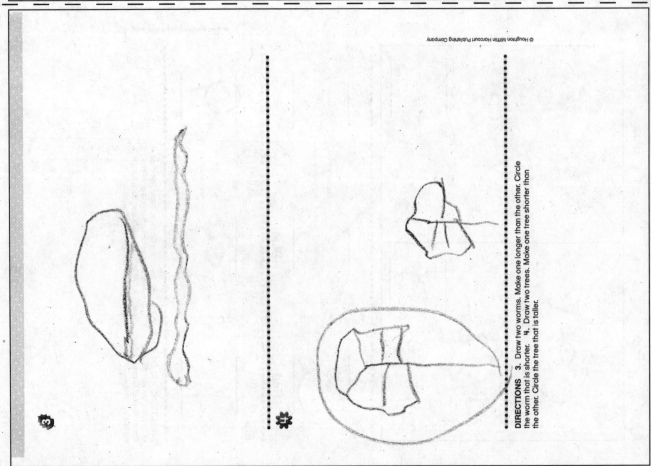

5

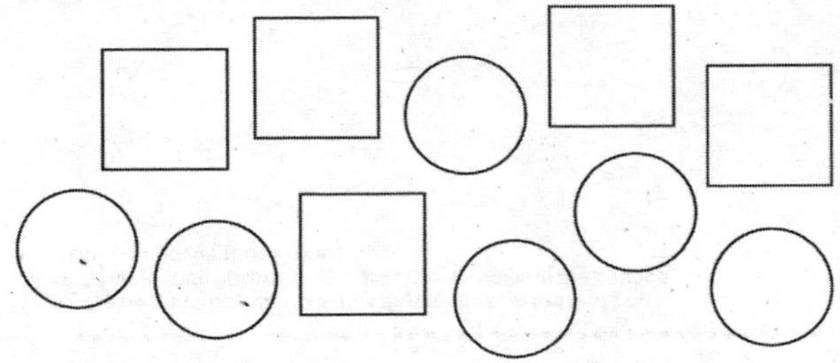

Circles and Squares					
○	○	○	○	○	○
□	□	□	□	□	

6

○ 6

□ 5

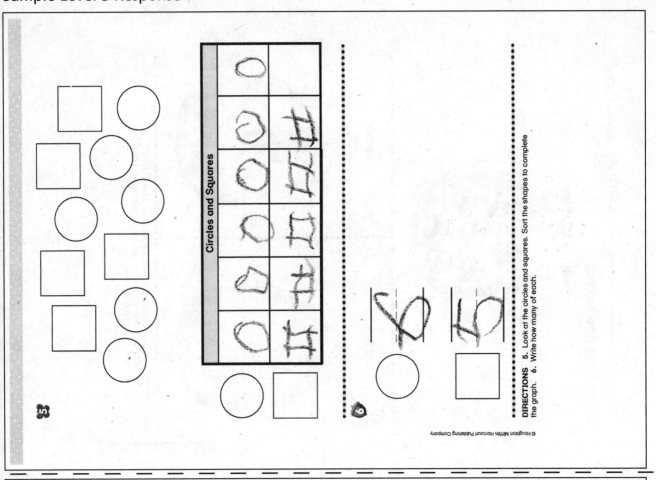

DIRECTIONS 5. Look at the circles and squares. Sort the shapes to complete the graph. 6. Write how many of each.

7

Red	Blue
3	1

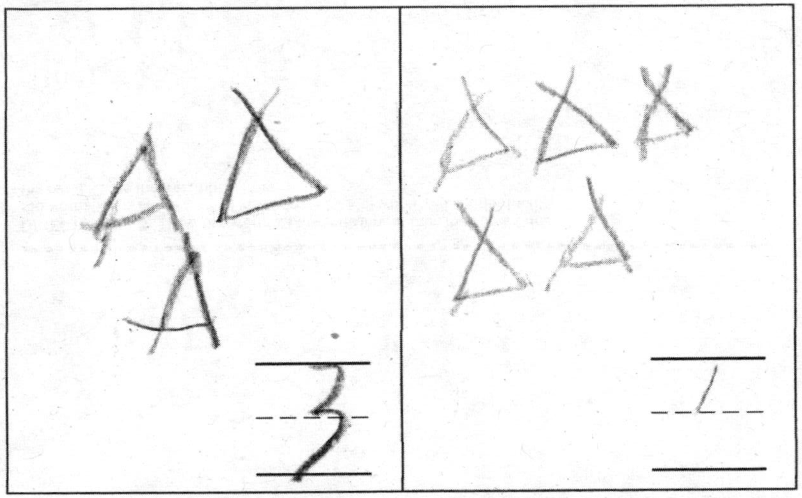

8

3 + 5 = 8

Red Blue

9

5 + 3 = ___

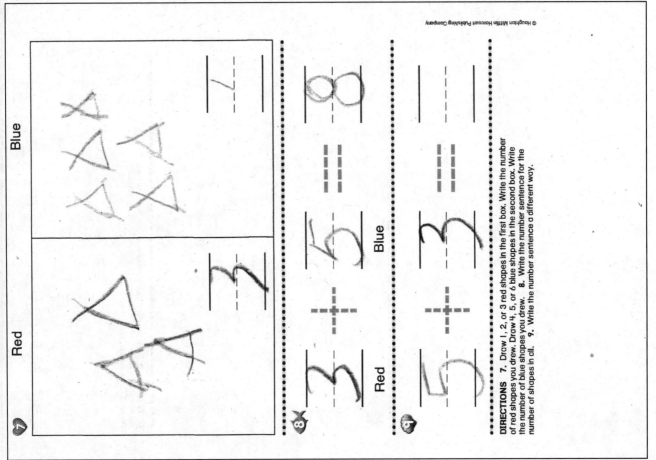

DIRECTIONS 7. Draw 1, 2, or 3 red shapes in the first box. Write the number of red shapes you drew. Draw 4, 5, or 6 blue shapes in the second box. Write the number of blue shapes you drew. 8. Write the number sentence for the number of shapes in all. 9. Write the number sentence a different way.

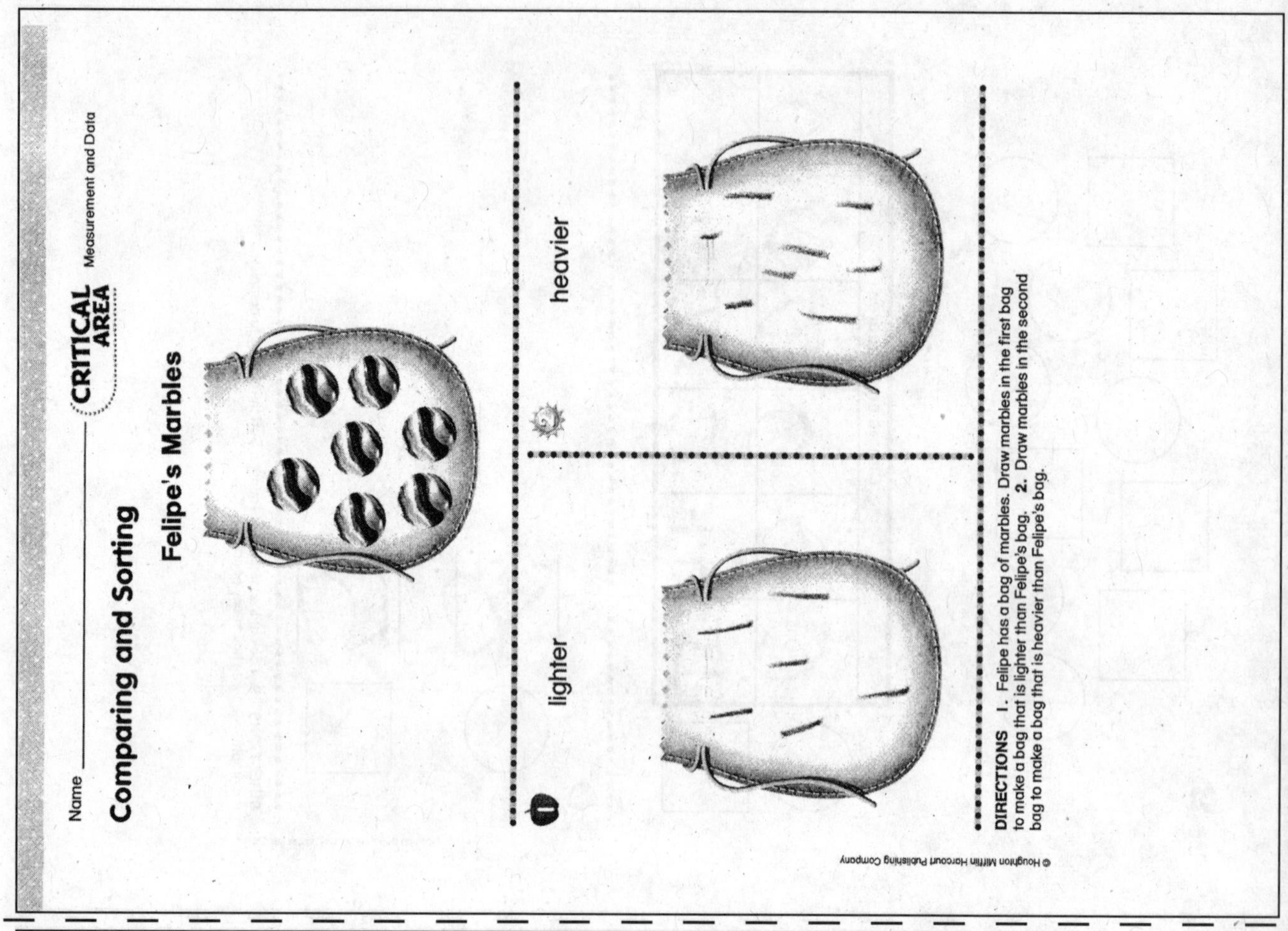

Name ______________________

CRITICAL AREA Measurement and Data

Comparing and Sorting

Felipe's Marbles

1 lighter

2 heavier

DIRECTIONS 1. Felipe has a bag of marbles. Draw marbles in the first bag to make a bag that is lighter than Felipe's bag. 2. Draw marbles in the second bag to make a bag that is heavier than Felipe's bag.

3

4

DIRECTIONS 3. Draw two worms. Make one longer than the other. Circle the worm that is shorter. 4. Draw two trees. Make one tree shorter than the other. Circle the tree that is taller.

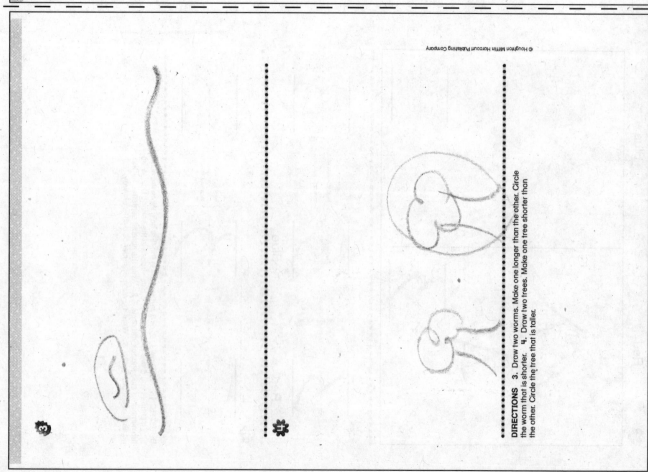

5

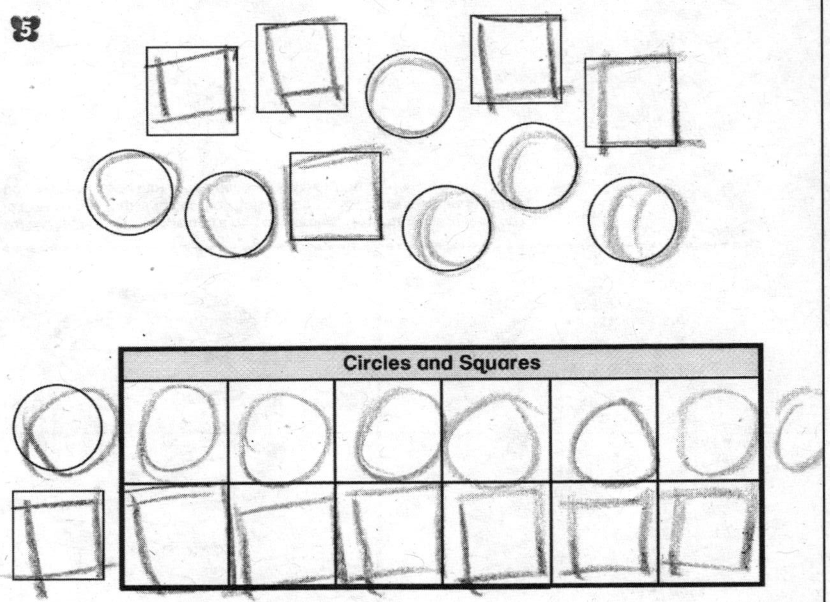

Circles and Squares

6

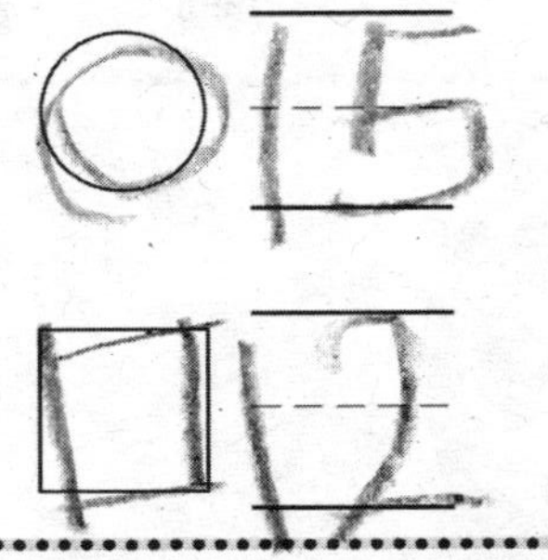

DIRECTIONS 5. Look at the circles and squares. Sort the shapes to complete the graph. 6. Write how many of each.

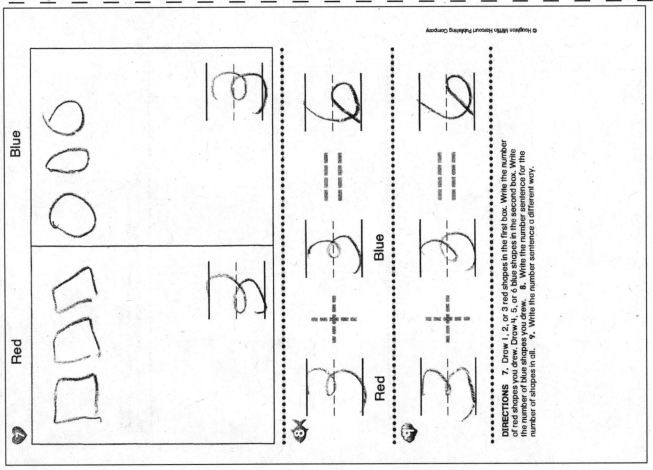

7

Red

Blue

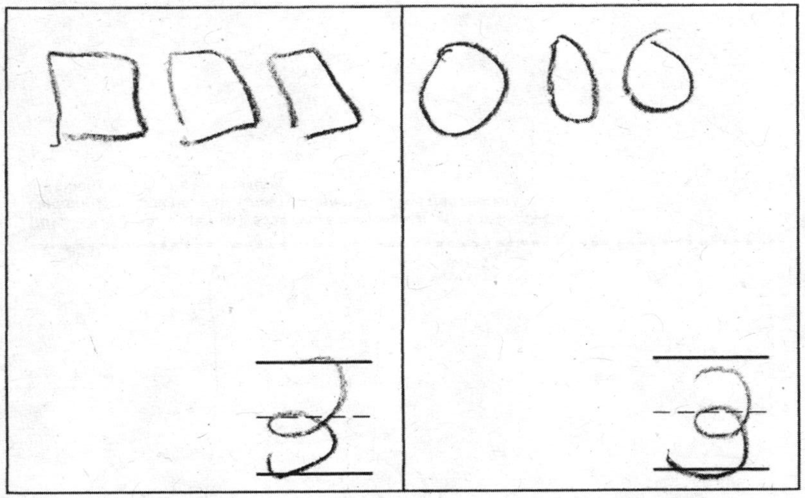

8

Red

Blue

9

DIRECTIONS 7. Draw 1, 2, or 3 red shapes in the first box. Write the number of red shapes you drew. Draw 4, 5, or 6 blue shapes in the second box. Write the number of blue shapes you drew. 8. Write the number sentence for the number of shapes in all. 9. Write the number sentence a different way.

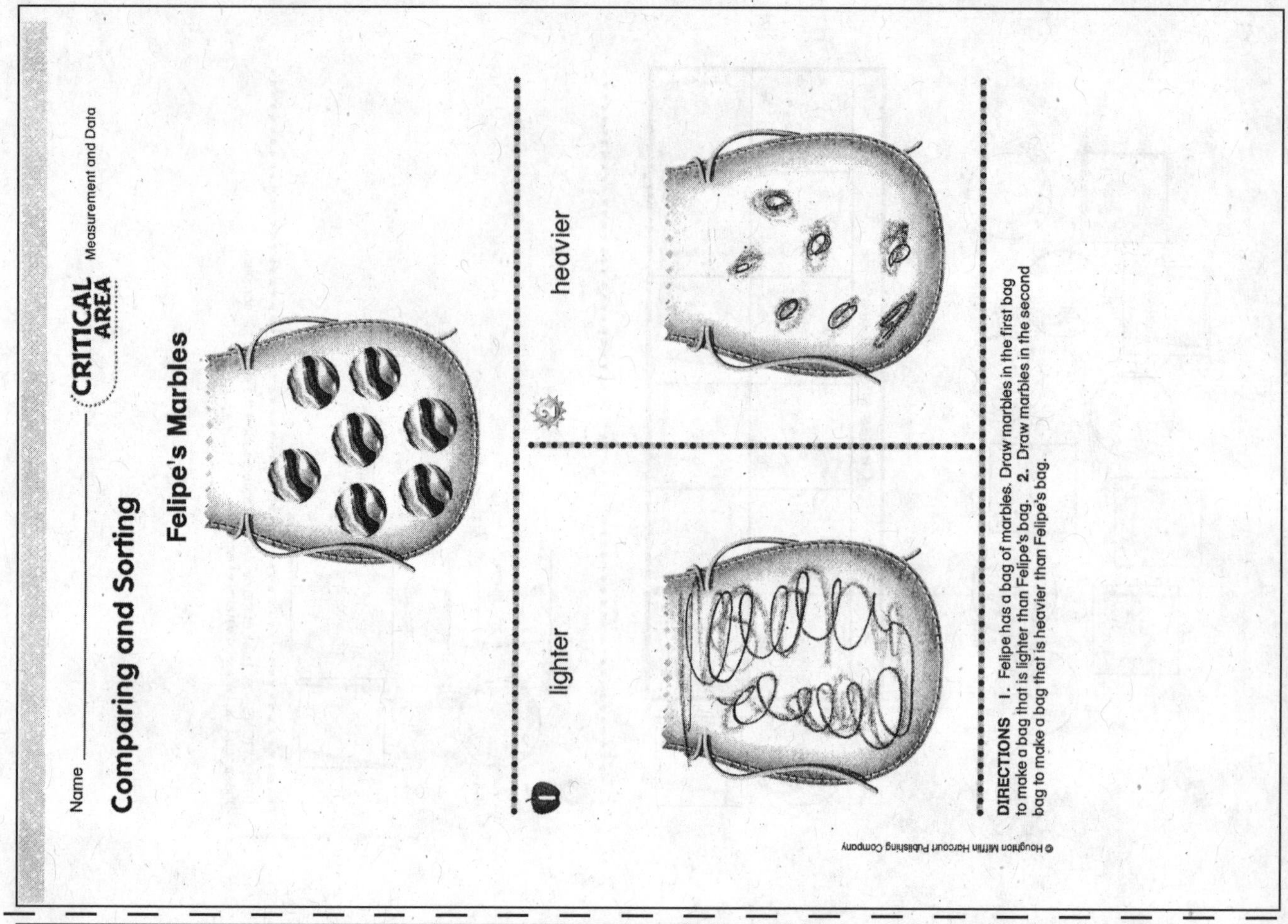

Name ______________________ CRITICAL AREA Measurement and Data

Comparing and Sorting

Felipe's Marbles

1 lighter

2 heavier

DIRECTIONS **1.** Felipe has a bag of marbles. Draw marbles in the first bag to make a bag that is lighter than Felipe's bag. **2.** Draw marbles in the second bag to make a bag that is heavier than Felipe's bag.

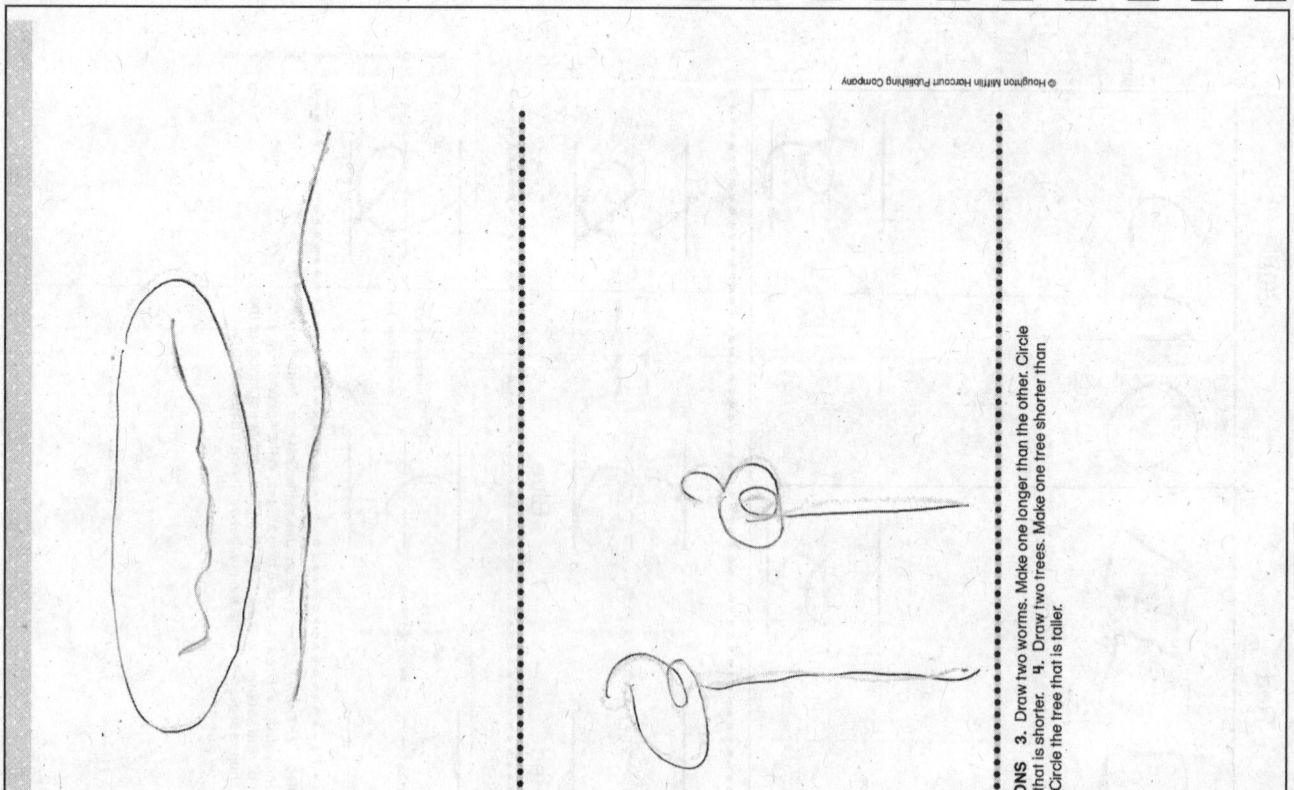

3

4

DIRECTIONS **3.** Draw two worms. Make one longer than the other. Circle the worm that is shorter. **4.** Draw two trees. Make one tree shorter than the other. Circle the tree that is taller.

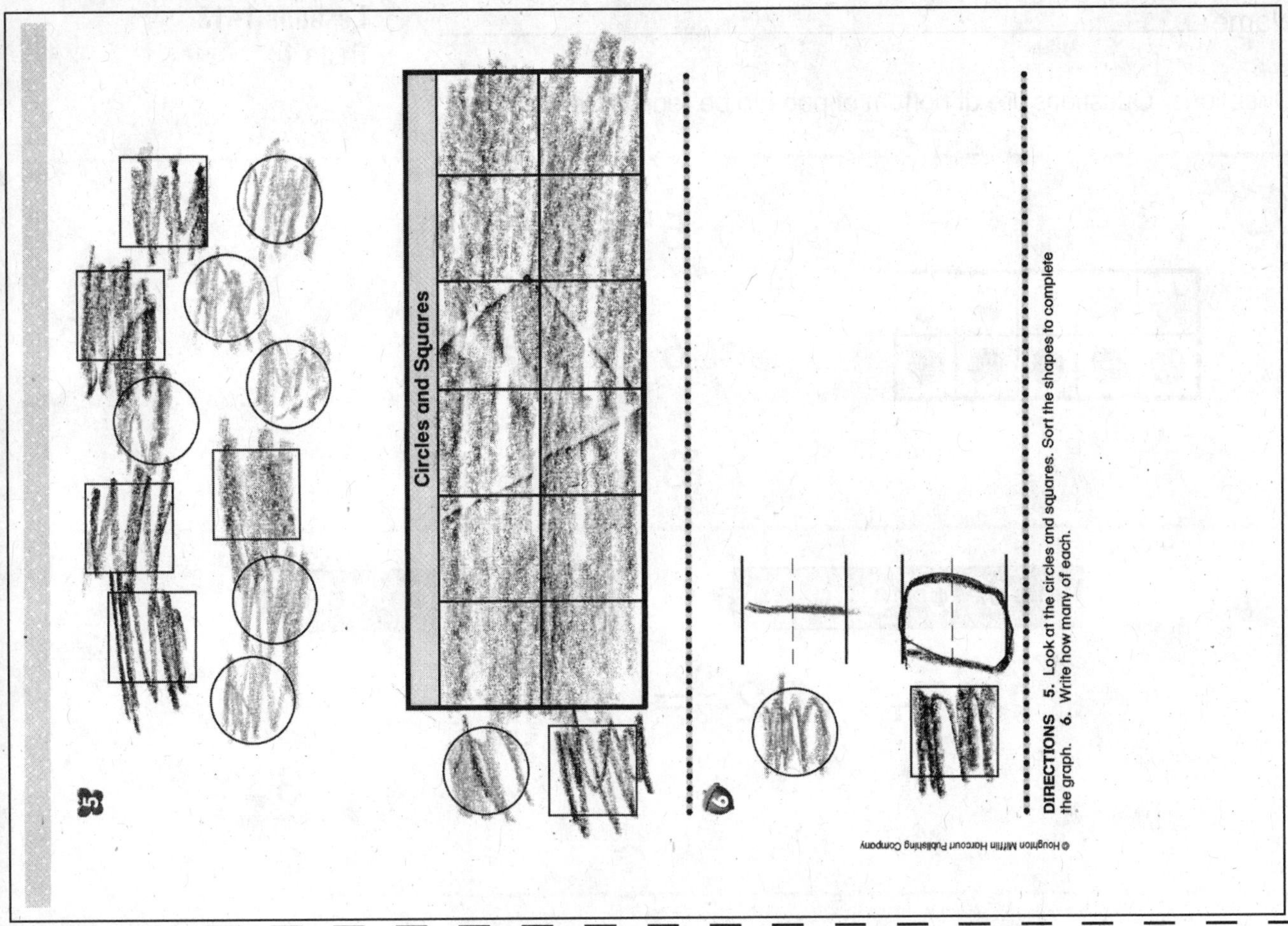

5

Circles and Squares

6

DIRECTIONS 5. Look at the circles and squares. Sort the shapes to complete the graph. 6. Write how many of each.

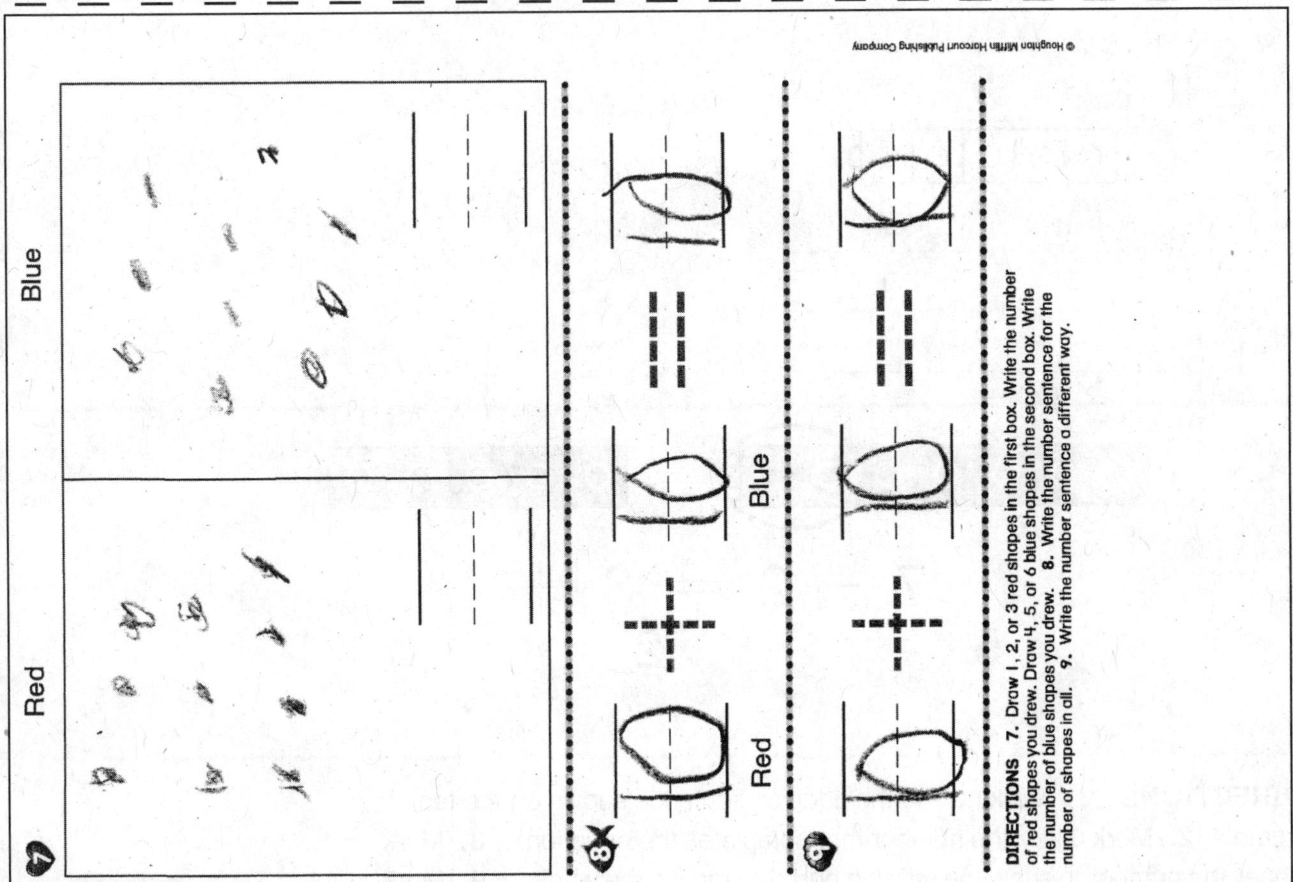

7

Red

Blue

8

__ + __ = __

Red Blue

9

__ + __ = __

DIRECTIONS 7. Draw 1, 2, or 3 red shapes in the first box. Write the number of red shapes you drew. Draw 4, 5, or 6 blue shapes in the second box. Write the number of blue shapes you drew. 8. Write the number sentence for the number of shapes in all. 9. Write the number sentence a different way.

Name ____________________

Directions/Questions are at bottom of page to be read by teacher.

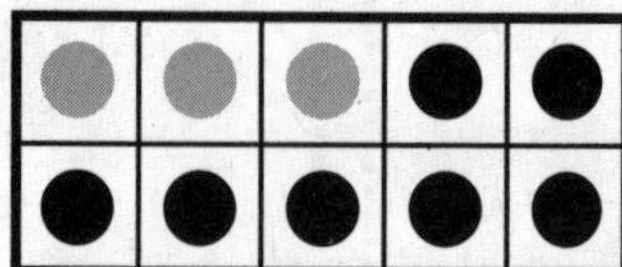

○ $5 + 5 = 10$

○ $6 + 4 = 10$

○ $3 + 7 = 10$

$4 + 2 = 5 + \_\_\_$

1	2	3
○	○	○

Whole	
5	
Part	Part
5	0
4	

1	2	4
○	○	○

$7 - 2 = 3 + \_\_\_$

5	2	1
○	○	○

DIRECTIONS **1.** Mark next to the addition sentence shown on the ten frame. **2.** Mark under the number that completes the equation. **3.** Mark under the number to show the missing part that makes the whole. **4.** Mark under the number that completes the equation.

GO ON

Name ________________________________

5

$5 + \_\_\_ = 6$

1 ○   2 ○   3 ○

6 

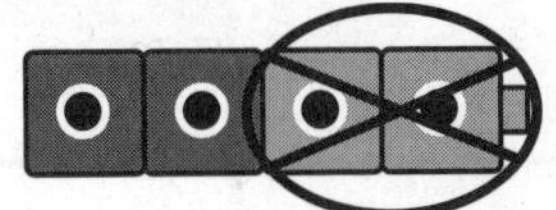

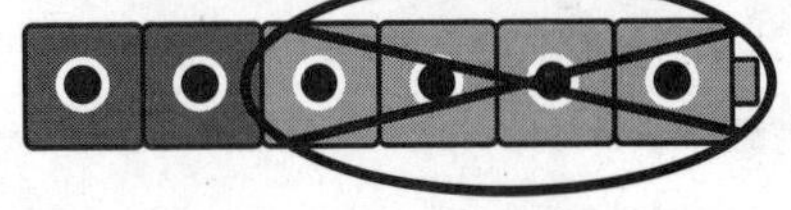

$4 - 2 = 6 - \_\_\_$

4 ○   3 ○   2 ○

7 

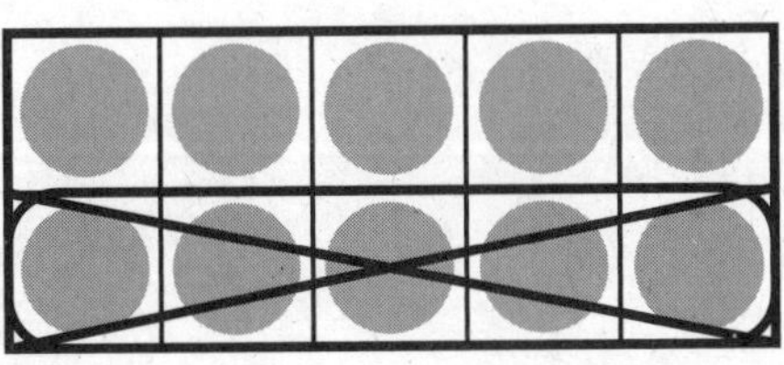

$10 - 5 = \_\_\_$

5 ○   4 ○   3 ○

8 

$4 + 1 = \_\_\_ + 2$

2 ○   3 ○   4 ○

DIRECTIONS **5.** Mark under the number that completes the addition sentence. **6.** Mark under the number that completes the equation. **7.** Mark under the number that completes the subtraction sentence. **8.** Mark under the number that completes the equation.

GO ON

Name ______________________________

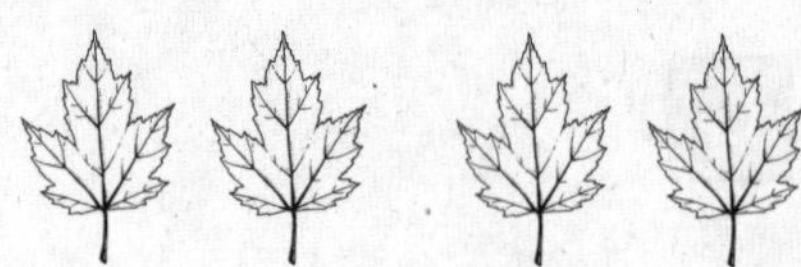

2 + 2 = ____

2 ○ 4 ○ 5 ○

Whole	
3	
Part	Part
3	0
2	1
1	

0 ○ 1 ○ 2 ○

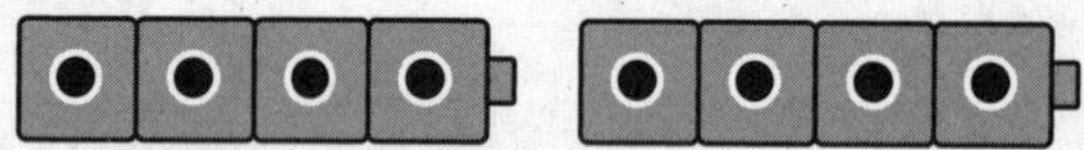

4 + ____ = 8

3 ○ 4 ○ 5 ○

DIRECTIONS **9.** Mark under the number that completes the addition sentence. **10.** Mark under the number to show the missing part that makes the whole. **11.** Mark under the number that completes the addition sentence.

GO ON

Name ______________________________

6 + 1 = ____

5 ○ 6 ○ 7 ○

4 − 2 = ____

4 ○ 3 ○ 2 ○

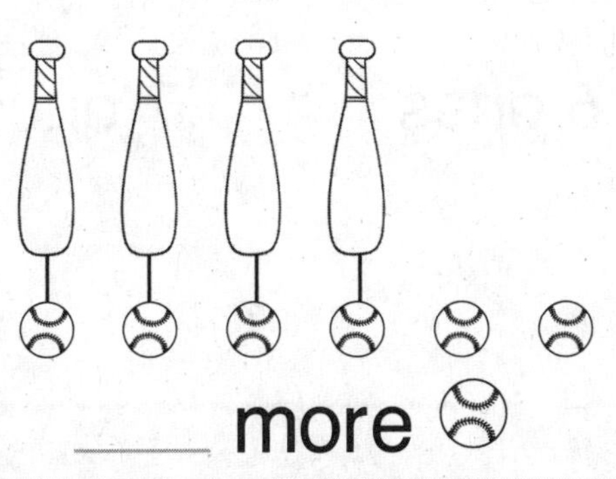

____ more

1 ○ 2 ○ 3 ○

8 − ____ = 7

2 ○ 1 ○ 0 ○

DIRECTIONS **12.** Mark under the number that completes the addition sentence. **13.** Mark under the number that completes the subtraction sentence. **14.** Compare the sets. Mark under the number that tells how many more balls than bats there are. **15.** Mark under the number that completes the subtraction sentence.

Name ________________________________

Directions/Questions are at bottom of page to be read by teacher.

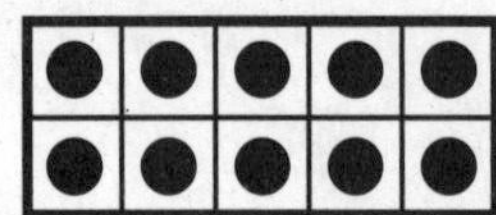 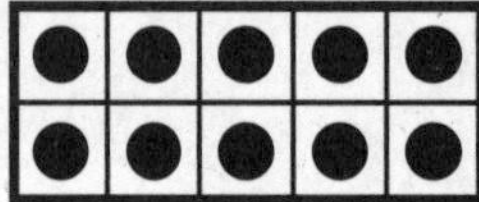 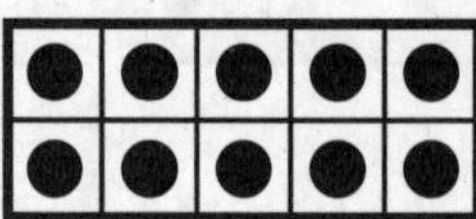 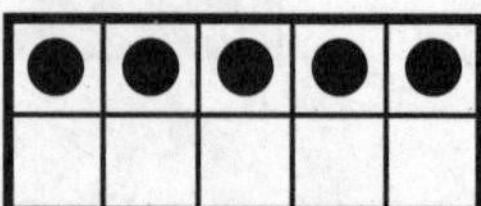

25	34	35
○	○	○

I o'clock	2 o'clock	3 o'clock
○	○	○

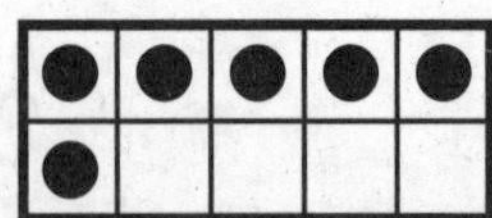

5 ones	6 ones	7 ones
○	○	○

4

I o'clock	3 o'clock	5 o'clock
○	○	○

DIRECTIONS **I.** How many counters are there? Mark under the number. **2.** About what time does the clock show? Mark under the time. **3.** How many ones are there? Mark under the number. **4.** What time does the clock show? Mark under the time.

GO ON

Name ______________________________________

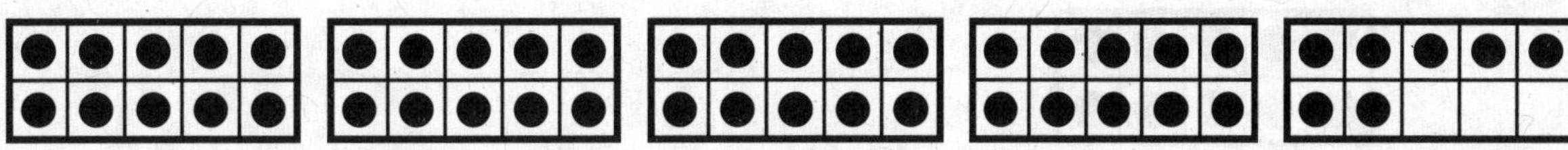

48 ○ 47 ○ 46 ○

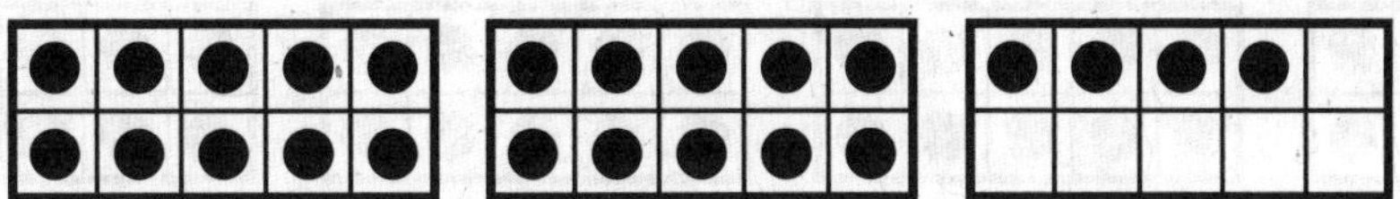

24 ○ 25 ○ 34 ○

8 o'clock ○ 10 o'clock ○ 12 o'clock ○

8

1 o'clock ○ 3 o'clock ○ 11 o'clock ○

DIRECTIONS **5.** How many counters are there? Mark under the number. **6.** How many counters are there? Mark under the number. **7.** About what time does the clock show? Mark under the time. **8.** What time does the clock show? Mark under the time.

GO ON

Name ______________________________

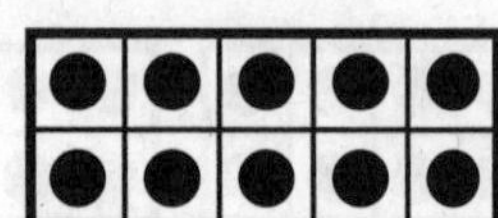

I ten ○ 2 tens ○ 10 tens ○

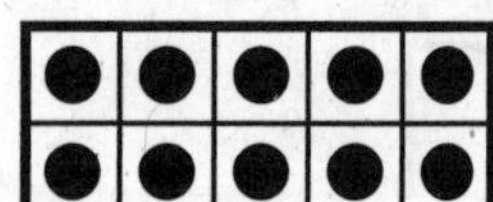
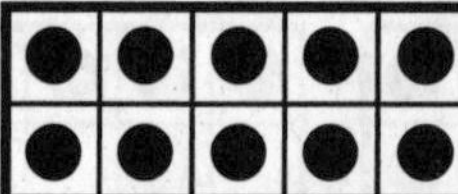
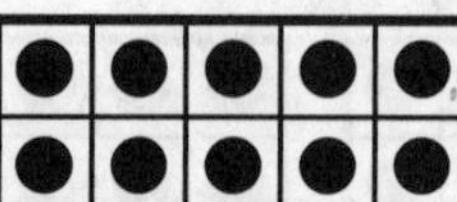
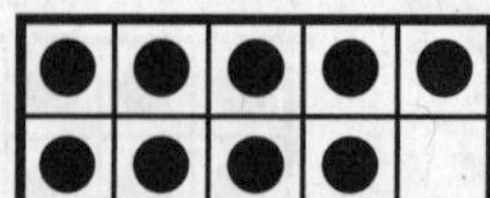

37 ○ 38 ○ 39 ○

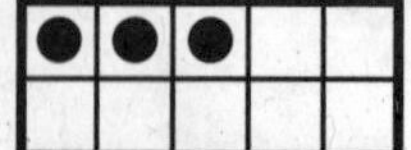

45 ○ 43 ○ 33 ○

8 ○ 9 ○ 12 ○

DIRECTIONS **9.** How many tens are shown? Mark under the answer. **10.** How many counters are shown? Mark under the number. **11.** How many counters are there? Mark under the number. **12.** What number is missing on the clock? Mark under the number.

Name ______________________________

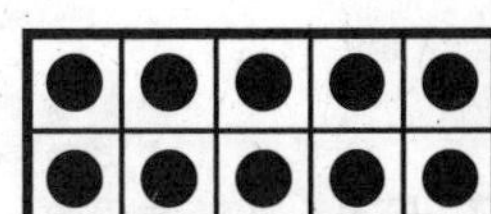 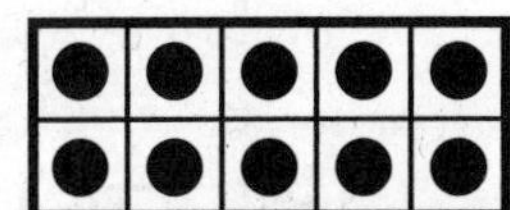 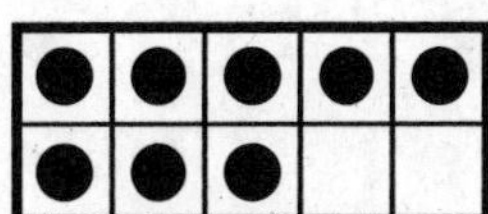

29	28	27
○	○	○

14

5 o'clock	7 o'clock	9 o'clock
○	○	○

15

6 o'clock	10 o'clock	12 o'clock
○	○	○

10	11	12
○	○	○

DIRECTIONS **13.** How many counters are there? Mark under the number. **14.** What time does the clock show? Mark under the time. **15.** About what time does the clock show? Mark under the time. **16.** What number is missing on the clock? Mark under the number.

Child's Name ______________

Prerequisite Skills Inventory
Page 1

1
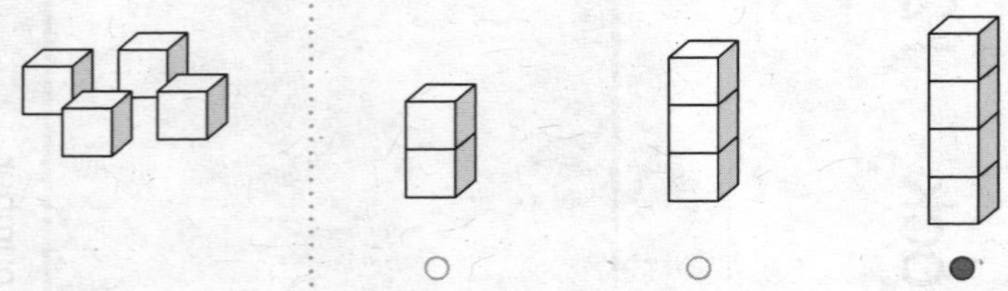

2
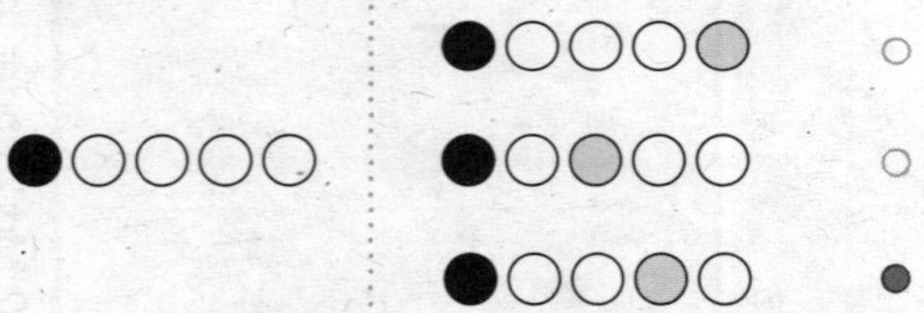

3
2
two
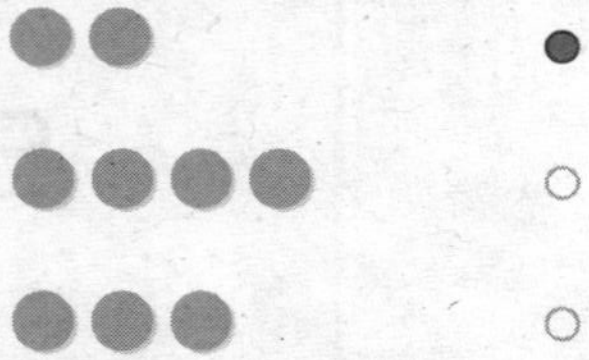

4
1 2 3 4 ___

6	5	4
○	●	○

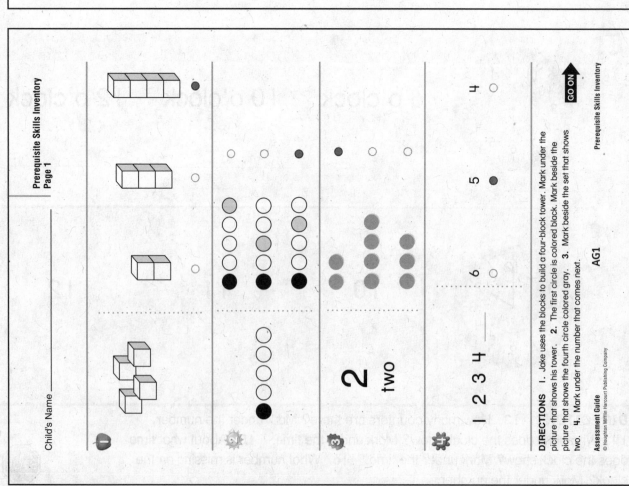

DIRECTIONS 1. Jake uses the blocks to build a four-block tower. Mark under the picture that shows his tower. 2. The first circle is colored black. Mark beside the picture that shows the fourth circle colored gray. 3. Mark beside the set that shows two. 4. Mark under the number that comes next.

GO ON

Assessment Guide AG1 **Prerequisite Skills Inventory**

Child's Name ______________

Prerequisite Skills Inventory
Page 2

5
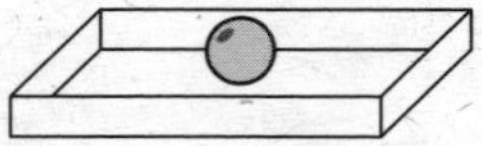

6	3	1
○	○	●

6
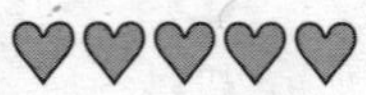

4	5	6
○	●	○

7
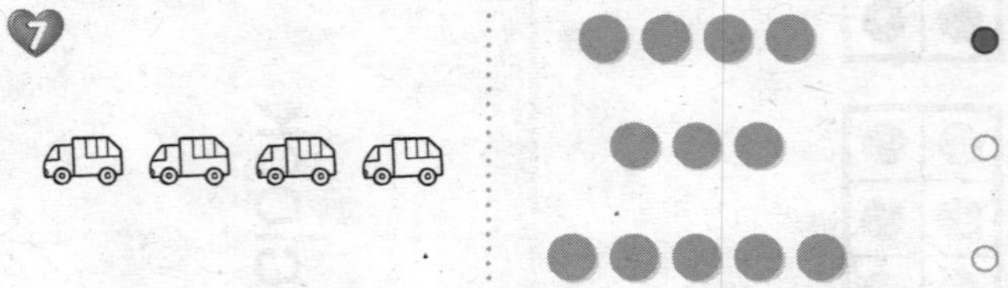

8
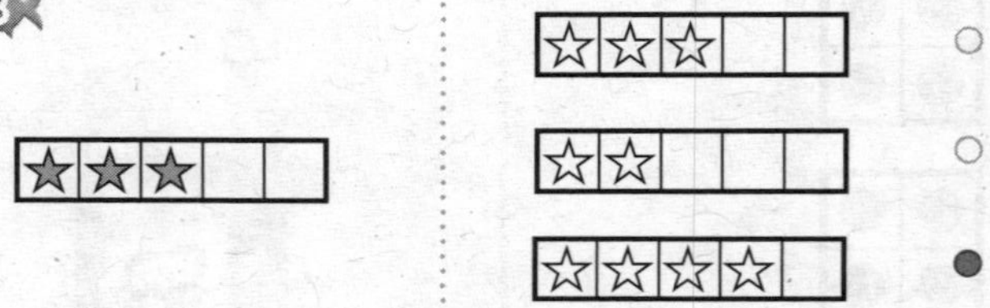

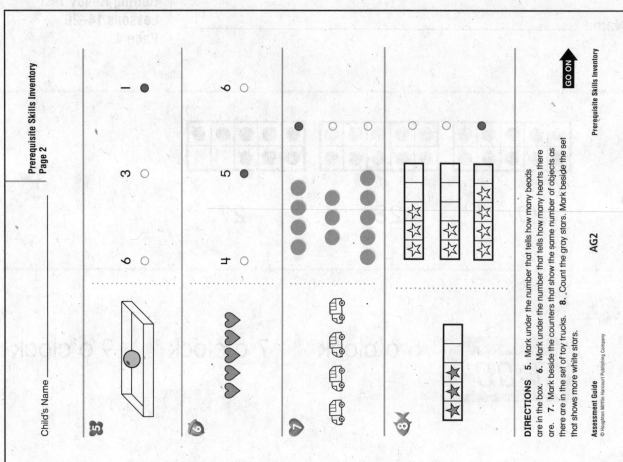

DIRECTIONS 5. Mark under the number that tells how many beads are in the box. 6. Mark under the number that tells how many hearts there are. 7. Mark beside the counters that show the same number of objects as there are in the set of toy trucks. 8. Count the gray stars. Mark beside the set that shows more white stars.

GO ON

Assessment Guide AG2 **Prerequisite Skills Inventory**

Child's Name ______________________

Prerequisite Skills Inventory
Page 3

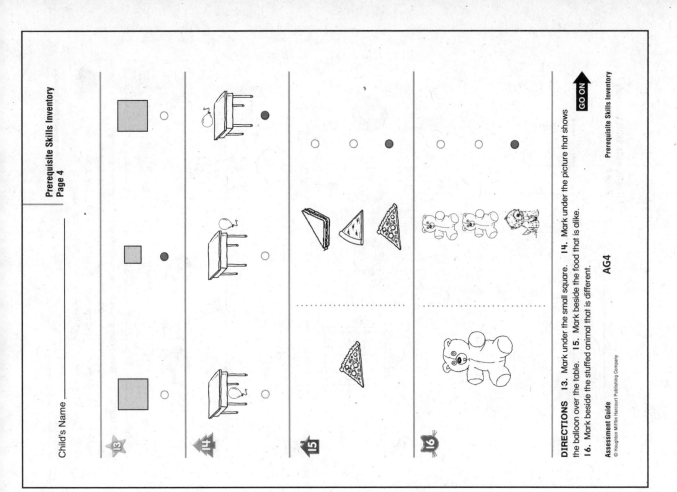

9

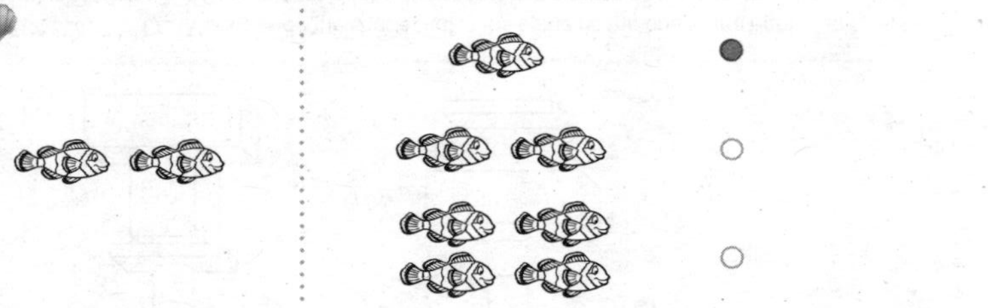

10

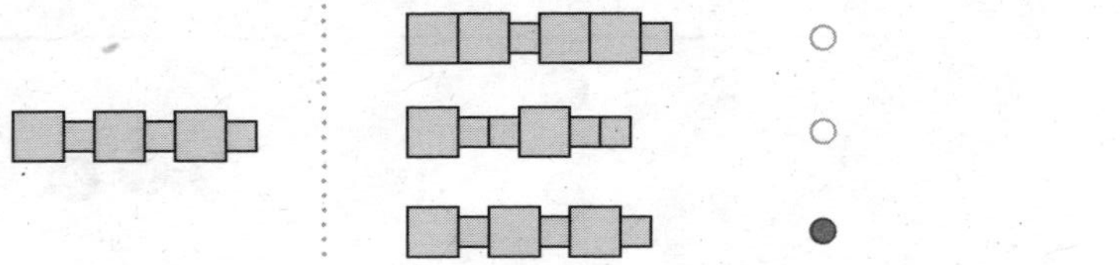

11

12

first

DIRECTIONS **9.** Mandy has 2 fish. The number of fish Ron has is less. Mark beside the number of fish Ron has. **10.** Mark beside the shape that is the same. **11.** Mark under the arrow that points down. **12.** Mark under the child that is last in line.

GO ON

Child's Name ______________________

Prerequisite Skills Inventory
Page 4

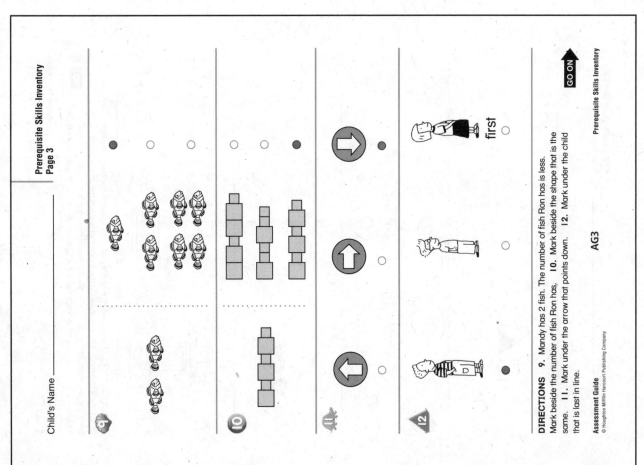

13

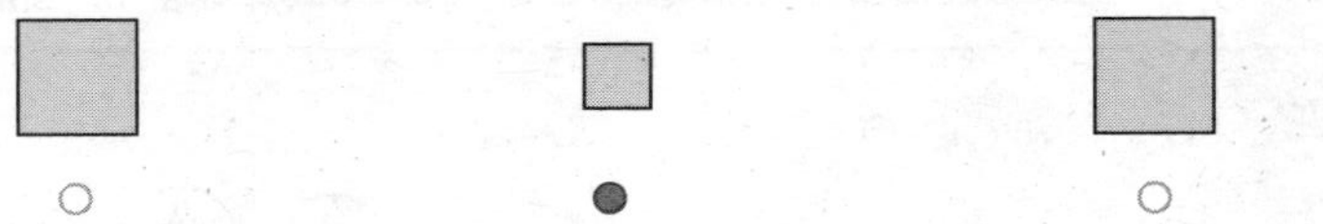

14

15

16

DIRECTIONS **13.** Mark under the small square. **14.** Mark under the picture that shows the balloon over the table. **15.** Mark beside the food that is alike. **16.** Mark beside the stuffed animal that is different.

GO ON

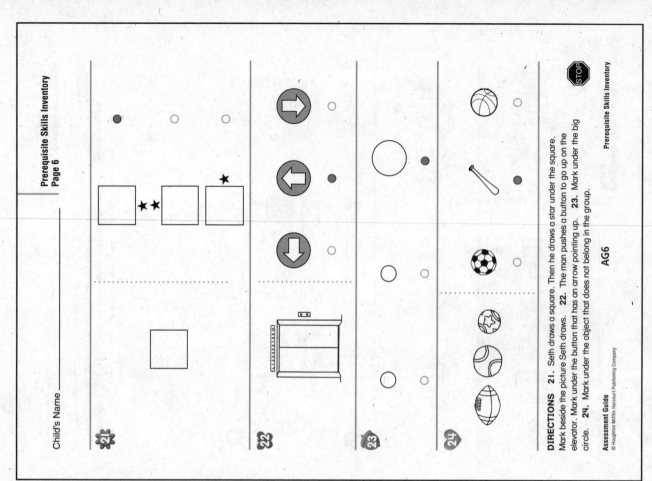

Child's Name ______________

Prerequisite Skills Inventory
Page 5

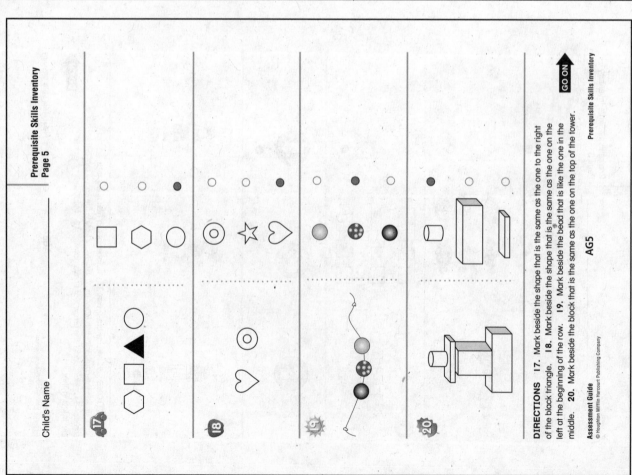

17

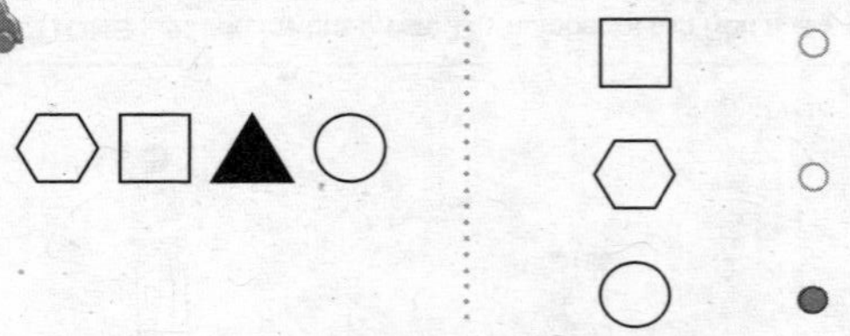

18

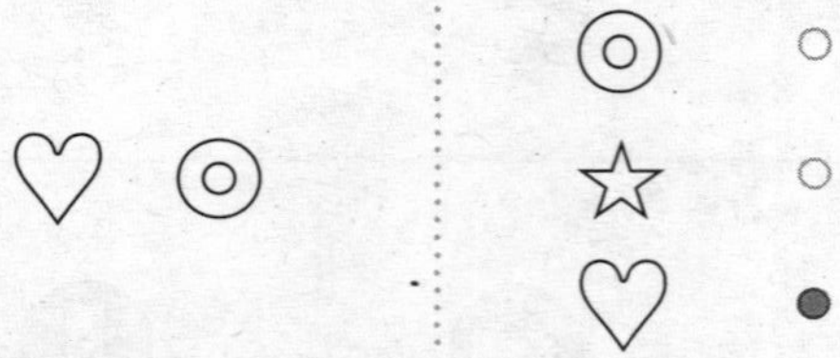

19

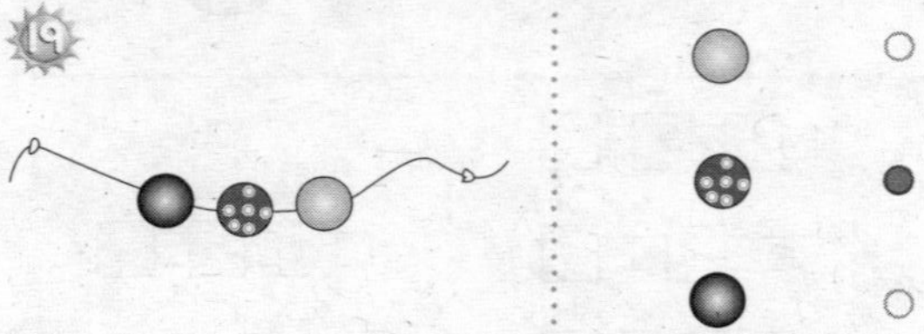

20

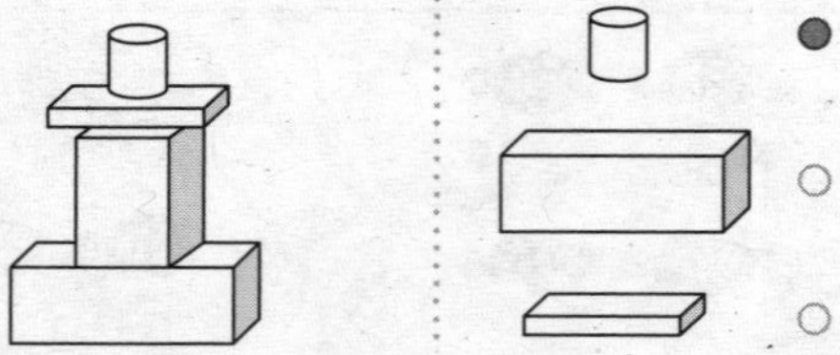

DIRECTIONS 17. Mark beside the shape that is the same as the one to the right of the black triangle. 18. Mark beside the shape that is the same as the one on the left at the beginning of the row. 19. Mark beside the bead that is like the one in the middle. 20. Mark beside the block that is the same as the one on the top of the tower.

GO ON

Child's Name ______________

Prerequisite Skills Inventory
Page 6

21

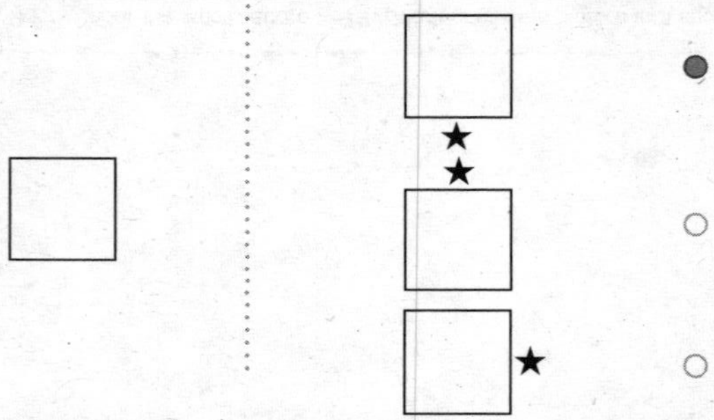

22

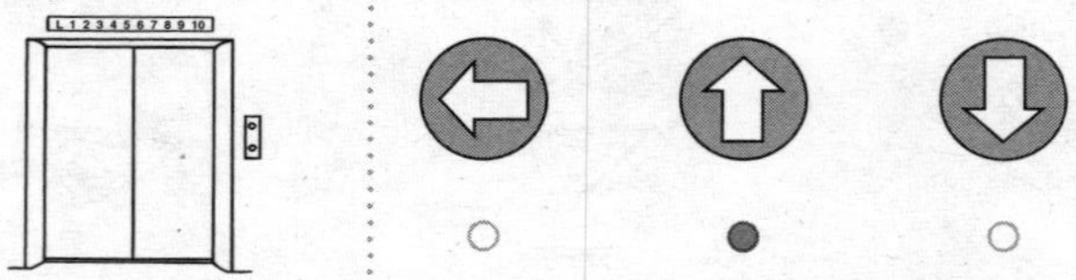

23

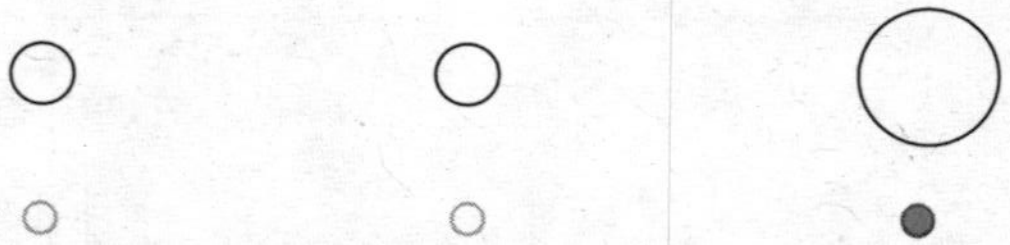

24

DIRECTIONS 21. Seth draws a square. Then he draws a star under the square. Mark beside the picture Seth draws. 22. The man pushes a button to go up on the elevator. Mark under the button that has an arrow pointing up. 23. Mark under the big circle. 24. Mark under the object that does not belong in the group.

STOP

Name ________________

Beginning-of-Year Test
Page 1

1

○ ● ○

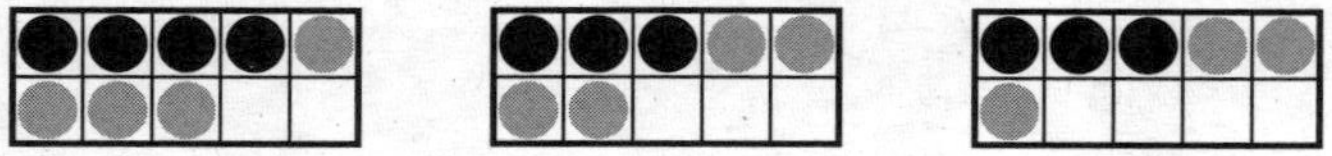

2 9

seven	eight	nine
○	○	●

3

___ − 3 = 5

3	5	8
○	○	●

4

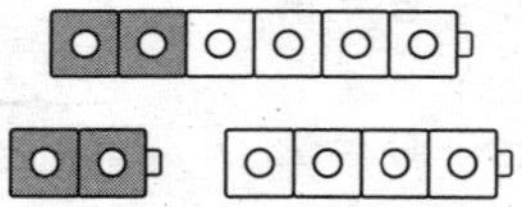

● $6 - 4 = 2$ ○ $6 - 3 = 3$ ○ $5 - 4 = 1$

DIRECTIONS **1.** Mark under the set that models a way to make seven. **2.** Mark under the word that matches the number at the beginning of the row. **3.** Mark under the number that shows how many you started with. **4.** Mark beside the subtraction sentence that shows the cube train being taken apart.

GO ON

Name ________________

Beginning-of-Year Test
Page 2

5 12 13 14 ___

14	15	16
○	●	○

6

71	72	73	74	75	76	77	78	79	80
81	82	83	84	85	86	87	88	89	90
91	92	93	94	___	96	97	98	99	100

90	95	100
○	●	○

7

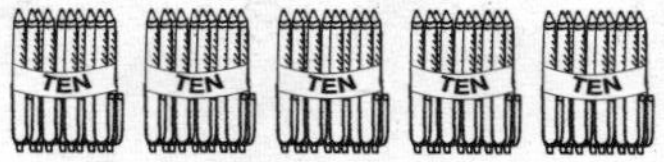

TEN TEN TEN TEN TEN

60	50	40
○	●	○

8

● $2 + 3$

○ $2 + 2$

○ $1 + 3$

DIRECTIONS **5.** Mark under the number that comes next. **6.** Begin with 71 and count to 100. Mark under the number that completes the counting order. **7.** Count the pens by tens. Mark under the number that shows how many pens in all. **8.** Mark beside the addition that shows the counters put together.

GO ON

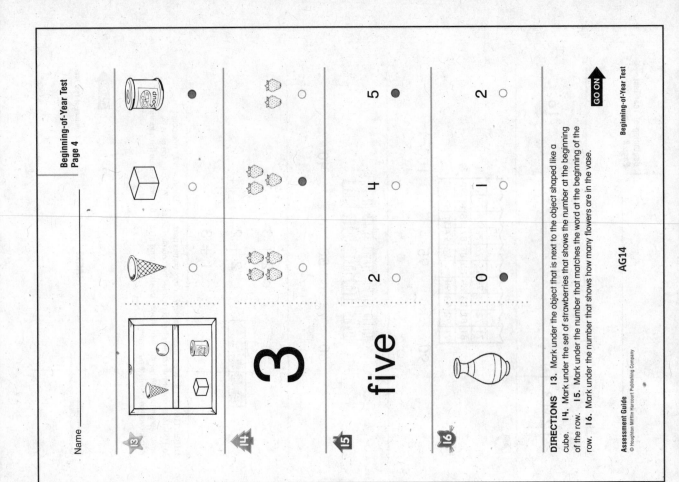

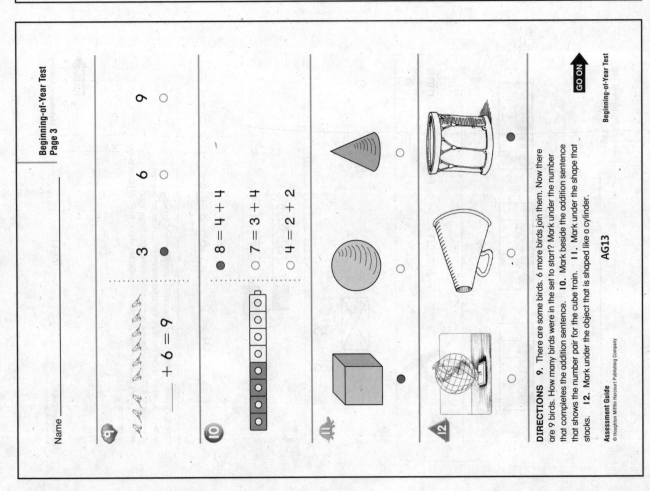

9

___ + 6 = 9

3 ● 6 ○ 9 ○

10

● 8 = 4 + 4

○ 7 = 3 + 4

○ 4 = 2 + 2

11

● ○ ○

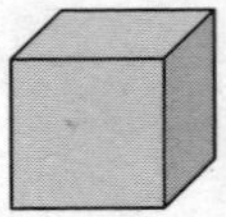

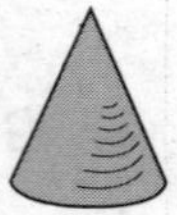

12

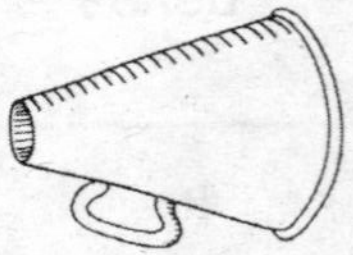

○ ○ ●

DIRECTIONS 9. There are some birds. 6 more birds join them. Now there are 9 birds. How many birds were in the set to start? Mark under the number that completes the addition sentence. 10. Mark beside the addition sentence that shows the number pair for the cube train. 11. Mark under the shape that stacks. 12. Mark under the object that is shaped like a cylinder.

GO ON

13

○ ○ ●

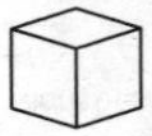

14

3

○ ● ○

15

five

2 ○ 4 ○ 5 ●

16

0 ● 1 ○ 2 ○

DIRECTIONS 13. Mark under the object that is next to the object shaped like a cube. 14. Mark under the set of strawberries that shows the number at the beginning of the row. 15. Mark under the number that matches the word at the beginning of the row. 16. Mark under the number that shows how many flowers are in the vase.

GO ON

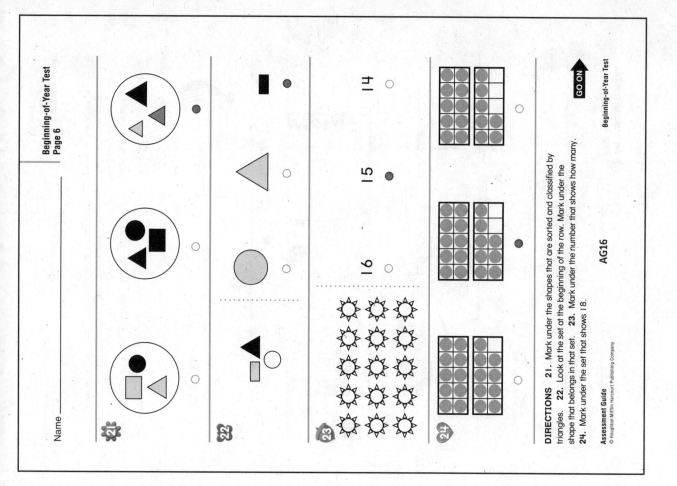

Name ____________

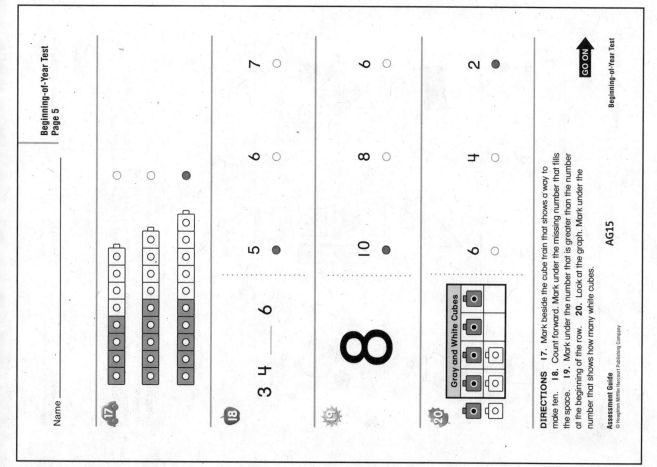

17

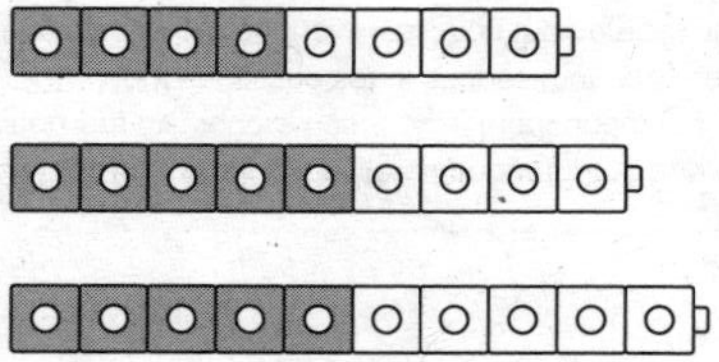

○
○
●

18

3 4 ___ 6

5	6	7
●	○	○

19

8

10	8	6
●	○	○

20

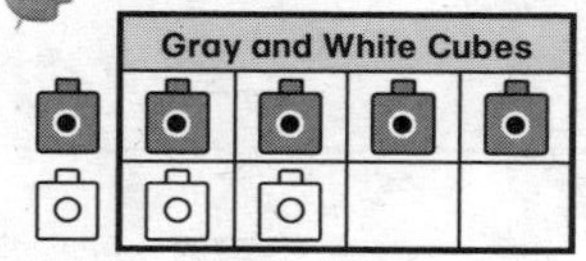

Gray and White Cubes

6	4	2
○	○	●

DIRECTIONS 17. Mark beside the cube train that shows a way to make ten. 18. Count forward. Mark under the missing number that fills the space. 19. Mark under the number that is greater than the number at the beginning of the row. 20. Look at the graph. Mark under the number that shows how many white cubes.

GO ON

Name ____________

21

○ ○ ●

22

○ ○ ●

23

16	15	14
○	●	○

24

○ ● ○

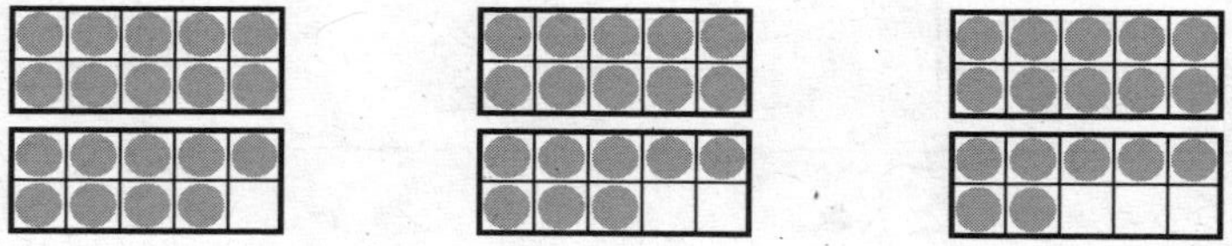

DIRECTIONS 21. Mark under the shapes that are sorted and classified by triangles. 22. Look at the set at the beginning of the row. Mark under the shape that belongs in that set. 23. Mark under the number that shows how many. 24. Mark under the set that shows 18.

GO ON

Name ________________

25 2 3 4

26

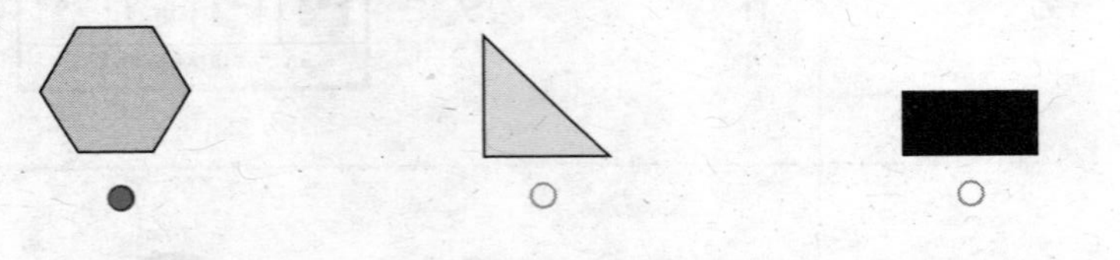

27

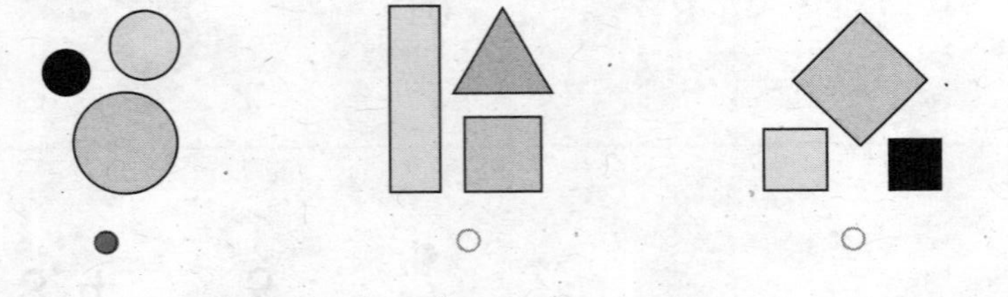

28

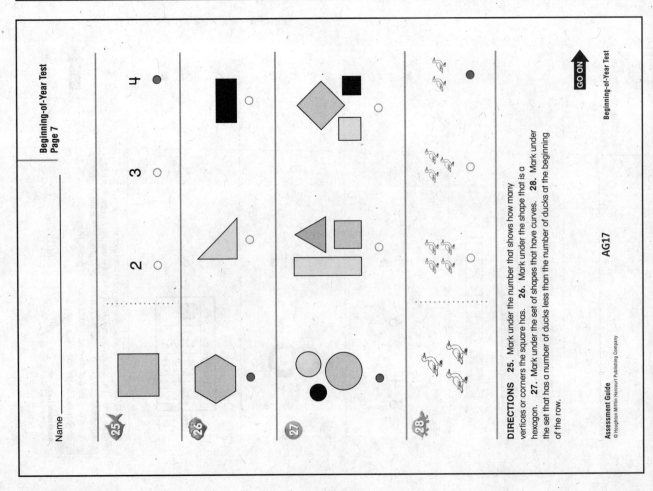

DIRECTIONS **25.** Mark under the number that shows how many vertices or corners the square has. **26.** Mark under the shape that is a hexagon. **27.** Mark under the set of shapes that have curves. **28.** Mark under the set that has a number of ducks less than the number of ducks at the beginning of the row.

GO ON

Name ________________

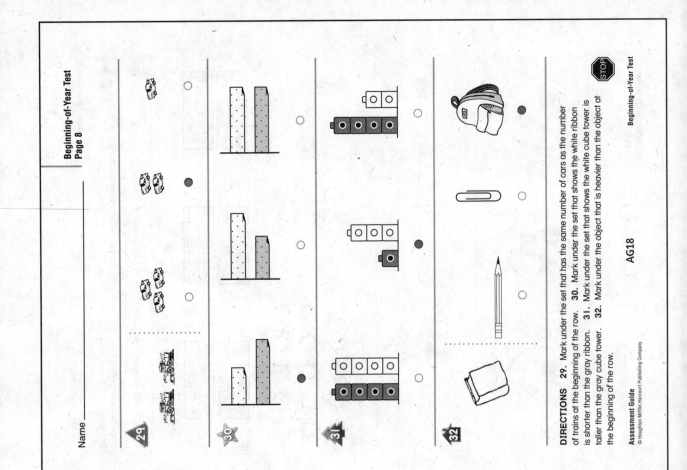

29

30

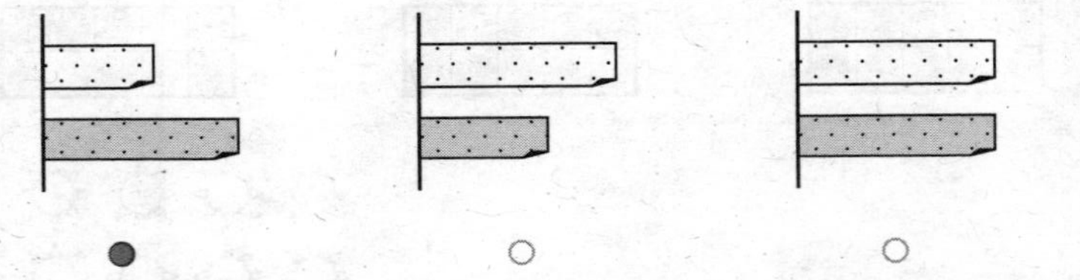

31

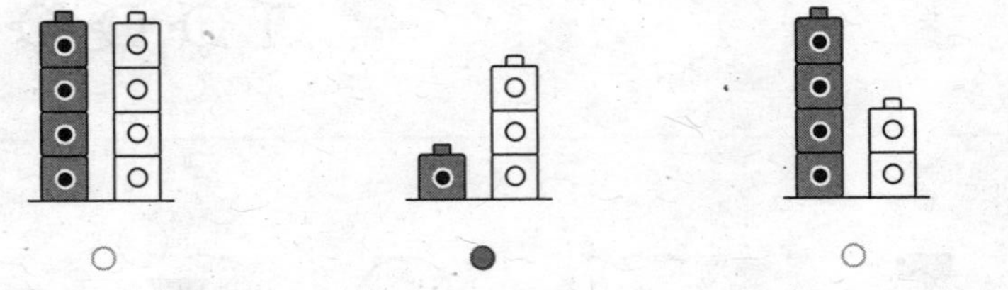

32

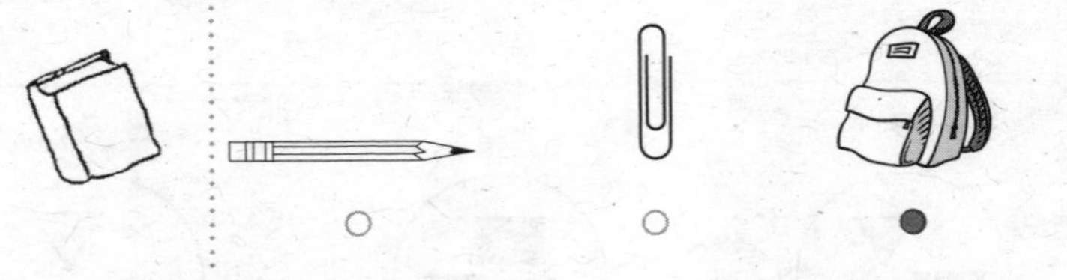

DIRECTIONS **29.** Mark under the set that has the same number of cars as the number of trains at the beginning of the row. **30.** Mark under the set that shows the white ribbon is shorter than the gray ribbon. **31.** Mark under the set that shows the white cube tower is taller than the gray cube tower. **32.** Mark under the object that is heavier than the object at the beginning of the row.

STOP

Name ______________________

Middle-of-Year Test
Page 1

1

● ○ ○

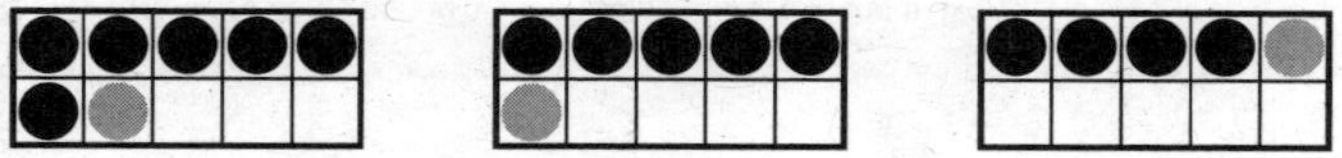

2

nine

6	8	9
○	○	●

3

___ − 2 = 6

6	8	9
○	●	○

4

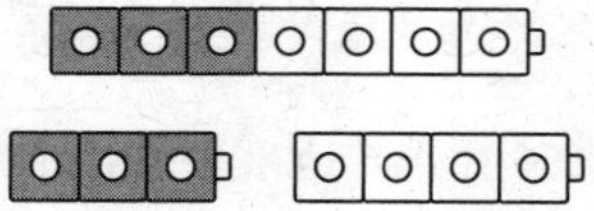

○ 7 − 5 = 2 ● 7 − 4 = 3 ○ 6 − 4 = 2

DIRECTIONS 1. Mark under the set that models a way to make seven. 2. Mark under the number that matches the word at the beginning of the row. 3. Mark under the number that shows how many suns you started with. 4. Mark beside the subtraction sentence that shows the cube train being taken apart.

GO ON

Name ______________________

Middle-of-Year Test
Page 2

5

17 18 19 ___

16	19	20
○	○	●

6

71	72	73	74	75	76	77	78	79	80
81	82	83	84	85	86	87	88	___	90
91	92	93	94	95	96	97	98	99	100

79	80	89
○	○	●

7

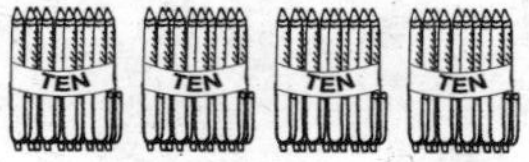

TEN TEN TEN TEN

4	40	50
○	●	○

8

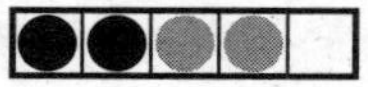

● 2 + 2

○ 1 + 3

○ 1 + 2

DIRECTIONS 5. Mark under the number that comes next. 6. Begin with 71 and count to 100. Mark under the number that completes the counting order. 7. Count the pens by tens. Mark under the number that shows how many pens in all. 8. Mark beside the addition that shows the counters put together.

GO ON

Name ______________

9

___ + 2 = 6

2 ○ 4 ● 8 ○

10

○ 9 = 6 + 3

○ 6 = 4 + 2

● 8 = 5 + 3

11

● ○ ○

12

● ○ ○

DIRECTIONS 9. There are some penguins. 2 more penguins join them. Now there are 6 penguins. How many penguins were in the set to start? Mark under the number that completes the addition sentence. 10. Mark beside the addition sentence that shows the number pair for the cube train. 11. Mark under the shape that rolls and stacks. 12. Mark under the object that is shaped like a cylinder.

GO ON

Name ______________

13

○ ● ○

14

4

○ ○ ●

15

5

two ○ four ○ five ●

16

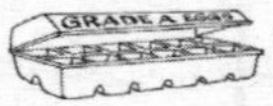

0 ● 1 ○ 2 ○

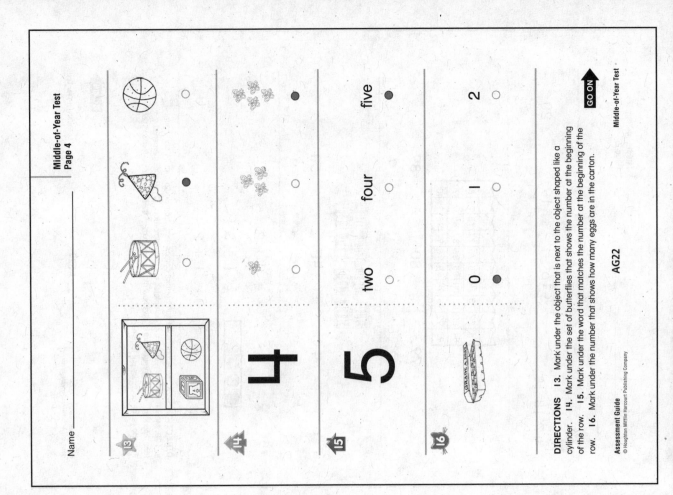

DIRECTIONS 13. Mark under the object that is next to the object shaped like a cylinder. 14. Mark under the set of butterflies that shows the number at the beginning of the row. 15. Mark under the word that matches the number at the beginning of the row. 16. Mark under the number that shows how many eggs are in the carton.

GO ON

Name ______________________

Middle-of-Year Test
Page 5

17

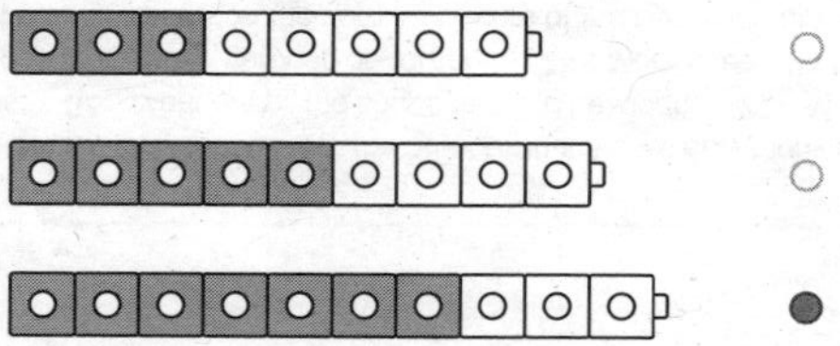

18

7 8 ___ 10

10 9 8

19

7

4 7 8

20

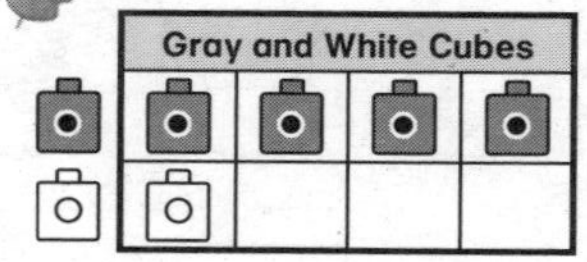

Gray and White Cubes

1 4 5

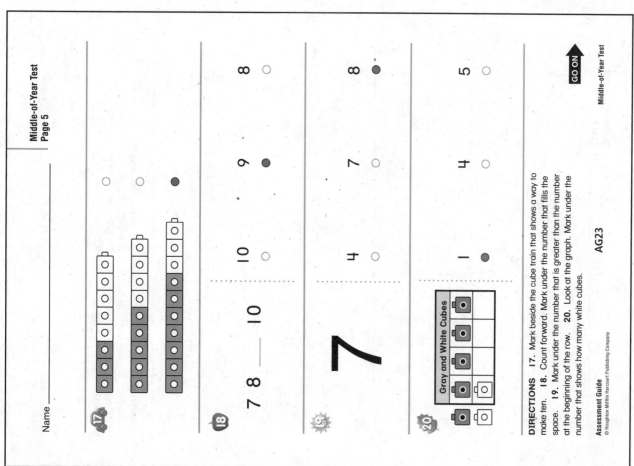

DIRECTIONS 17. Mark beside the cube train that shows a way to make ten. 18. Count forward. Mark under the number that fills the space. 19. Mark under the number that is greater than the number at the beginning of the row. 20. Look at the graph. Mark under the number that shows how many white cubes.

GO ON

Name ______________________

Middle-of-Year Test
Page 6

21

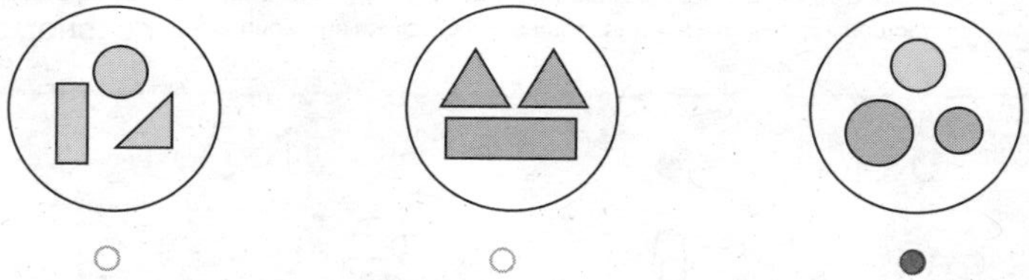

22

23

15 16 17

24

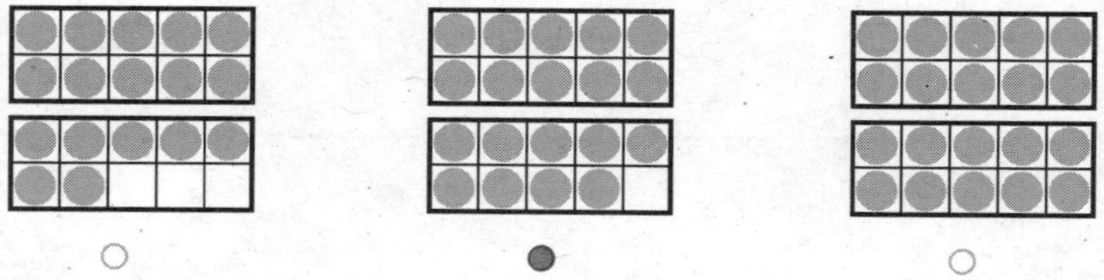

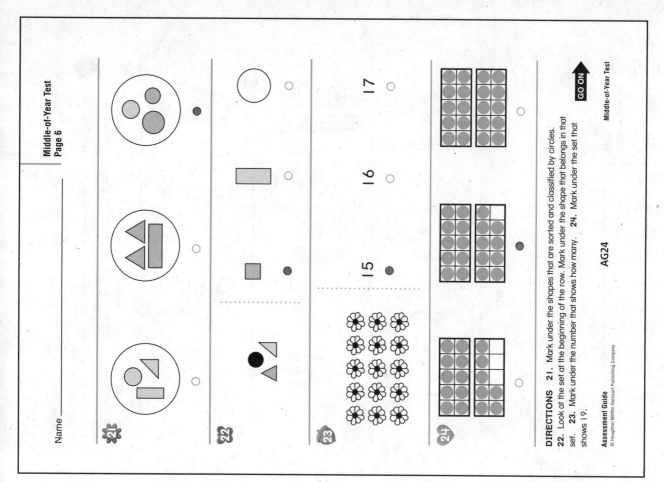

DIRECTIONS 21. Mark under the shapes that are sorted and classified by circles. 22. Look at the set at the beginning of the row. Mark under the shape that belongs in that set. 23. Mark under the number that shows how many. 24. Mark under the set that shows 19.

GO ON

Name ______________________

25

6 4 3

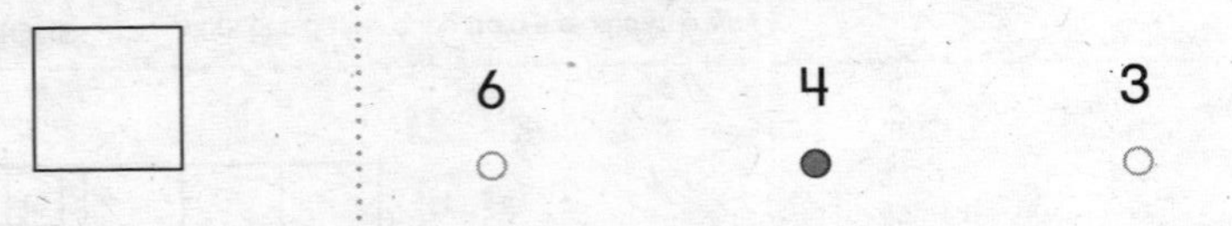

26

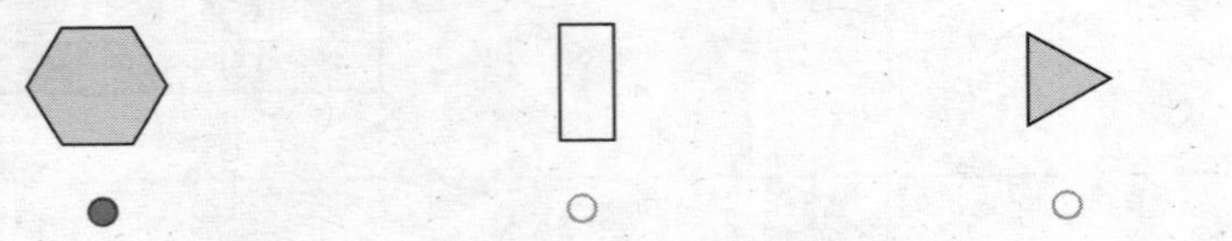

27

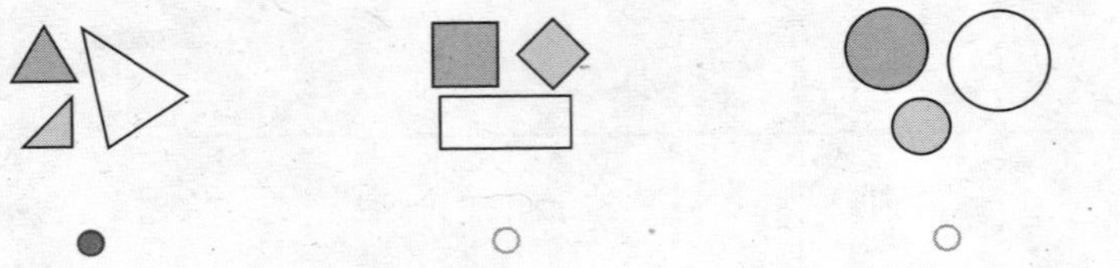

28

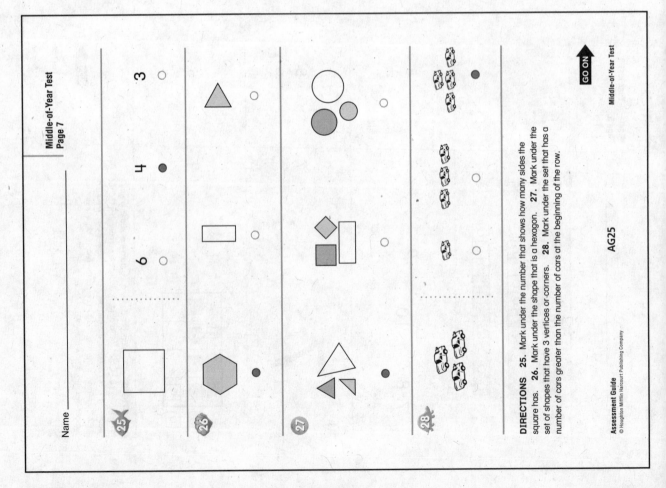

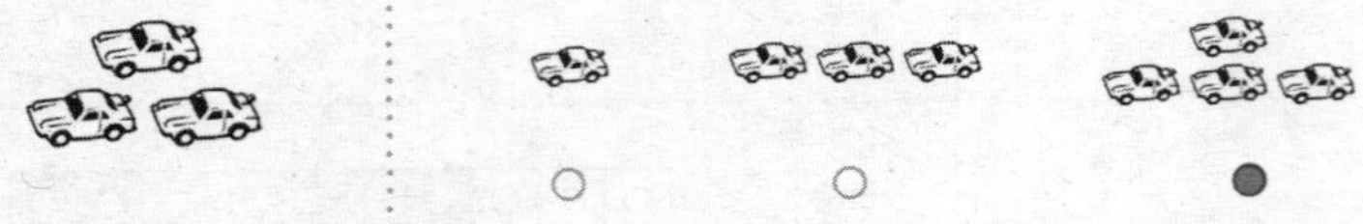

DIRECTIONS **25.** Mark under the number that shows how many sides the square has. **26.** Mark under the shape that is a hexagon. **27.** Mark under the set of shapes that have 3 vertices or corners. **28.** Mark under the set that has a number of cars greater than the number of cars at the beginning of the row.

GO ON

Name ______________________

29

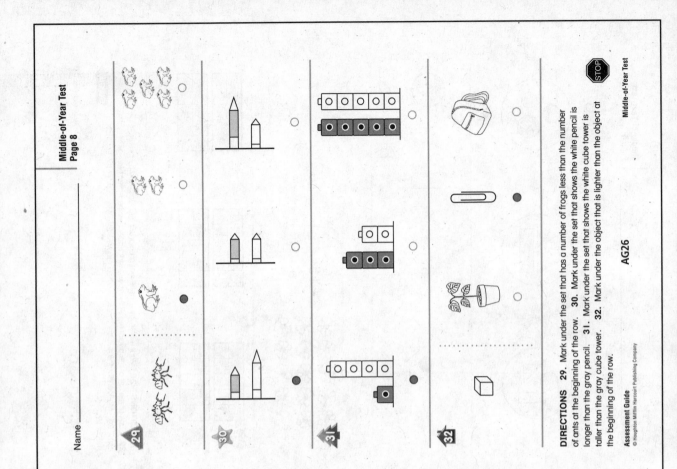

30

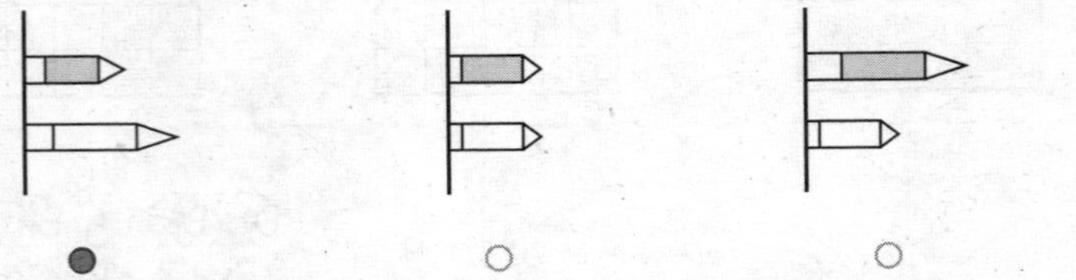

31

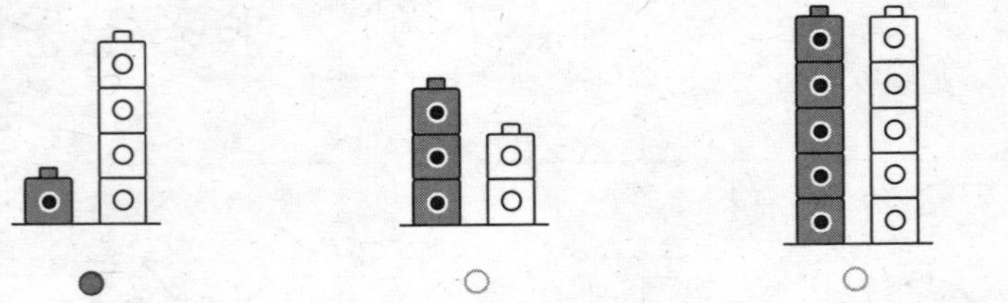

32

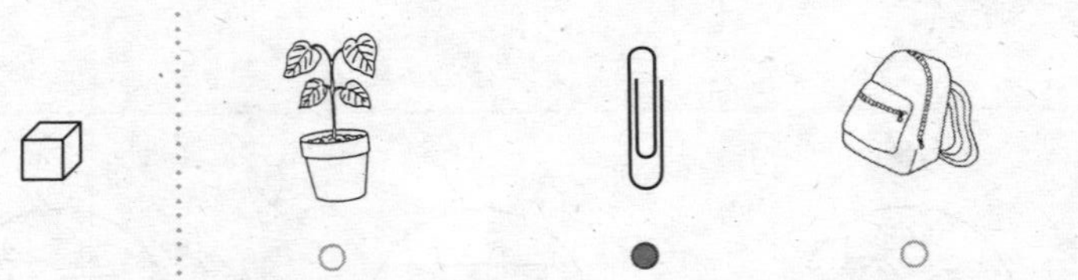

DIRECTIONS **29.** Mark under the set that has a number of frogs less than the number of ants at the beginning of the row. **30.** Mark under the set that shows the white pencil is longer than the gray pencil. **31.** Mark under the set that shows the white cube tower is taller than the gray cube tower. **32.** Mark under the object that is lighter than the object at the beginning of the row.

STOP

Name ______________________

End-of-Year Test
Page 1

1

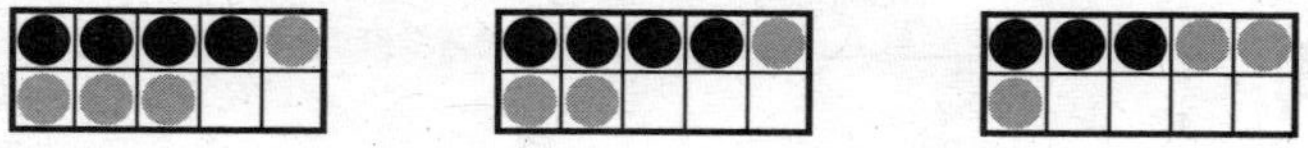

○ ● ○

2

nine

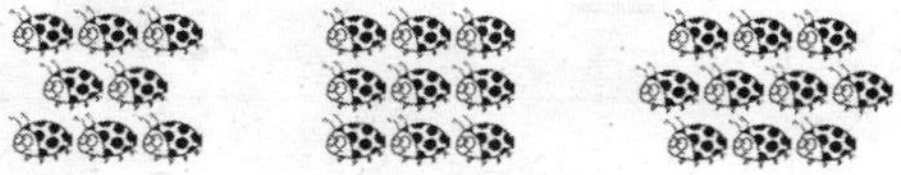

○ ● ○

3

___ − 1 = 5

5 ○ 6 ● 7 ○

4

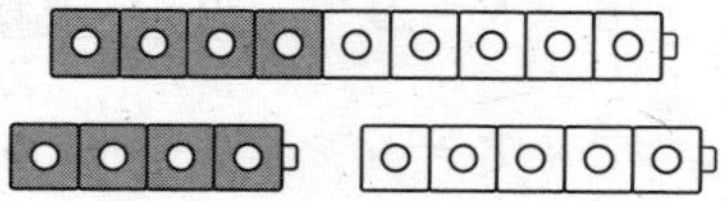

○ 8 − 5 = 3 ○ 9 − 6 = 3 ● 9 − 5 = 4

DIRECTIONS 1. Mark under the set that models a way to make seven. 2. Mark under the set that matches the word at the beginning of the row. 3. Mark under the number that shows how many stars you started with. 4. Mark beside the subtraction sentence that shows the cube train being taken apart.

GO ON

Name ______________________

End-of-Year Test
Page 2

5

16 17 18 ___

18 ○ 19 ● 20 ○

6

71	72	73	74	75	76	77	78	79	80
81	82	83	84	85	___	87	88	89	90
91	92	93	94	95	96	97	98	99	100

77 ○ 86 ● 90 ○

7

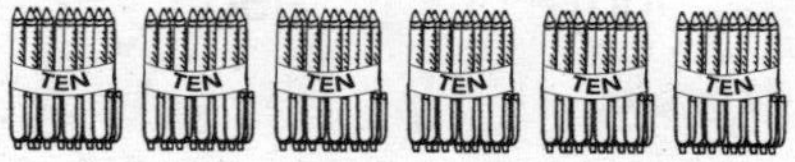

60 ● 50 ○ 6 ○

8

● 4 + 1
○ 3 + 2
○ 3 + 1

DIRECTIONS 5. Mark under the number that comes next. 6. Begin with 71 and count to 100. Mark under the number that completes the counting order. 7. Count the pens by tens. Mark under the number that shows how many pens in all. 8. Mark beside the addition that shows the counters put together.

GO ON

Name ____________________

9

_____ + 3 = 6

2 ○ 3 ● 6 ○

10

○ 4 = 2 + 2

● 8 = 6 + 2

○ 9 = 5 + 4

11

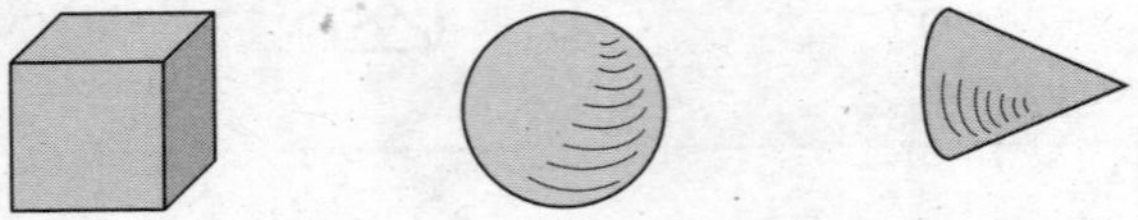

● ○ ○

12

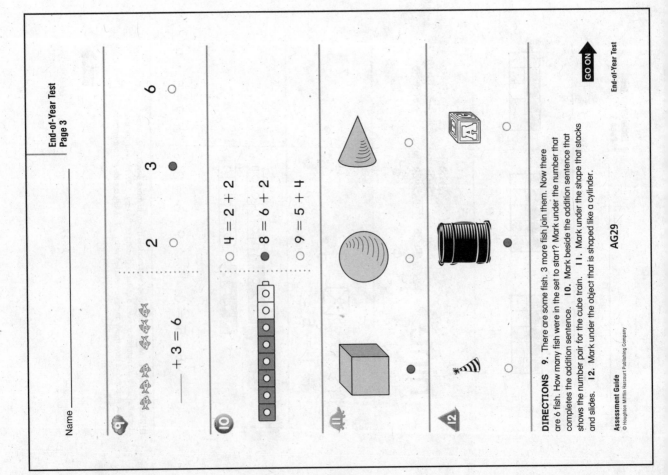

○ ● ○

DIRECTIONS 9. There are some fish. 3 more fish join them. Now there are 6 fish. How many fish were in the set to start? Mark under the number that completes the addition sentence. 10. Mark beside the addition sentence that shows the number pair for the cube train. 11. Mark under the shape that stacks and slides. 12. Mark under the object that is shaped like a cylinder.

GO ON

Name ____________________

13

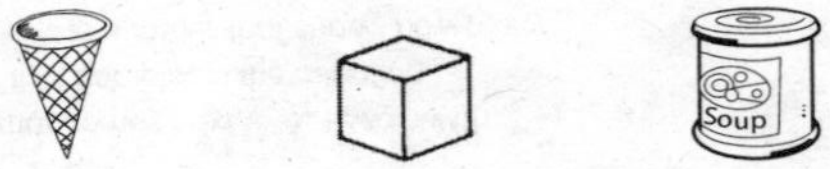

○ ● ○

14

3

○ ● ○

15

5

one ○ four ○ five ●

16

0 ● 2 ○ 3 ○

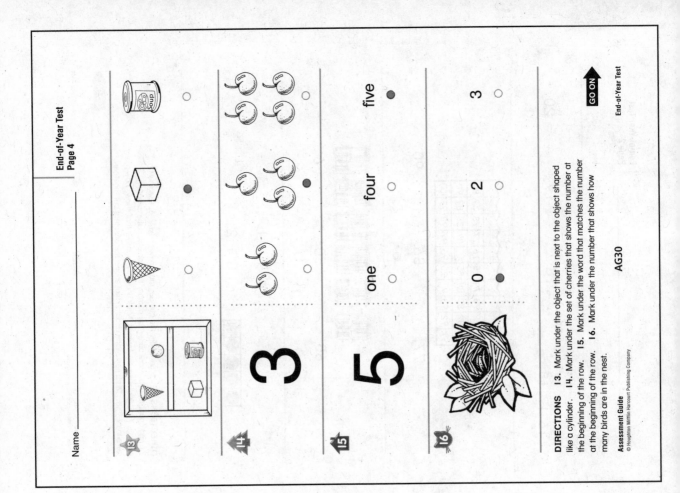

DIRECTIONS 13. Mark under the object that is next to the object shaped like a cylinder. 14. Mark under the set of cherries that shows the number at the beginning of the row. 15. Mark under the word that matches the number at the beginning of the row. 16. Mark under the number that shows how many birds are in the nest.

GO ON

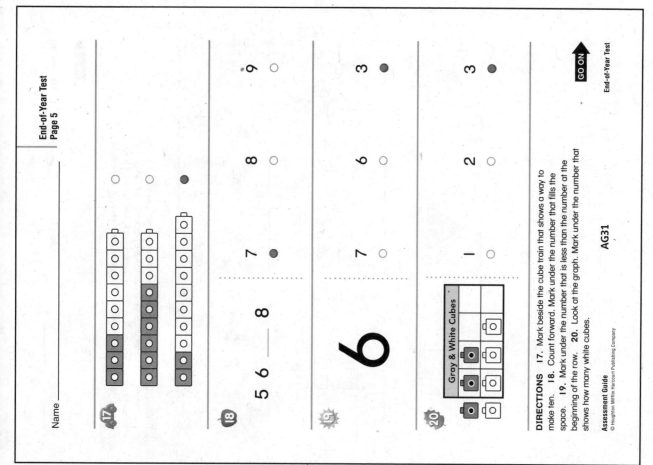

Name ________________

End-of-Year Test
Page 5

17

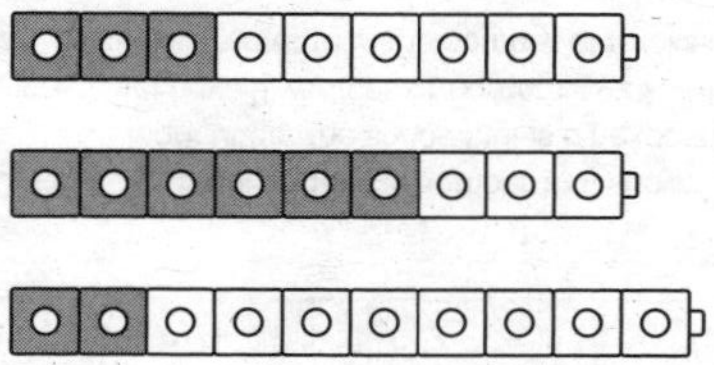

18

5 6 ___ 8

7 8 9

19

6

7 6 3

20

Gray & White Cubes				

1 2 3

DIRECTIONS **17.** Mark beside the cube train that shows a way to make ten. **18.** Count forward. Mark under the number that fills the space. **19.** Mark under the number that is less than the number at the beginning of the row. **20.** Look at the graph. Mark under the number that shows how many white cubes.

GO ON

Name ________________

End-of-Year Test
Page 6

21

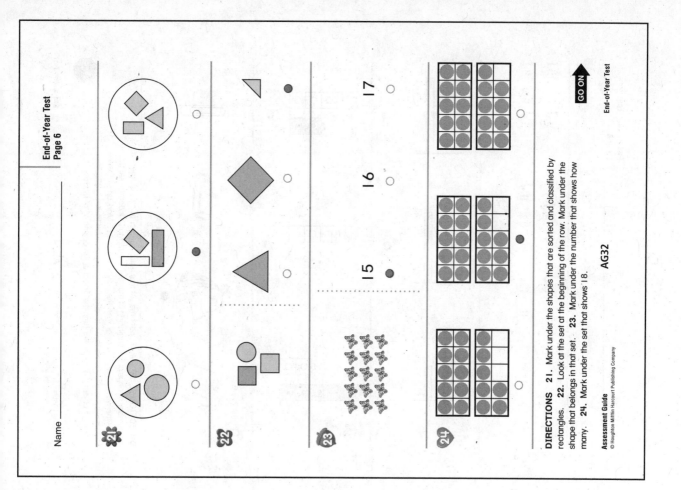

22

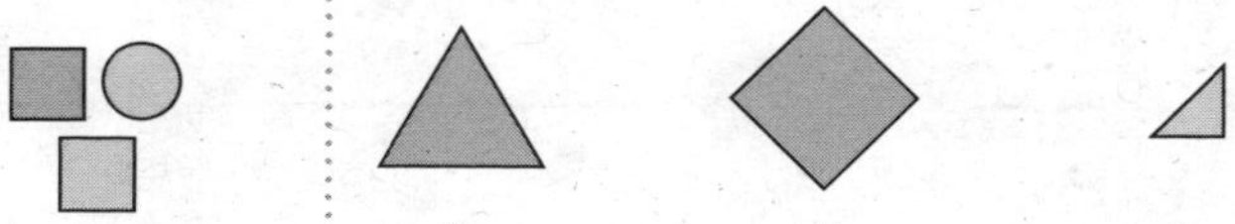

23

15 16 17

24

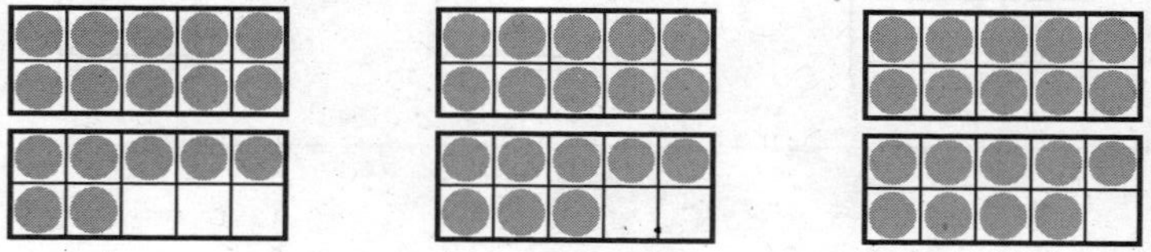

DIRECTIONS **21.** Mark under the shapes that are sorted and classified by rectangles. **22.** Look at the set at the beginning of the row. Mark under the shape that belongs in that set. **23.** Mark under the number that shows how many. **24.** Mark under the set that shows 18.

GO ON

25

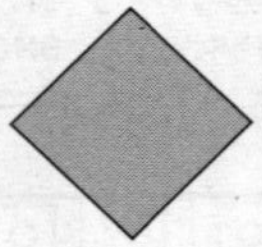

3 4 8

26

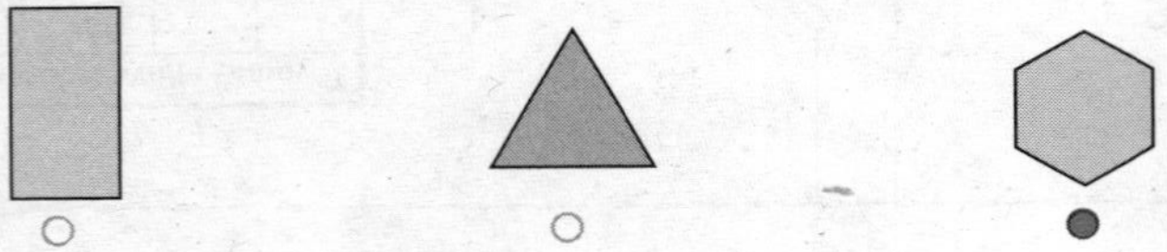

27

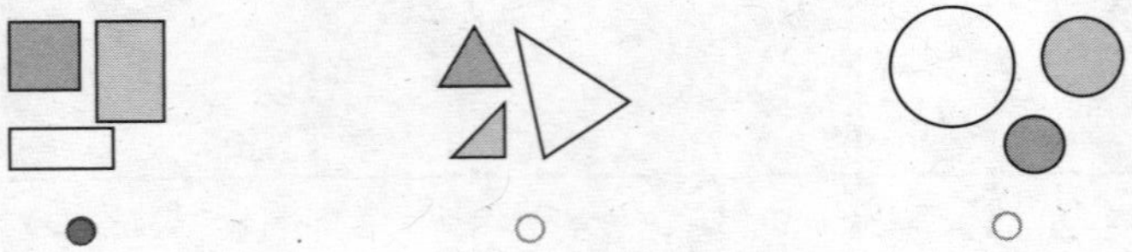

28

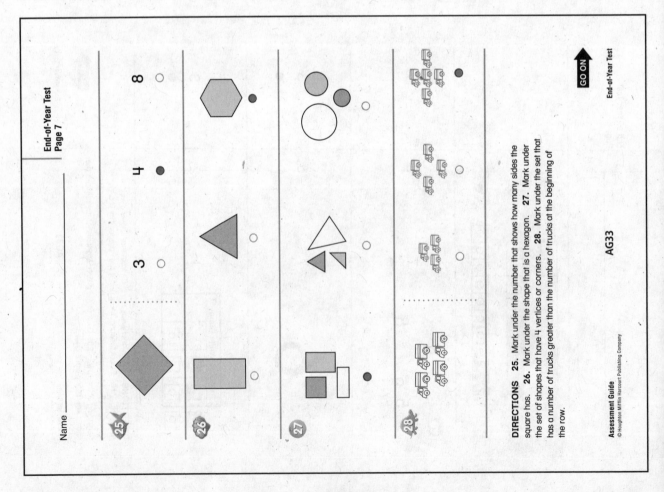

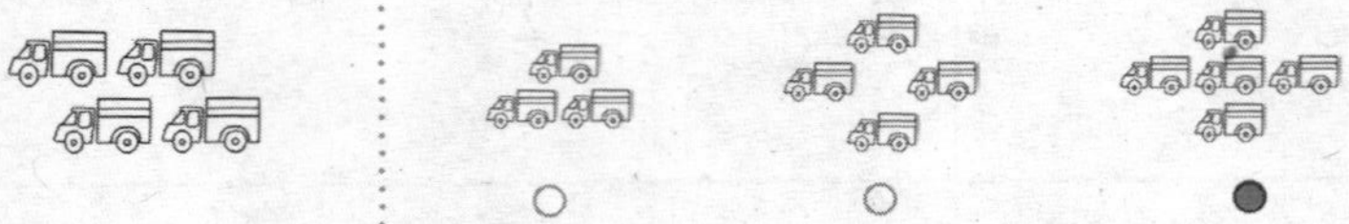

DIRECTIONS **25.** Mark under the number that shows how many sides the square has. **26.** Mark under the shape that is a hexagon. **27.** Mark under the set of shapes that have 4 vertices or corners. **28.** Mark under the set that has a number of trucks greater than the number of trucks at the beginning of the row.

GO ON

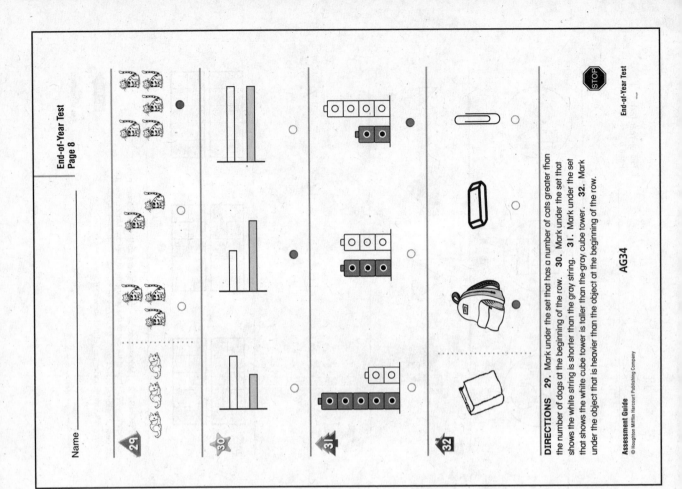

29

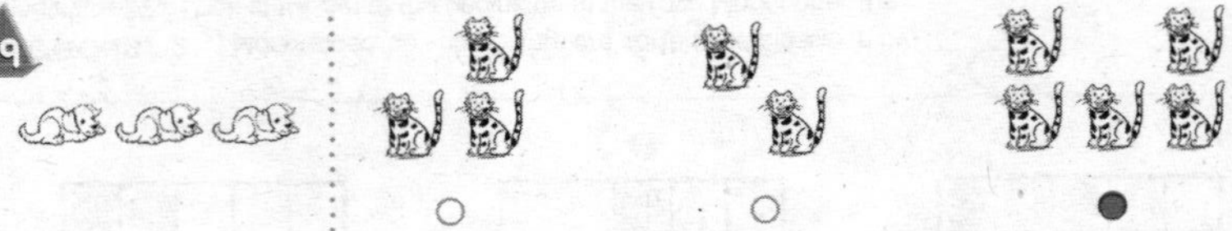

30

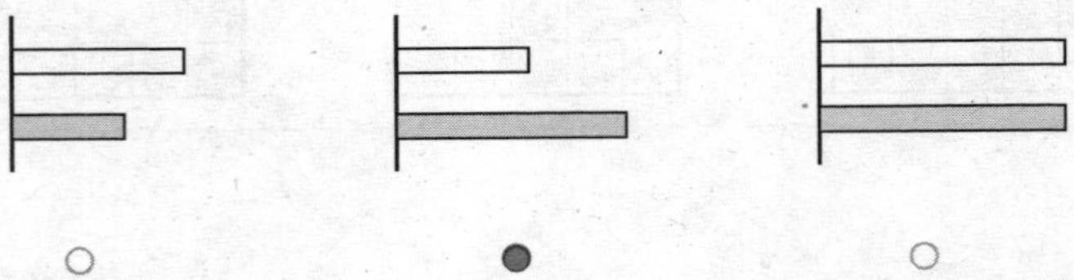

31

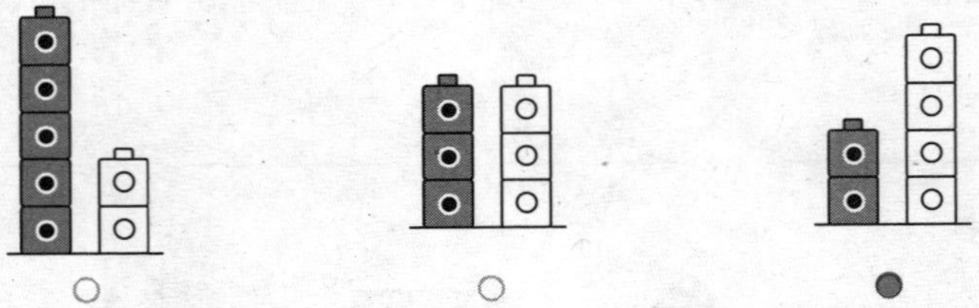

32

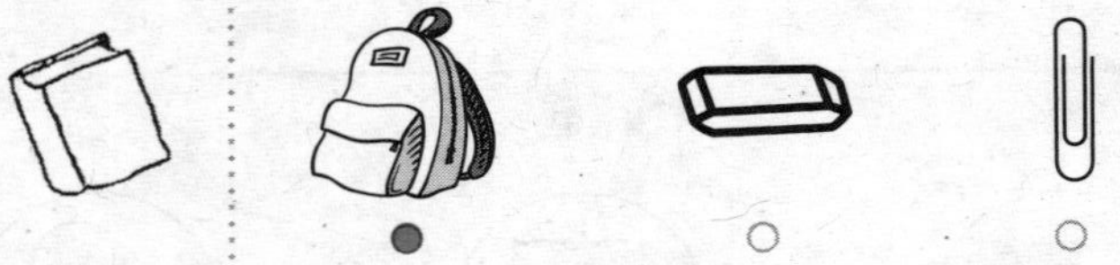

DIRECTIONS **29.** Mark under the set that has a number of cats greater than the number of dogs at the beginning of the row. **30.** Mark under the set that shows the white string is shorter than the gray string. **31.** Mark under the set that shows the white cube tower is taller than the gray cube tower. **32.** Mark under the object that is heavier than the object at the beginning of the row.

STOP

Name ______________________

Chapter 1 Test
Page 1

1

○ 1
● 2
● two

2

● 5
● five
○ 4

3

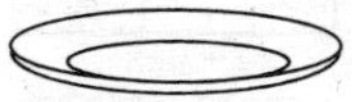

0

4

1

5

4

DIRECTIONS **1–2.** Choose all the answers that tell how many. **3.** How many muffins are on the plate? Write the number. **4–5.** Count how many. Write the number.

GO ON

Name ______________________

Chapter 1 Test
Page 2

6

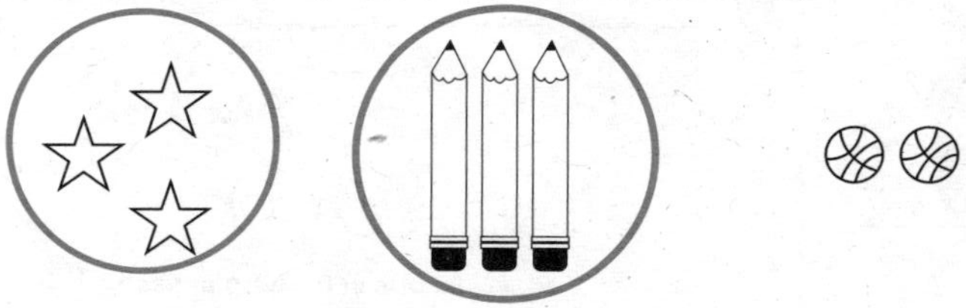

7

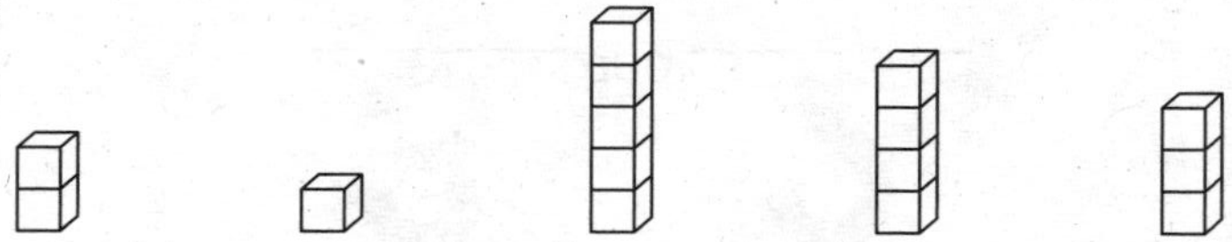

2 1 5 4 3

8

1 2 3 4 5

DIRECTIONS **6.** Circle all the sets that show 3. **7.** Count the cubes in each tower. Write the number. **8.** Write the numbers 1 to 5 in counting order.

GO ON

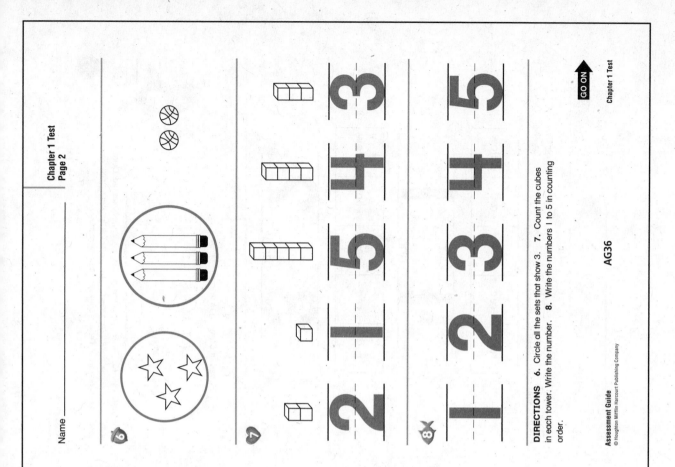

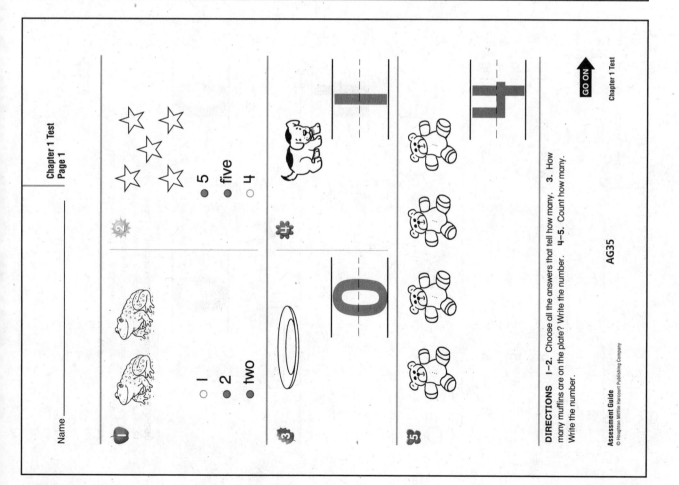

Name ______________________

9

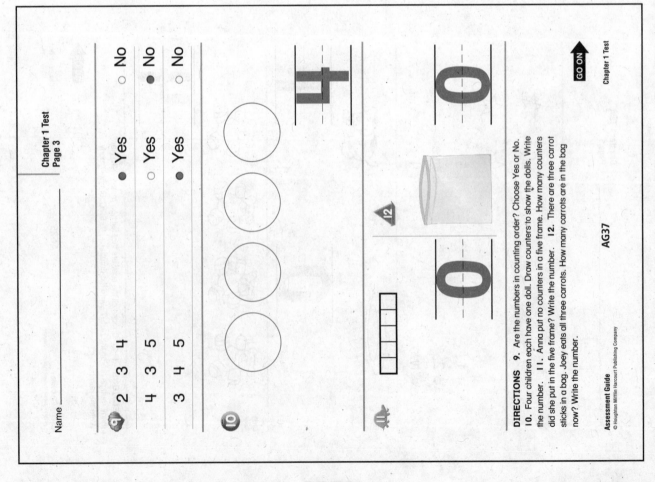

2	3	4	● Yes	○ No
4	3	5	○ Yes	● No
3	4	5	● Yes	○ No

10

4

11

0

12

0

DIRECTIONS **9.** Are the numbers in counting order? Choose Yes or No. **10.** Four children each have one doll. Draw counters to show the dolls. Write the number. **11.** Anna put no counters in a five frame. How many counters did she put in the five frame? Write the number. **12.** There are three carrot sticks in a bag. Joey eats all three carrots. How many carrots are in the bag now? Write the number.

GO ON

Name ______________________

13

Answers will vary. Possible answers are given.

red	red	red	red	yellow

4 and 1

red	red	red	yellow	yellow

3 and 2

14

Possible drawing is shown.

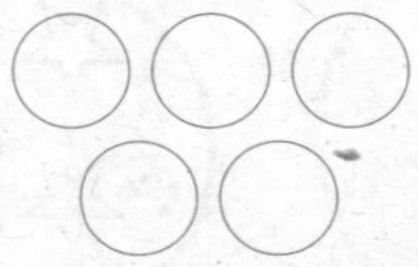

5

DIRECTIONS **13.** Show 2 ways to make 5. Color some boxes red. Color some boxes yellow. Write the numbers. **14.** Write the number that comes after 4 in counting order. Draw counters to show the number.

STOP

Name ____________________

Chapter 2 Test
Page 1

1

2

2

2

3

4

DIRECTIONS 1. Draw a counter below each kitten to show the same number of counters as kittens. Write how many kittens. Write how many counters. 2. How many counters are there in each row? Write the numbers. Compare the sets by matching. Circle the number that is greater.

GO ON

Name ____________________

Chapter 2 Test
Page 2

3

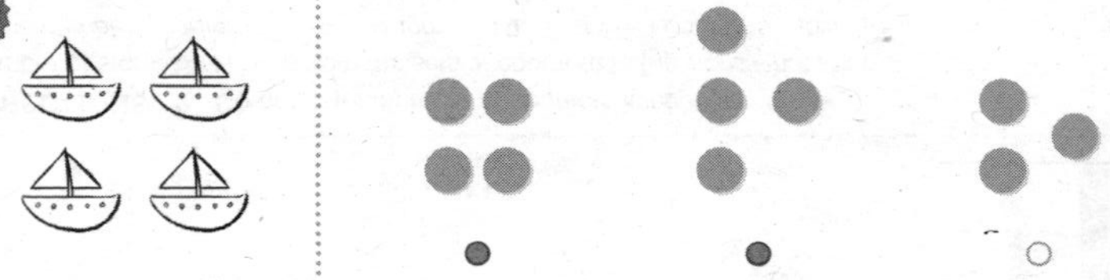

4

5

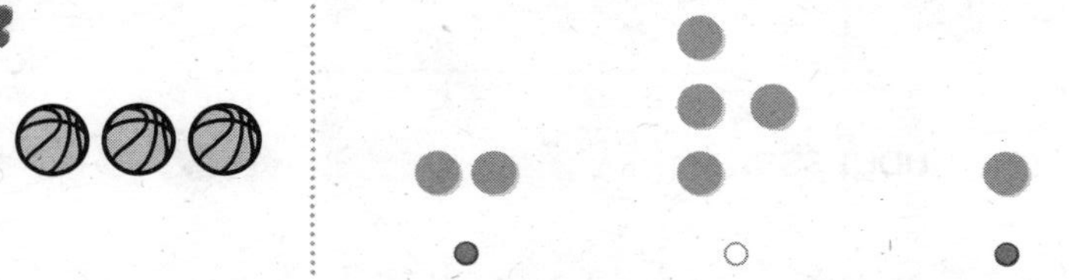

6

2 3 5

DIRECTIONS 3. Mark under all the sets that have the same number of counters as the number of boats. 4. Mark under all the sets that have a number of counters greater than the number of bats. 5. Mark under all the sets that have a number of counters less than the number of basketballs. 6. Mark all the numbers less than 5.

GO ON

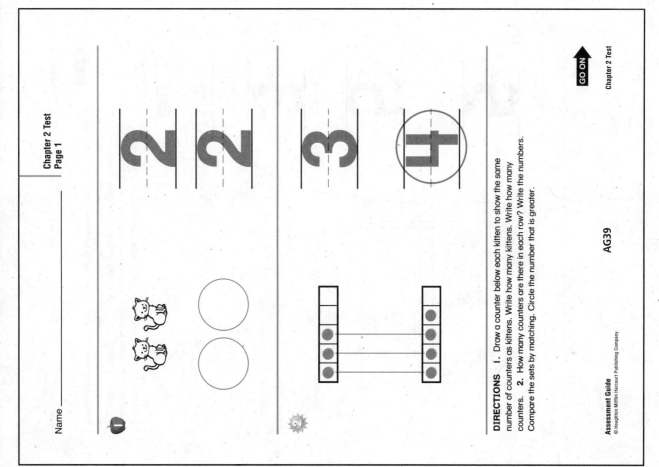

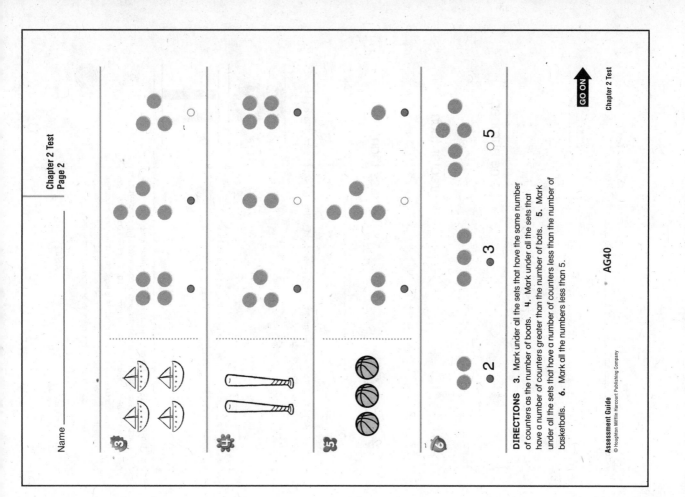

Name ______________________

Chapter 2 Test
Page 3

7

5

5

Check children's drawings.

8

Check children's drawings.

3

2

DIRECTIONS 7. Maria has these books. Draw a set of books on the shelf below that has the same number. Compare the sets by matching. Write how many books in each set. **8.** Raul has three flowers. Draw Raul's flowers. Jenna has a number of flowers that is one less than the number of flowers Raul has. How many flowers does Jenna have? Draw her flowers. Write how many in each set.

Name ______________________

Chapter 2 Test
Page 4

9

same number

greater than

less than

10

Check children's drawings. Children should color the set of 5 counters red and the other set blue.

Answers may vary. A possible answer is given.

5

4

DIRECTIONS 9. Compare the number of counters in each set to the number of stars. Draw lines from the sets of counters to the words that show *same number*, *greater than*, or *less than*. **10.** Draw five counters. Now draw a set that has a number of counters that is less. How many are in each set? Write the numbers. Use red to color the set with a greater number of counters. Use blue to color the set with a number of counters that is less.

STOP

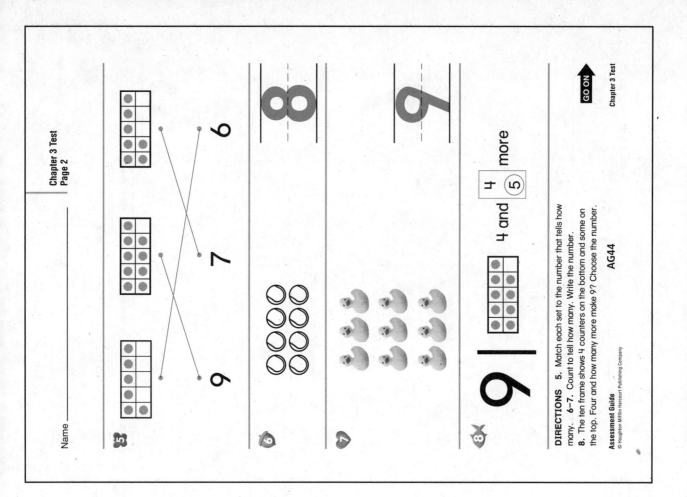

Name ____________

1

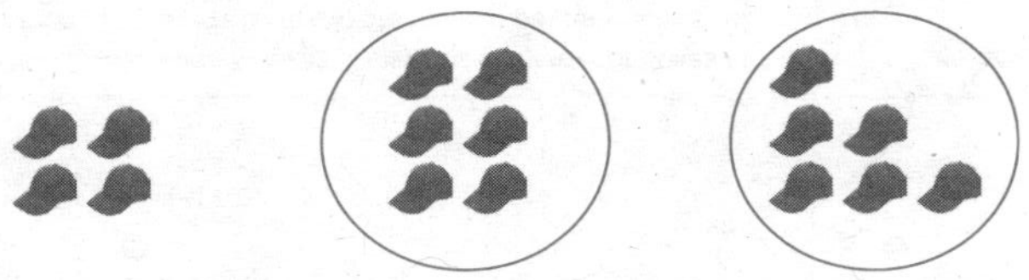

2

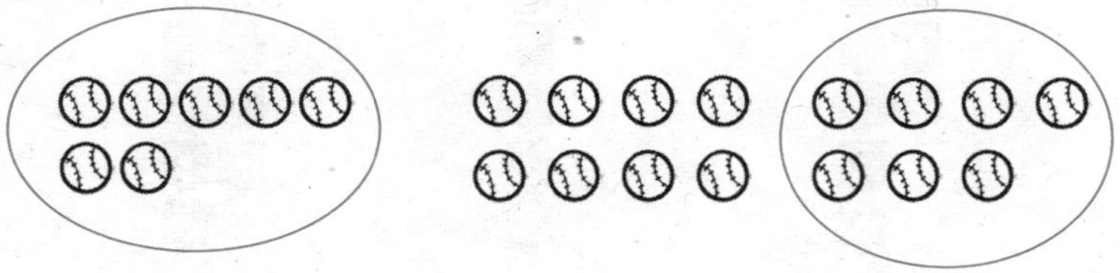

3

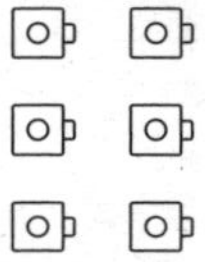

6

4

7

DIRECTIONS **1.** Circle all the sets that show 6. **2.** Circle all the sets that show 7. **3–4.** Count and tell how many. Write the number.

GO ON

Name ____________

5

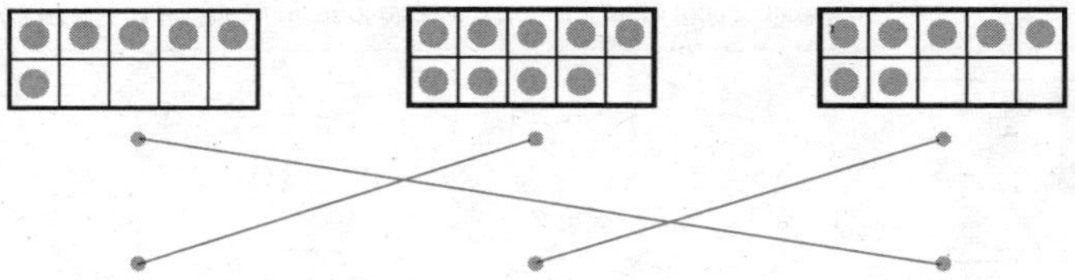

9 7 6

6

8

7

9

8

9

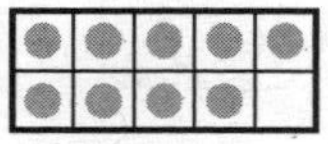

4 and 4 / (5) more

DIRECTIONS **5.** Match each set to the number that tells how many. **6–7.** Count to tell how many. Write the number.
8. The ten frame shows 4 counters on the bottom and some on the top. Four and how many more make 9? Choose the number.

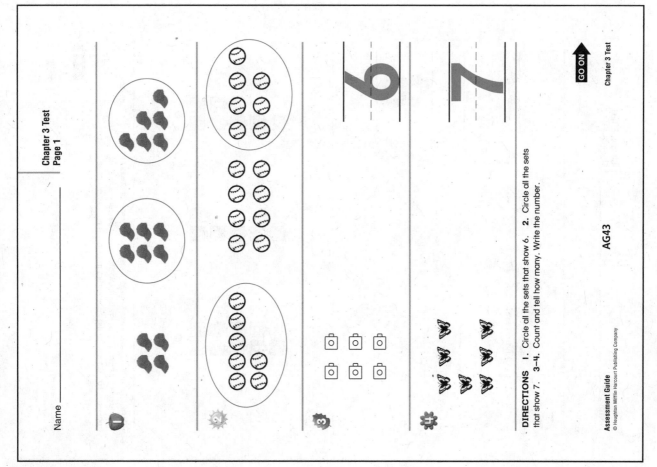

GO ON

Name ________________ Chapter 3 Test Page 3

9

Children should draw 7 squares.

7

Children should draw 8 squares.

8

10

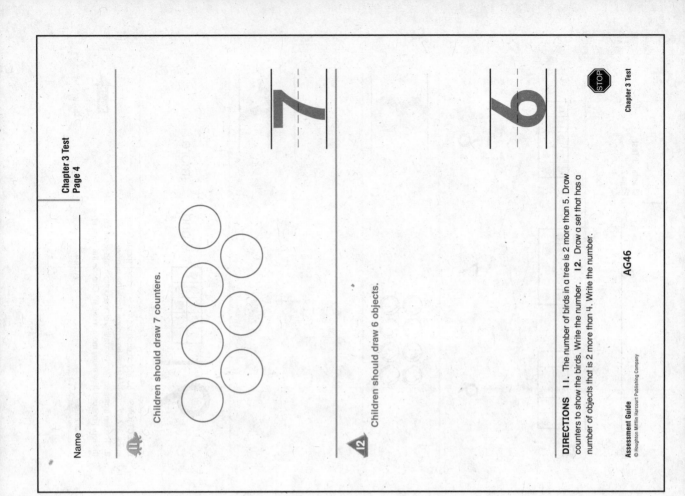

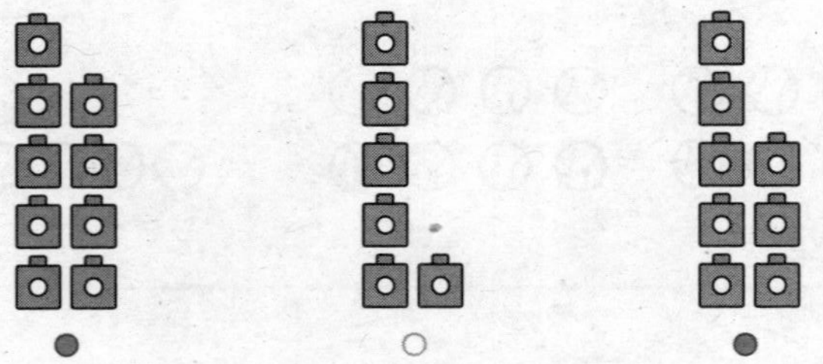

DIRECTIONS 9. Mike has 7 boxes. Daisy has a number of boxes that is one greater than 7. Draw the boxes. Write the number for each set of boxes. 10. Choose all the cube towers that have a number of cubes greater than 6.

GO ON

Name ________________ Chapter 3 Test Page 4

11

Children should draw 7 counters.

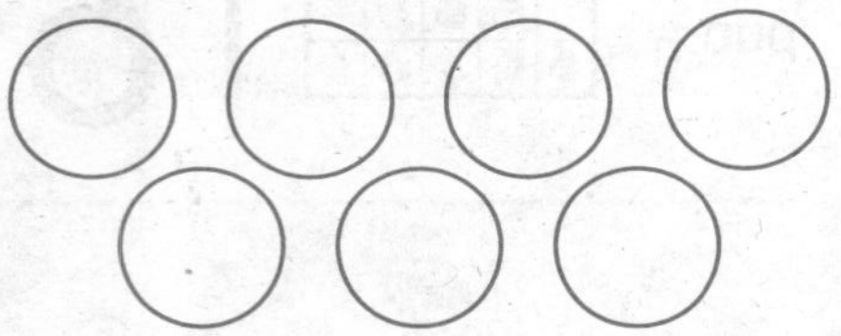

7

12

Children should draw 6 objects.

6

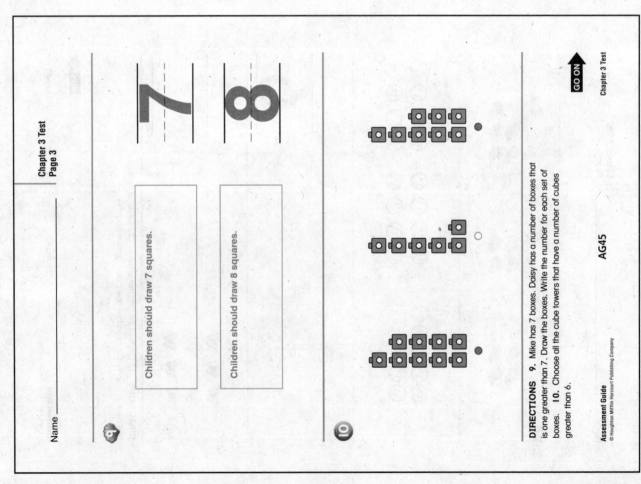

DIRECTIONS 11. The number of birds in a tree is 2 more than 5. Draw counters to show the birds. Write the number. 12. Draw a set that has a number of objects that is 2 more than 4. Write the number.

STOP

Name ____________

Chapter 4 Test
Page 1

1

●　○　●

2

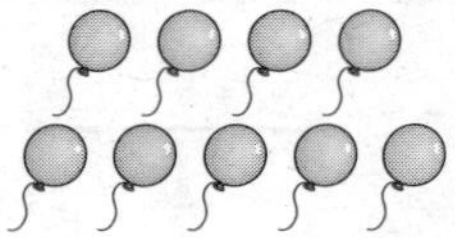

9

3

6

five
(six)

DIRECTIONS 1. Mark under all the sets that have 10 items. 2. How many balloons are shown? Write the number. 3. What is another way to write 6? Circle the word.

GO ON

Name ____________

Chapter 4 Test
Page 2

4

4 　6

10 cubes

5

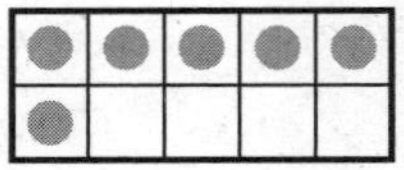

6　4

6

5	7	6	8	○ Yes	● No
7	8	9	10	● Yes	○ No
5	6	7	8	● Yes	○ No

DIRECTIONS 4. Write how many gray cubes. Write how many white cubes. Write how many cubes in all. 5. How many counters are there? Write the number. How many more counters do you need to make 10? Write the number. 6. Are the numbers in counting order? Choose Yes or No.

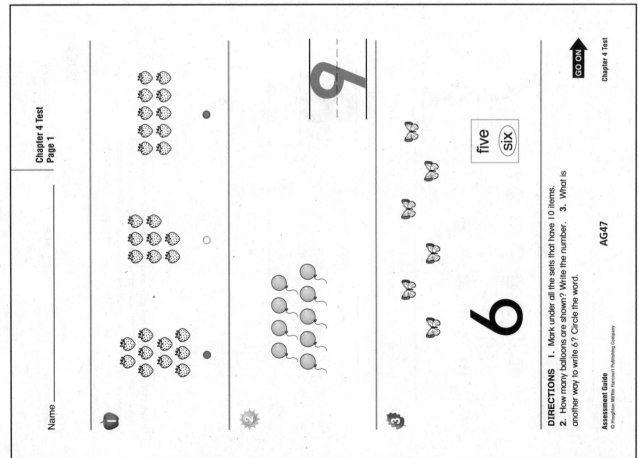

GO ON

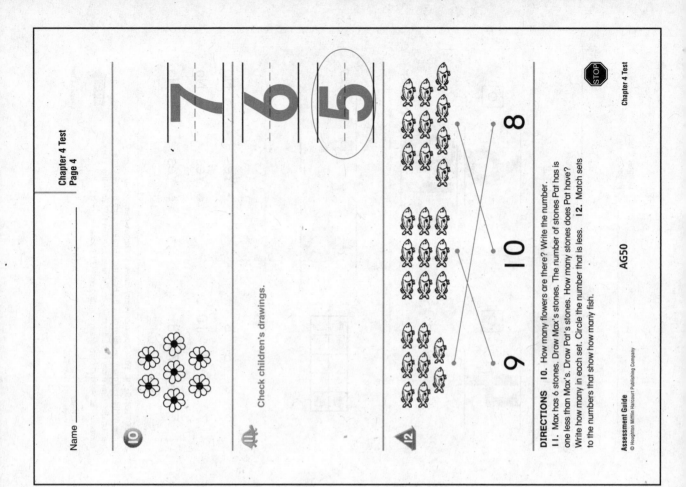

Name ______________________

7 Check children's work. Answers may vary.

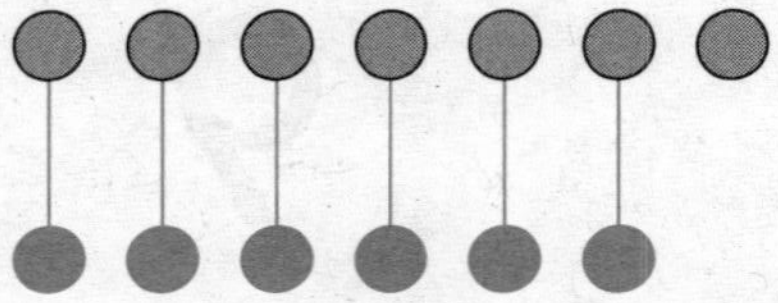

7

6

8 Children should circle 8.

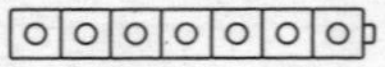

7 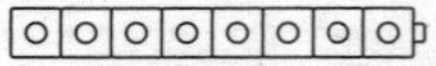 8

9

8 5 6

DIRECTIONS 7. Write how many counters are in the set. Use matching lines to draw a set of counters less than the number of counters shown. Circle the number that is less. 8. Count how many in each set. Write the numbers. Circle the greater number. 9. Think about counting order. Choose the number that is more than 7.

GO ON

Name ______________________

10

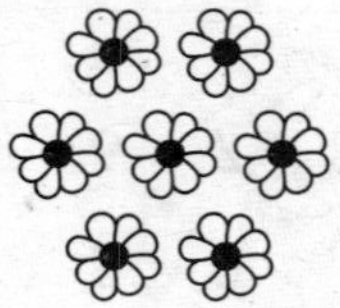

7

11 Check children's drawings.

6

5

12

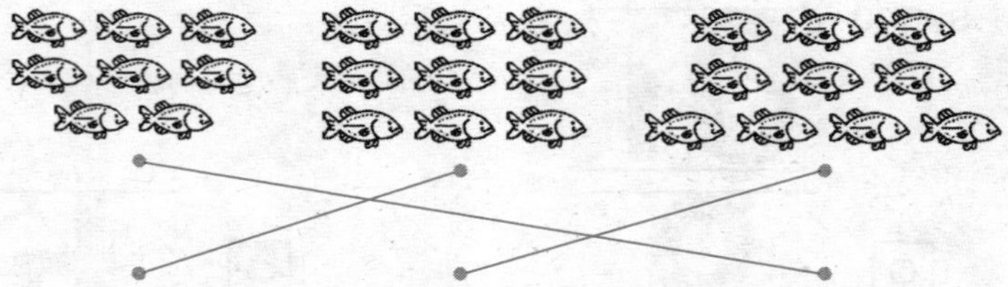

9 10 8

DIRECTIONS 10. How many flowers are there? Write the number. 11. Max has 6 stones. Draw Max's stones. The number of stones Pat has is one less than Max's. Draw Pat's stones. How many stones does Pat have? Write how many in each set. Circle the number that is less. 12. Match sets to the numbers that show how many fish.

STOP

Name ______________ Chapter 5 Test Page 1

1

2 and 1

2

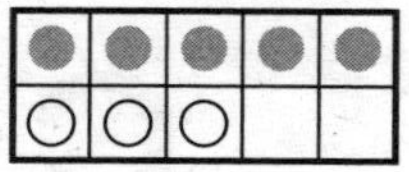

○ 5 plus 1
● 5 plus 3
● 5 + 3

3

4 + 1 = 5

DIRECTIONS 1. How many children are facing right? How many children are being added to the group? Write the numbers. 2. Keri put 5 gray counters in the ten frame. Then she put 3 white counters in the ten frame. Choose all the ways that show the counters being put together. 3. How many of each color cube is being added? Trace the numbers and symbols. Write the number that shows how many cubes in all.

GO ON

Name ______________ Chapter 5 Test Page 2

4 Possible drawing shown.

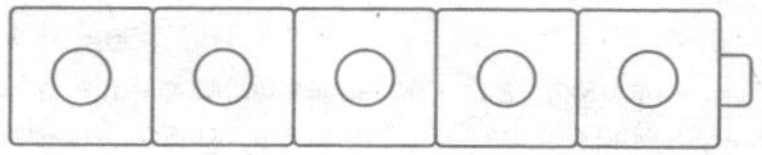

2 + 3 = 5

5 Children should draw 5 cubes.

5 + 5 = 10

6

2 + 3 = 5

DIRECTIONS 4. Jeff has 2 red cubes. He has 3 yellow cubes. How many cubes does he have? Draw the cubes. Trace the numbers and symbols. Write how many in all. 5. Look at the cube train. How many gray cubes do you see? How many more cubes are added to make 10? Draw the cubes. Write and trace to show this in an addition sentence. 6. Write and trace to complete the addition sentence.

GO ON

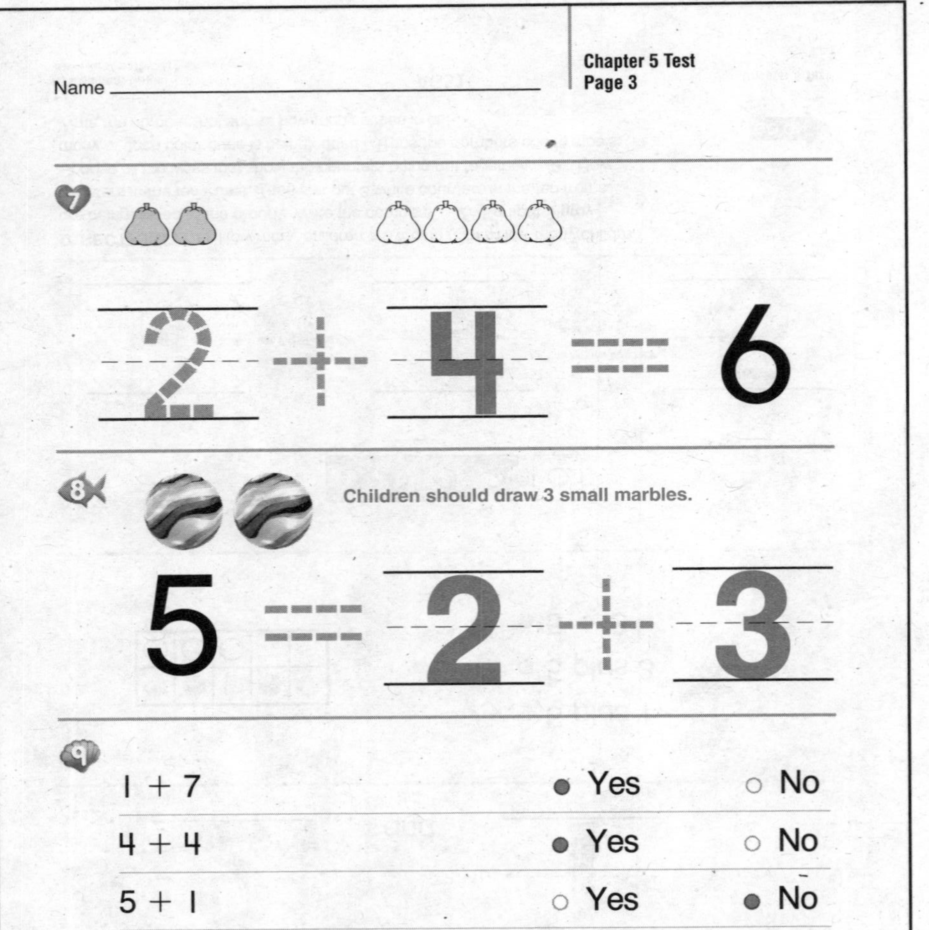

Name ______

Chapter 5 Test
Page 3

7

$2 + 4 = 6$

8 Children should draw 3 small marbles.

$5 = 2 + 3$

9

1 + 7	● Yes	○ No
4 + 4	● Yes	○ No
5 + 1	○ Yes	● No

DIRECTIONS **7.** Write the numbers and trace the symbols to complete the addition sentence. **8.** Ryan has 2 big marbles. Dani has some small marbles. Together they have 5 marbles. Draw to show how many small marbles Dani has. Complete the number pair. **9.** Does the number pair make a number greater than 6? Choose Yes or No.

GO ON

Assessment Guide
© Houghton Mifflin Harcourt Publishing Company

AG53

Chapter 5 Test

Name ______

Chapter 5 Test
Page 4

10

(8 + 0) 6 + 1 (5 + 3)

11 Answers may vary. One possible solution provided.

red red red red red red red blue blue

$9 = 7 + 2$

12 Answers may vary. One possible solution provided.

$10 = 5 + 5$

DIRECTIONS **10.** Circle all the number pairs for 8. **11.** Paul has 9 tokens. Each token is either red or blue. How many red and blue tokens could he have? Color the tokens to show the number of red and blue tokens. Write the numbers to complete the addition sentence. **12.** Complete the addition sentence to show a number pair for 10.

STOP

Assessment Guide
© Houghton Mifflin Harcourt Publishing Company

AG54

Chapter 5 Test

Name ______

Chapter 6 Test
Page 1

1

5 take away 3

2

2

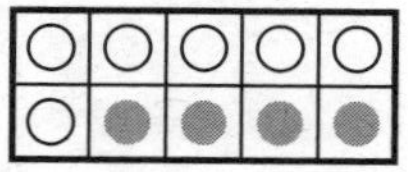

10 − 4	● Yes	○ No
6 − 4	○ Yes	● No
10 − 1	○ Yes	● No

3

Children should draw 3 gray cubes and 2 white cubes.

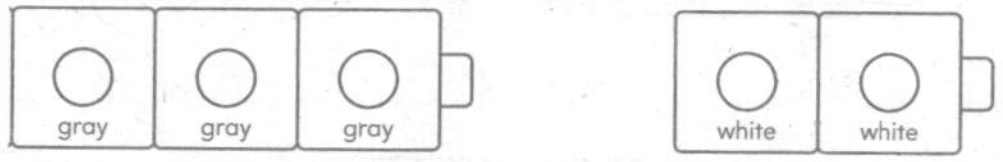

gray gray gray

white white

5 − 3 = 2

DIRECTIONS 1. Write how many people there are. Write how many people are leaving. Write how many people are left. 2. Which answers show how many counters are white? Choose Yes or No. 3. Model a five-cube train. Three cubes are gray and the rest are white. Take apart the cube train to show how many are white. Draw the cube trains. Trace and write to complete the subtraction sentence.

GO ON

Name ______

Chapter 6 Test
Page 2

4

5 − 4 = 1

5

3 − 1 = 2

6

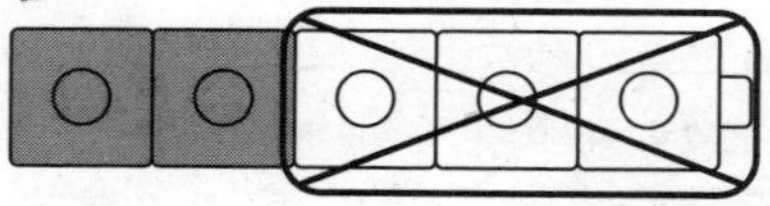

5 − 4 = 1	Yes	(No)
1 + 4 = 5	Yes	(No)
5 − 3 = 2	(Yes)	No

7

10 = 6 + 4	8 = 4 + 4	4 + 6 = 10
●	○	●

DIRECTIONS 4. There are 5 horses. Some horses are taken from the set. Trace and write to complete the subtraction sentence. 5. There are some cats. One is taken from the set. How many cats were there to start? Write and trace to complete the subtraction sentence. 6. Does the number sentence match the picture? Circle Yes or No. 7. Mark under all the number sentences that match the cubes.

GO ON

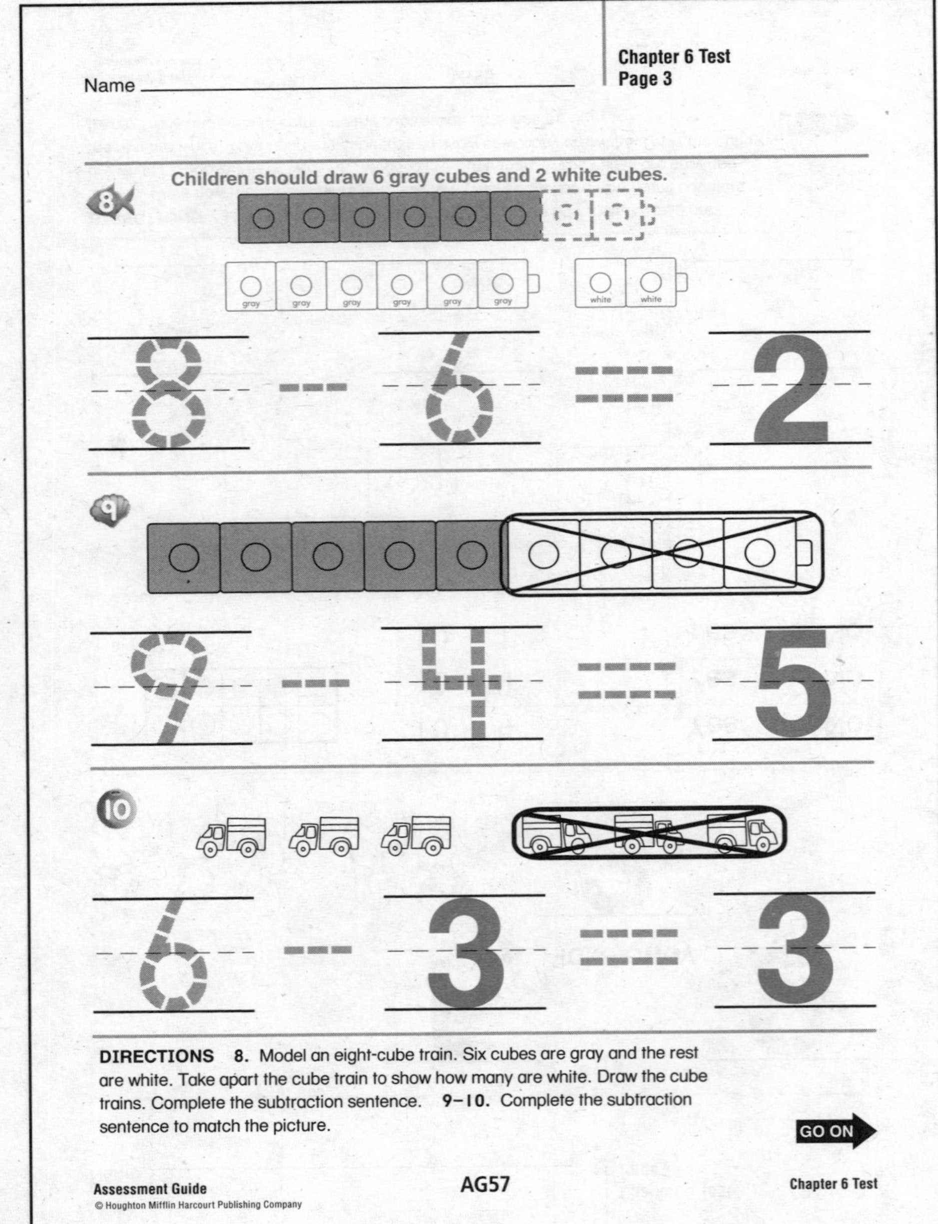

Name ____________ Chapter 6 Test Page 3

8. Children should draw 6 gray cubes and 2 white cubes.

8 − 6 = 2

9. 9 − 4 = 5

10. 6 − 3 = 3

DIRECTIONS **8.** Model an eight-cube train. Six cubes are gray and the rest are white. Take apart the cube train to show how many are white. Draw the cube trains. Complete the subtraction sentence. **9–10.** Complete the subtraction sentence to match the picture.

GO ON

Assessment Guide AG57 Chapter 6 Test

© Houghton Mifflin Harcourt Publishing Company

Name ____________ Chapter 6 Test Page 4

11. Check children's drawings. A possible answer is given.

6 − 6 = 0

12. Check children's drawings. Children should draw 1 more butterfly.

4 − 3 = 1

13. Children should draw 7 baseballs with 3 crossed out.

7 − 3 = 4

DIRECTIONS **11.** Arthur had some grapes. He ate some grapes. Now there are zero grapes left. Draw to show how many grapes there could have been to start. Cross out grapes to show how many were eaten. Complete the subtraction sentence. **12.** There are some butterflies. Three of the butterflies are taken from the set. Draw more butterflies to show how many butterflies there were to start. Write the number to complete the subtraction sentence. **13.** Mabel started a game with 7 baseballs. Some of the baseballs were lost. Now Mabel has 4 baseballs. How many baseballs were lost? Draw to solve the problem. Complete the subtraction sentence.

STOP

Assessment Guide AG58 Chapter 6 Test

© Houghton Mifflin Harcourt Publishing Company

Name ______________________

Chapter 7 Test
Page 1

1. 12

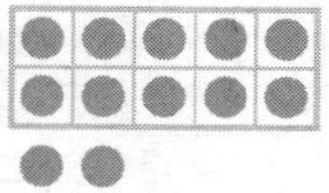

2. 13

3. 11 — (10 + 1) — [group of 11 fish circled]

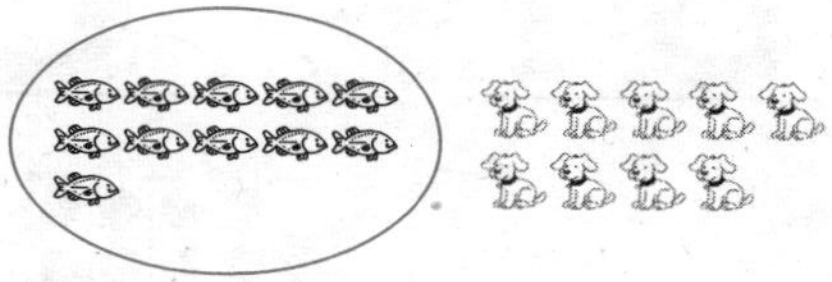

4.

15	○ Yes	● No
14	● Yes	○ No
10 + 4	● Yes	○ No

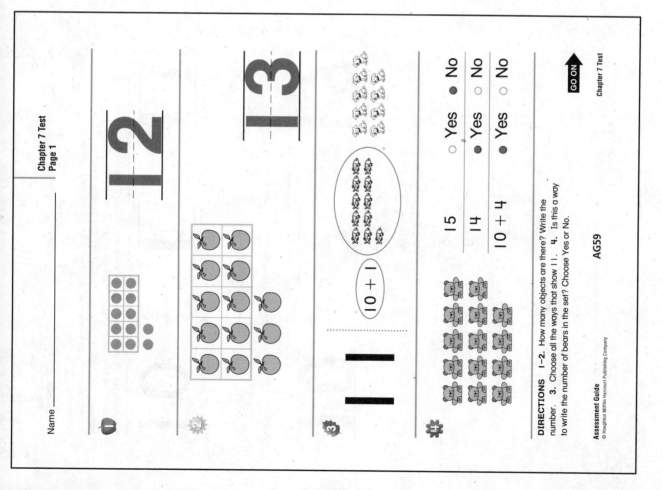

DIRECTIONS 1–2. How many objects are there? Write the number. 3. Choose all the ways that show 11. 4. Is this a way to write the number of bears in the set? Choose Yes or No.

GO ON

Name ______________________

Chapter 7 Test
Page 2

5. 17

10 + 7 = 17

6. 15

9 + 6 = 15

7. 16 17

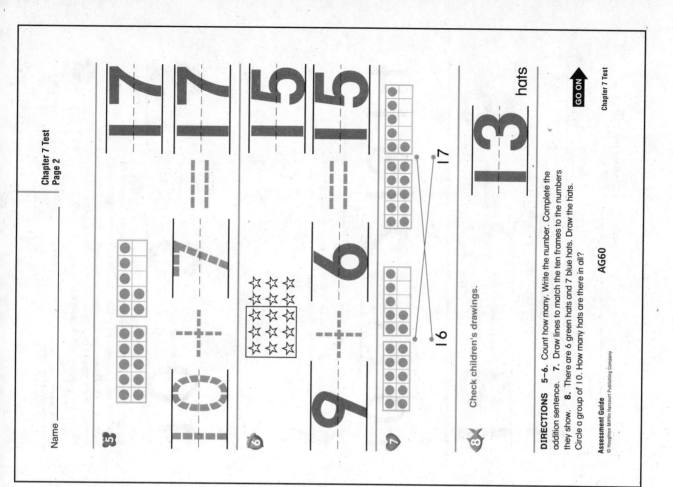

8. Check children's drawings.

13 hats

DIRECTIONS 5–6. Count how many. Write the number. Complete the addition sentence. 7. Draw lines to match the ten frames to the numbers they show. 8. There are 6 green hats and 7 blue hats. Draw the hats. Circle a group of 10. How many hats are there in all?

GO ON

Name ______________________

Chapter 7 Test
Page 3

9

10 ones and (8) / 9 ones

10

10 + 9 = 19

11

Children should draw a group of 10 sticks and 1 stick.

10 + 1 = 11

DIRECTIONS 9. How many more ones are needed to show the number of lemons? Circle the number. **10.** Look at the ten frames. Complete the addition sentence. **11.** Vicki was told to pick up 10 sticks. She picked up one extra stick. How many sticks are there in all? Draw the sticks. Complete the addition sentence.

GO ON

Name ______________________

Chapter 7 Test
Page 4

12

18 = 10 + 8

13

10 11 12 13 14

14

Children should draw 8 blue buttons and 5 green buttons, then circle a combination of 10.

10 + 3 = 13

DIRECTIONS 12. What number do the ten frames show? Complete the addition sentence to show the number. **13.** Count in order. Fill in the missing numbers. **14.** Franklin has 8 blue buttons and 5 green buttons. Draw the buttons. Circle a group of 10 buttons. Count the remaining buttons starting from 10. Complete the addition sentence.

STOP

Name ____________

Chapter 8 Test
Page 1

1.

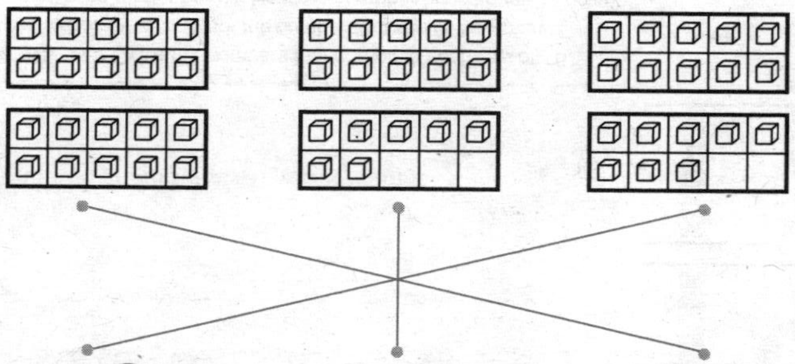

18 17 20

2.

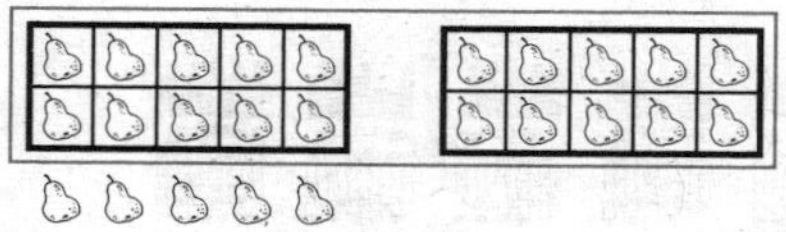

20

3.

14 15 16

17 18 19

DIRECTIONS **1.** Match the ten frames to the numbers that tell how many cubes. **2.** Harry has 20 pears. Circle how many pears he has. Write the number of pears. **3.** Start with 14. Count forward. Write the numbers in order.

GO ON

Name ____________

Chapter 8 Test
Page 2

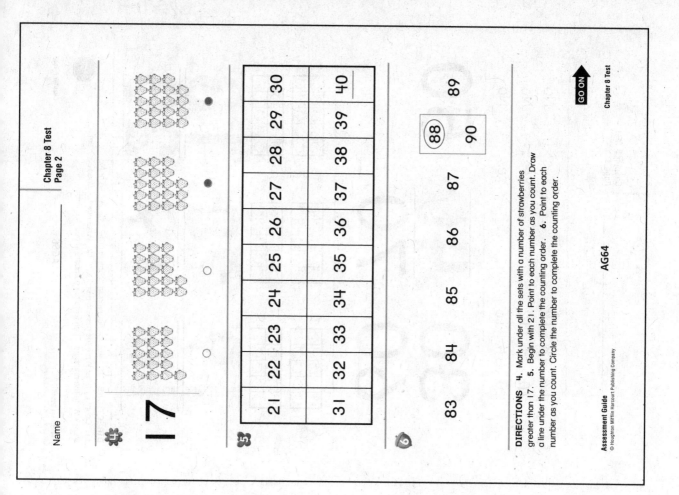

4.

17

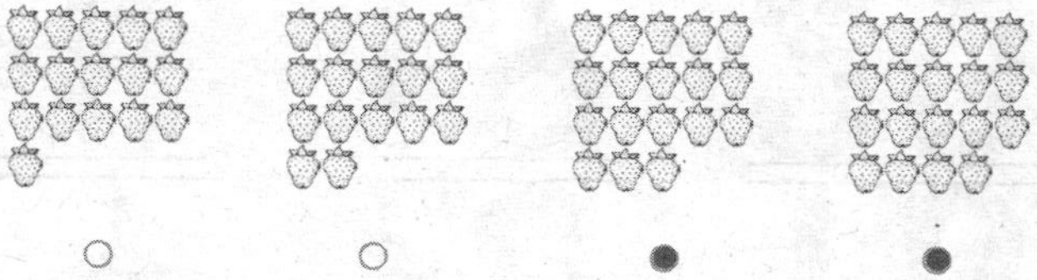

5.

21	22	23	24	25	26	27	28	29	30
31	32	33	34	35	36	37	38	39	40

6.

83 84 85 86 87 88 90 89

DIRECTIONS **4.** Mark under all the sets with a number of strawberries greater than 17. **5.** Begin with 21. Point to each number as you count. Draw a line under the number to complete the counting order. **6.** Point to each number as you count. Circle the number to complete the counting order.

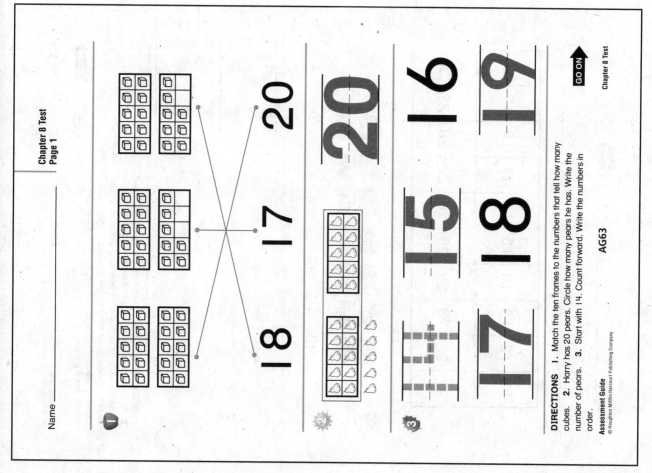

GO ON

Name ______________________

7

11	12	13	14	15	16	17	18	19	(20)
21	22	23	24	25	26	27	28	29	(30)

8

10 straws · 10 straws · 10 straws · 10 straws · 10 straws · 10 straws · 10 straws

○ 40 ○ 50 ○ 60 ● 70

9

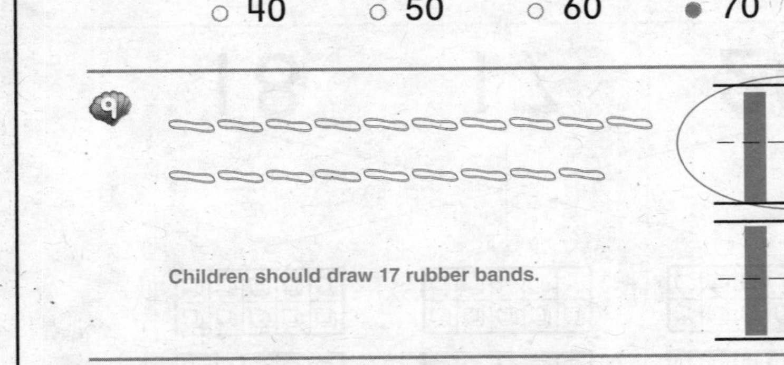

(19)

17

Children should draw 17 rubber bands.

DIRECTIONS **7.** Circle the numbers that complete each row of 10. **8.** Count the straws by tens. Mark the number that shows how many. **9.** Barney has these rubber bands. How many rubber bands does he have? Write the number. Sarah has a number of rubber bands 2 less than Barney. Draw the number of rubber bands Sarah has. Write the number. Circle the number that is greater.

GO ON

Name ______________________

10

17	18	19	(Yes)	No
10	11	12	(Yes)	No
20	14	16	Yes	(No)

11

30 40 50
60 70

12

19 20 18

18 19 20

DIRECTIONS **10.** Are the numbers in counting order? Circle Yes or No. **11.** Count by tens. Write the missing number. **12.** What number does each set show? Write the numbers. Then write the numbers in counting order.

STOP

Name ______________________

Chapter 9 Test
Page 1

1

● Yes ○ No

○ Yes ● No

● Yes ○ No

2

● ○ ○ ●

3

3 squares

DIRECTIONS **1.** Is the shape a circle? Choose Yes or No. **2.** Mark under all of the shapes that have curves. **3.** How many squares are in the picture? Write the number.

GO ON

Name ______________________

Chapter 9 Test
Page 2

4

4 vertices

5

○ ● ● ○

6

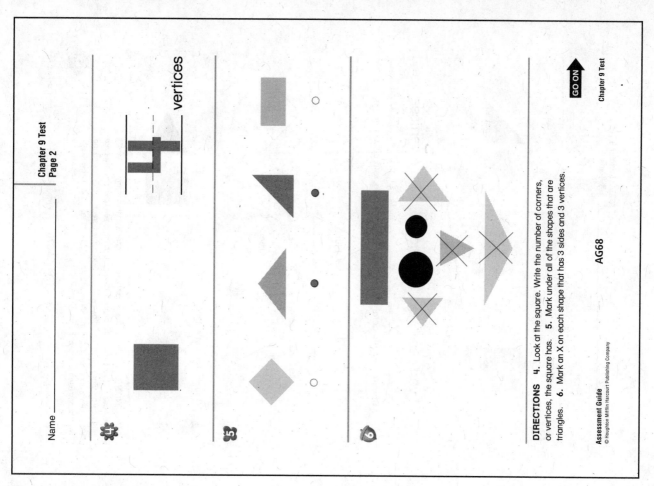

DIRECTIONS **4.** Look at the square. Write the number of corners, or vertices, the square has. **5.** Mark under all of the shapes that are triangles. **6.** Mark an X on each shape that has 3 sides and 3 vertices.

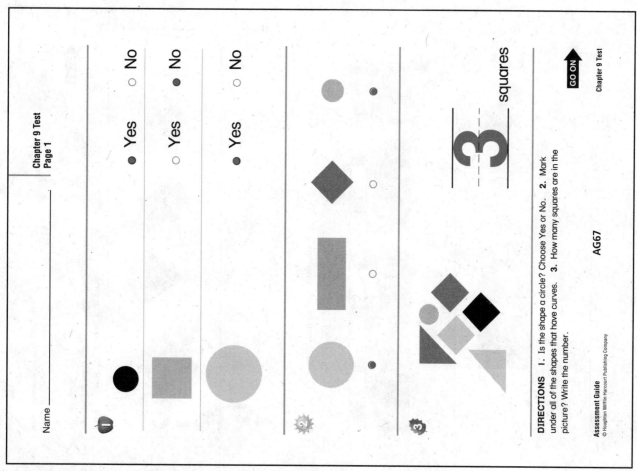

GO ON

Name ____________________

Chapter 9 Test
Page 3

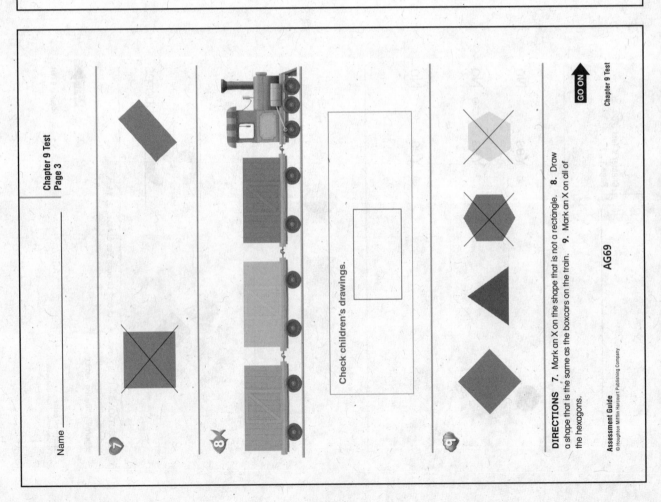

7

8

Check children's drawings.

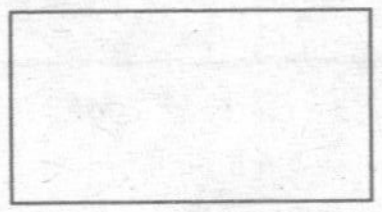

9

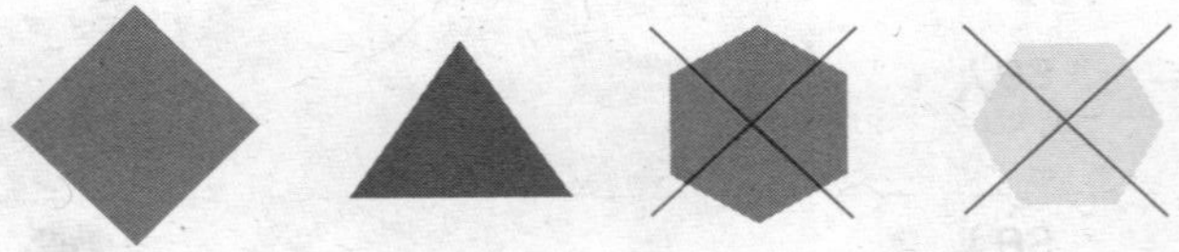

DIRECTIONS 7. Mark an X on the shape that is not a rectangle. 8. Draw a shape that is the same as the boxcars on the train. 9. Mark an X on all of the hexagons.

GO ON

Name ____________________

Chapter 9 Test
Page 4

10

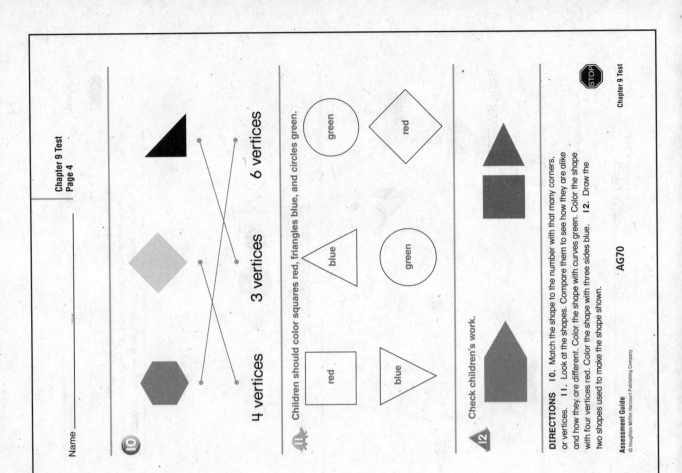

4 vertices   3 vertices   6 vertices

11 Children should color squares red, triangles blue, and circles green.

red   blue   green

blue   green   red

12 Check children's work.

DIRECTIONS 10. Match the shape to the number with that many corners, or vertices. 11. Look at the shapes. Compare them to see how they are alike and how they are different. Color the shape with curves green. Color the shape with four vertices red. Color the shape with three sides blue. 12. Draw the two shapes used to make the shape shown.

STOP

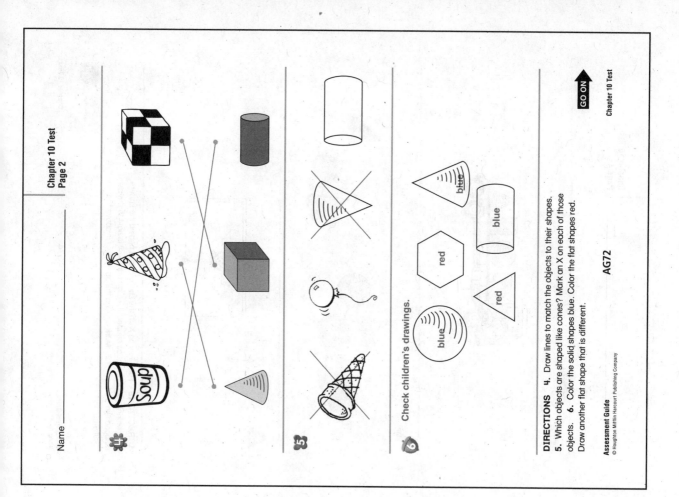

Name ____________

1

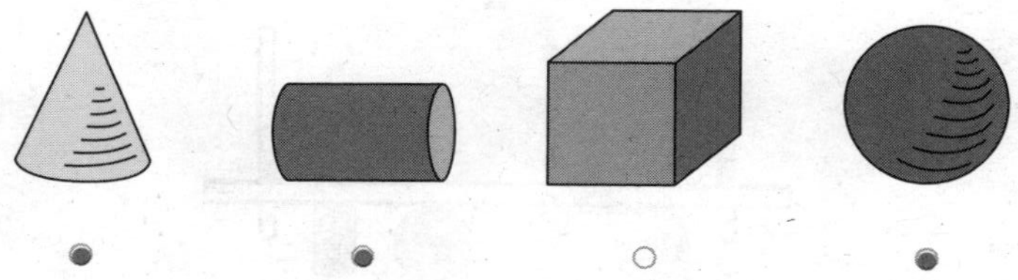

2

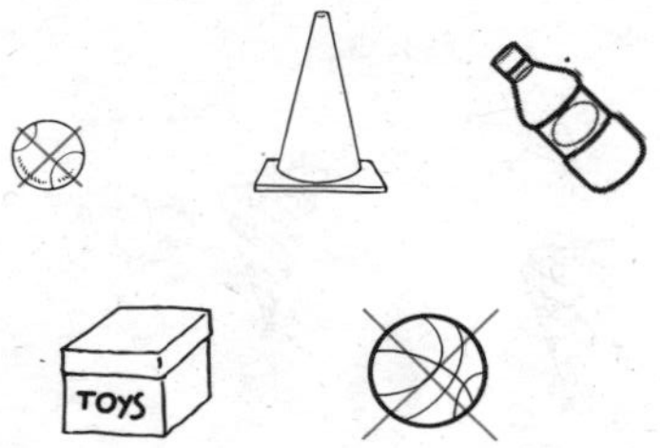

3

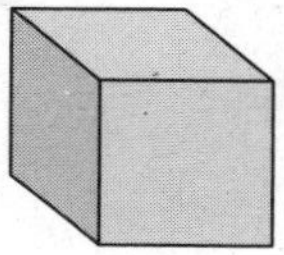

slides (Yes) No

stacks (Yes) No

DIRECTIONS **1.** Mark under all the shapes that roll. **2.** Which objects are shaped like a sphere? Mark an X on each of those objects. **3.** Do the words describe a cube? Circle Yes or No.

GO ON

Name ____________

4

Soup

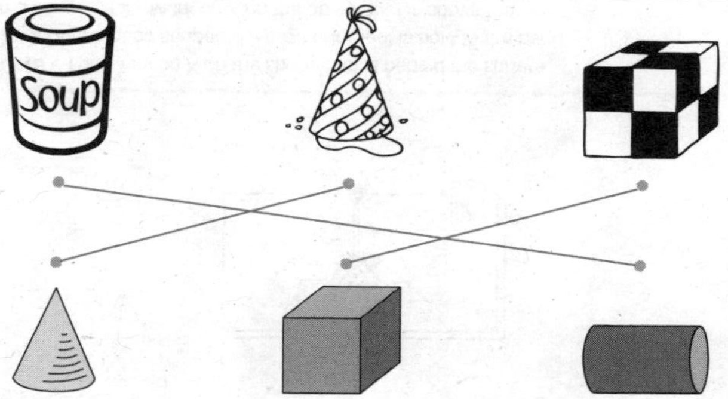

5

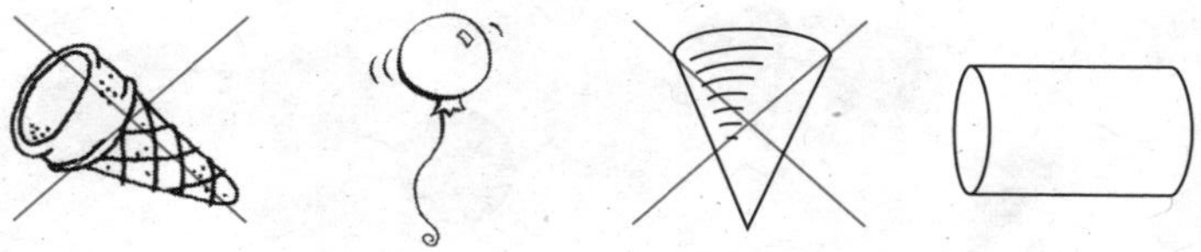

6 Check children's drawings.

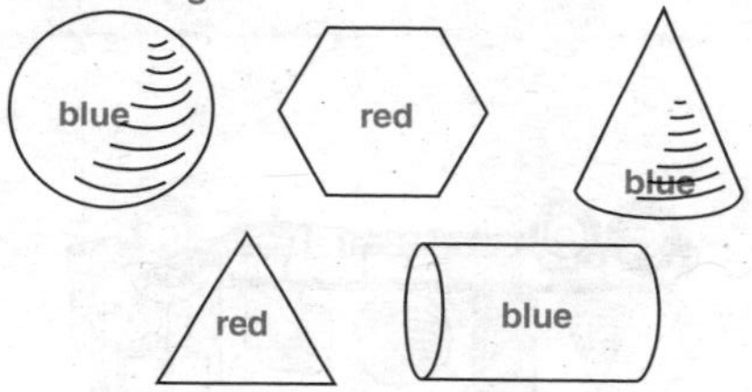

blue red blue

red blue

DIRECTIONS **4.** Draw lines to match the objects to their shapes. **5.** Which objects are shaped like cones? Mark an X on each of those objects. **6.** Color the solid shapes blue. Color the flat shapes red. Draw another flat shape that is different.

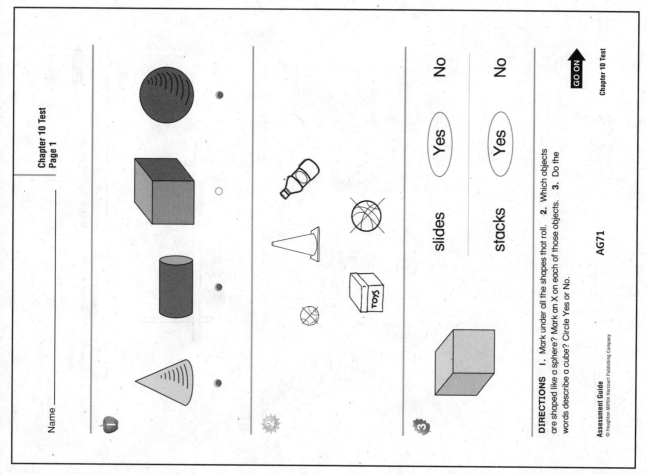

GO ON

Name ____________

7 Check children's drawings.

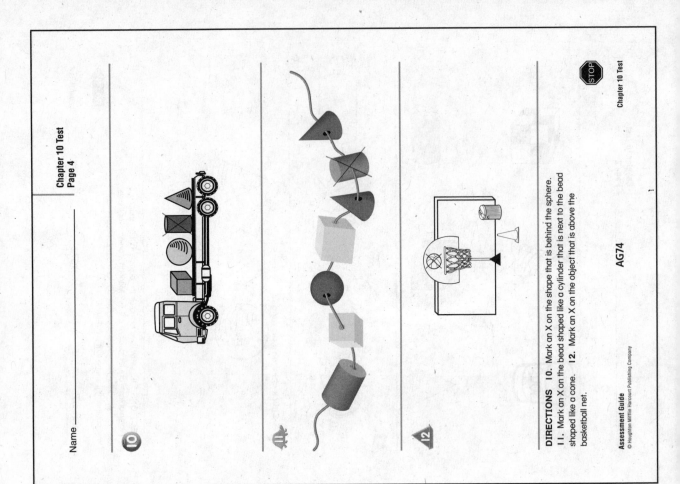

8

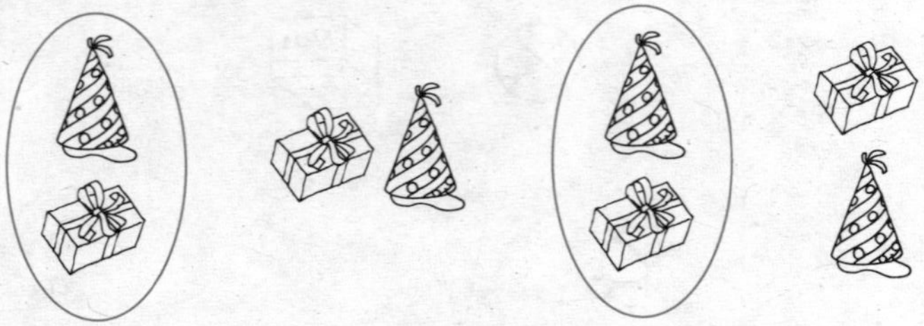

9

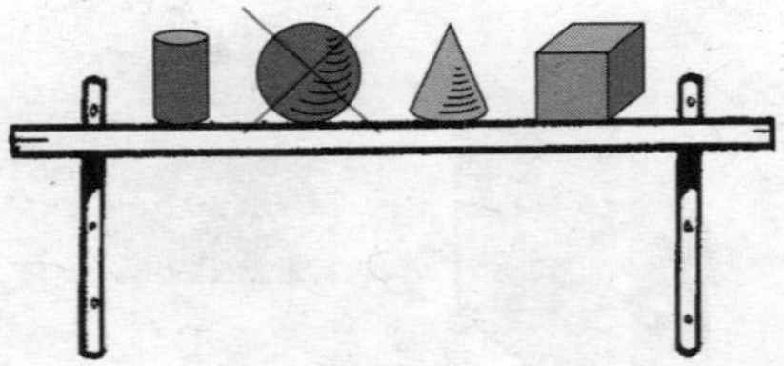

GO ON

DIRECTIONS **7.** Draw an object that has the shape of a cone. **8.** Circle the shapes that show the cone above the cube. **9.** Mark an X on the shape that is next to the cylinder.

Name ____________

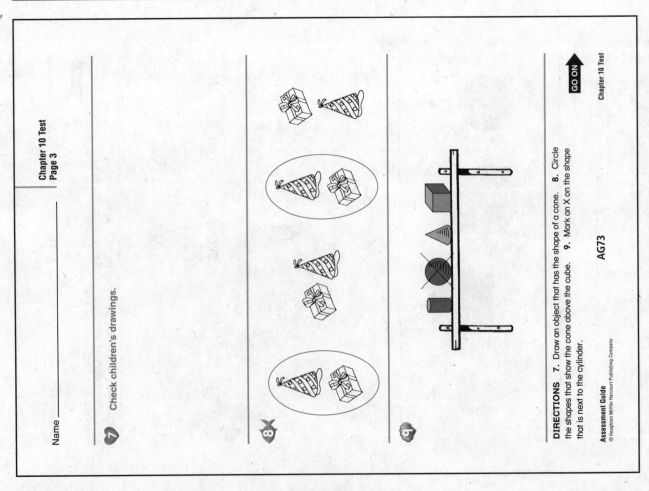

10

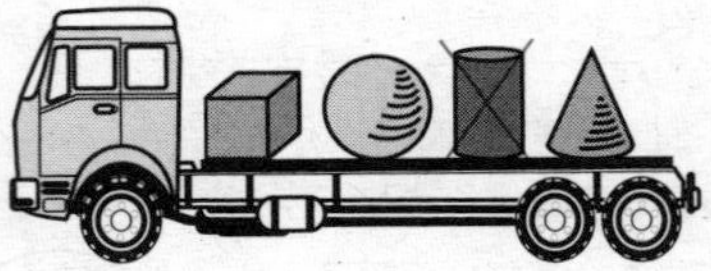

11

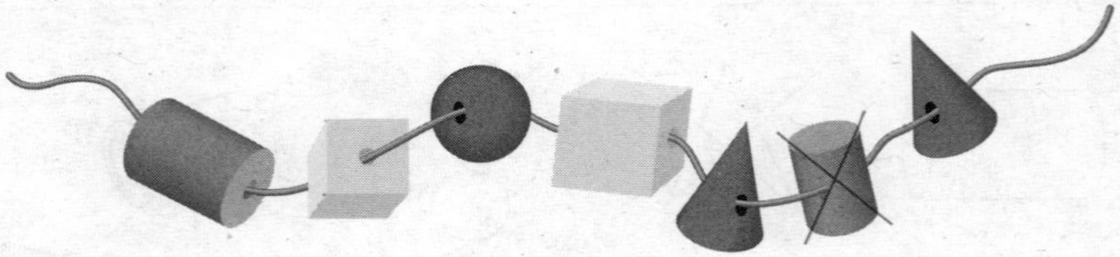

12

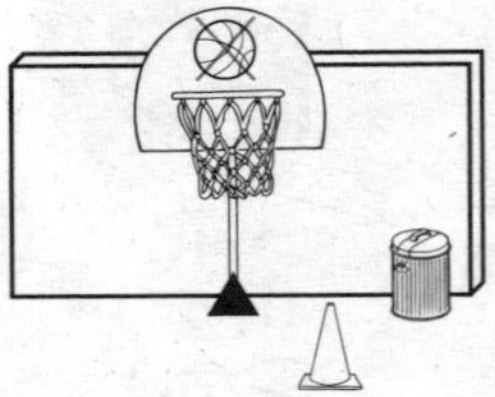

DIRECTIONS **10.** Mark an X on the shape that is behind the sphere. **11.** Mark an X on the bead shaped like a cylinder that is next to the bead shaped like a cone. **12.** Mark an X on the object that is above the basketball net.

STOP

Name ______________ Chapter 11 Test Page 1

1

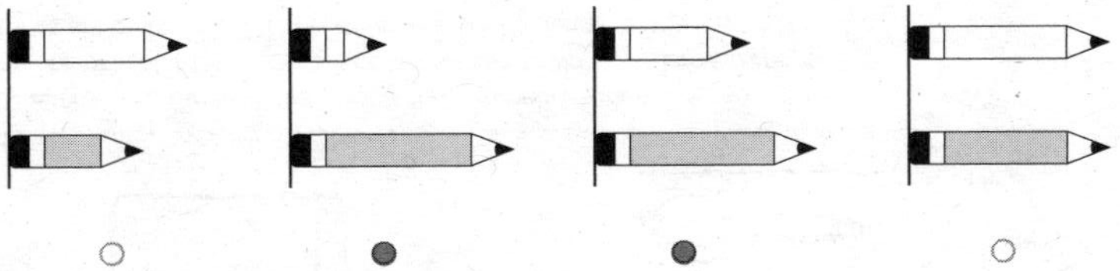

2 Check children's drawings. Possible drawing shown.

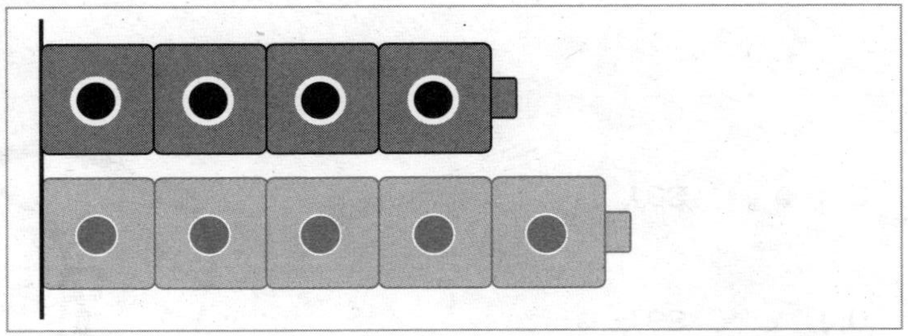

3

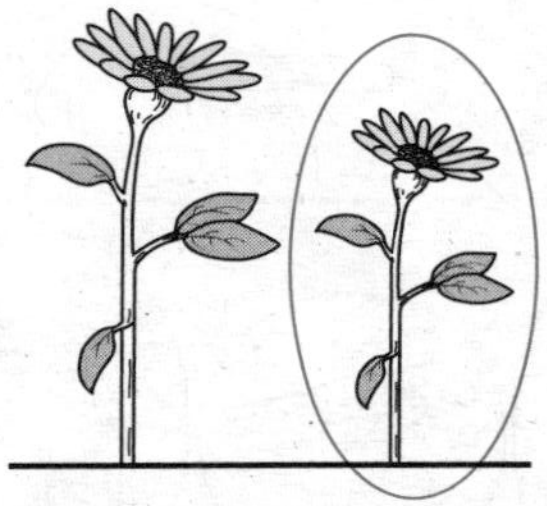

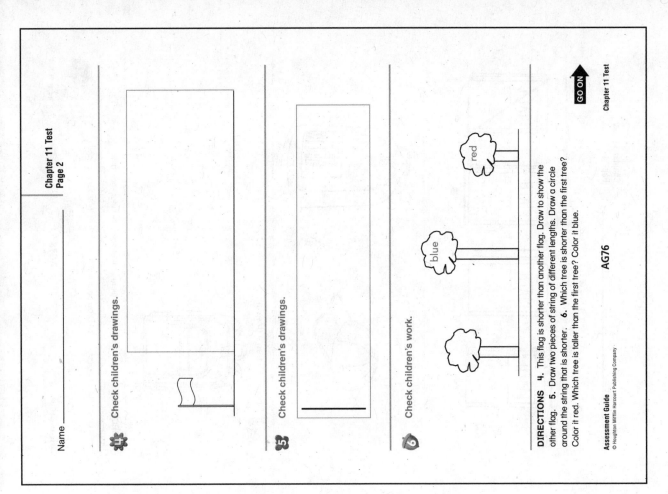

DIRECTIONS **1.** Choose all the sets that have a white pencil that is shorter than the gray pencil. **2.** Draw a cube train that is longer. **3.** Circle the flower that is shorter.

GO ON

Name ______________ Chapter 11 Test Page 2

4 Check children's drawings.

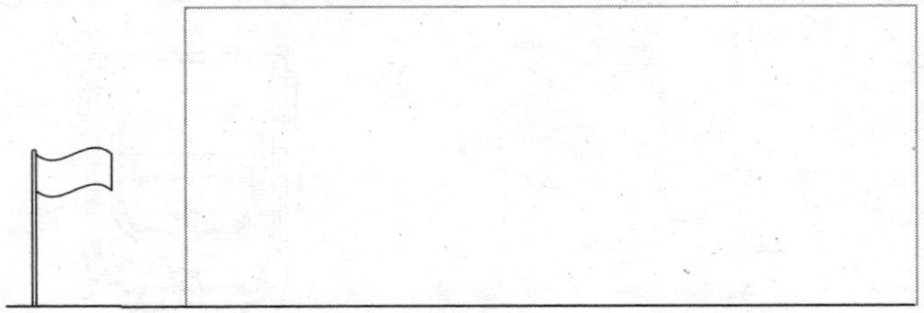

5 Check children's drawings.

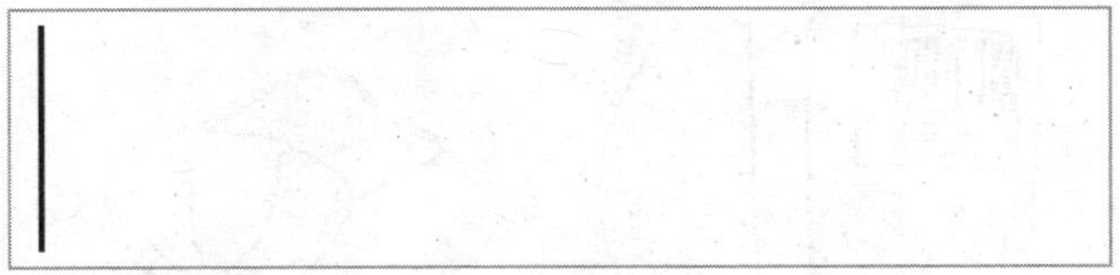

6 Check children's work.

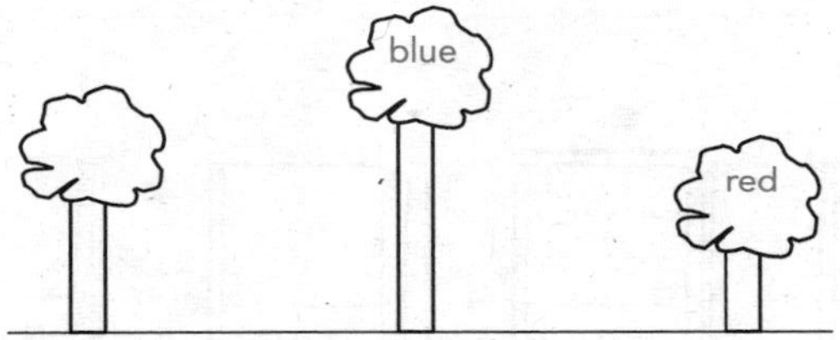

blue

red

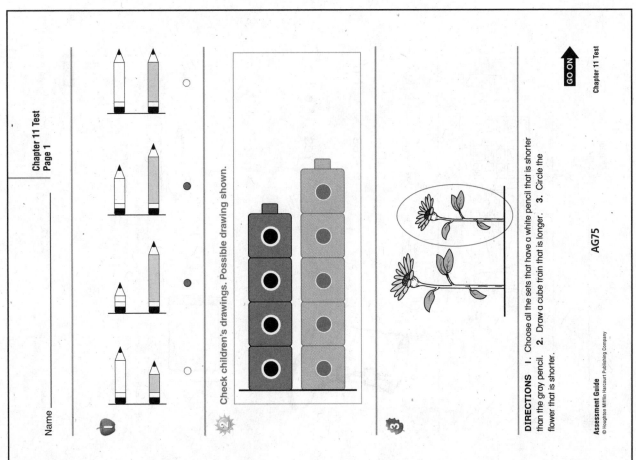

DIRECTIONS **4.** This flag is shorter than another flag. Draw to show the other flag. **5.** Draw two pieces of string of different lengths. Draw a circle around the string that is shorter. **6.** Which tree is shorter than the first tree? Color it red. Which tree is taller than the first tree? Color it blue.

GO ON

Name ______________________ Chapter 11 Test Page 3

7

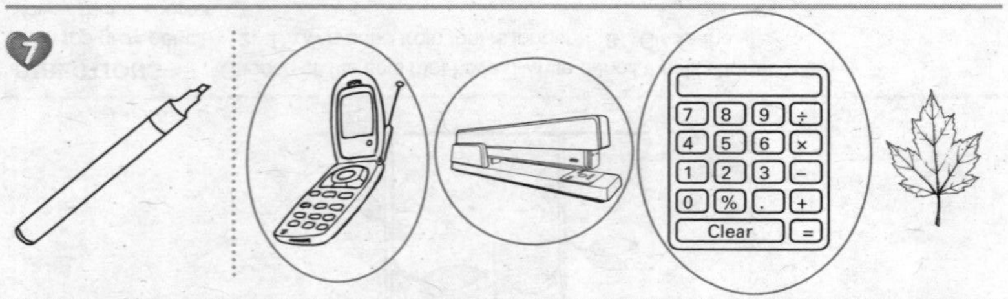

8

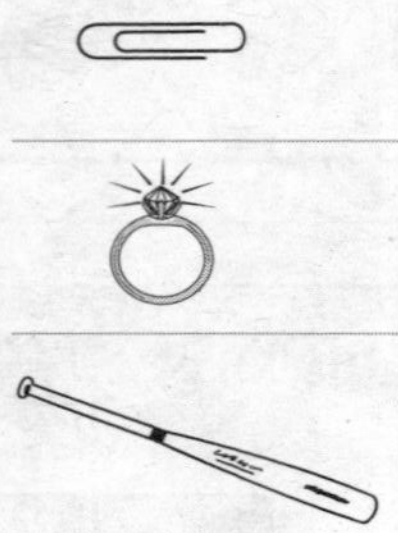

Yes ● No ○

Yes ● No ○

Yes ○ No ●

9 Check children's work.

DIRECTIONS **7.** Circle all the objects that are heavier than a marker. **8.** Is the object lighter than the boot? Choose Yes or No. **9.** Draw a line to show the height of the folder. Draw a line to show the length of the key.

GO ON

Name ______________________ Chapter 11 Test Page 4

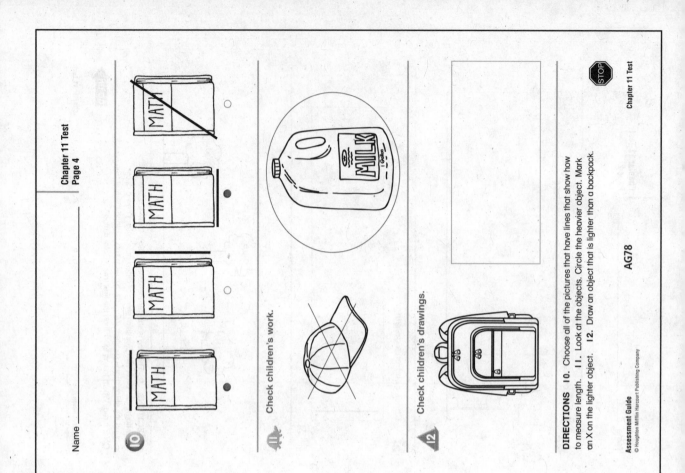

10

11 Check children's work.

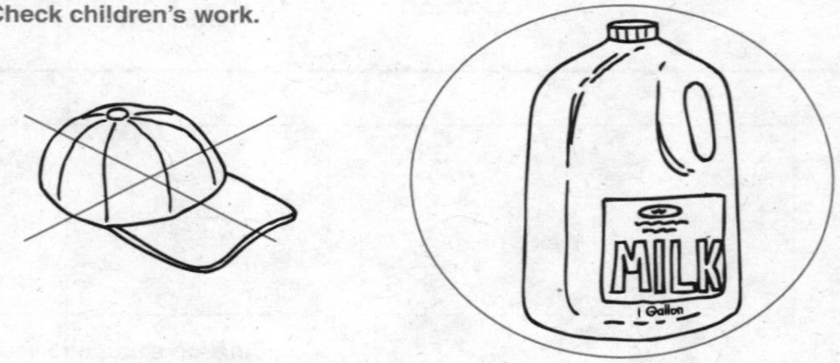

12 Check children's drawings.

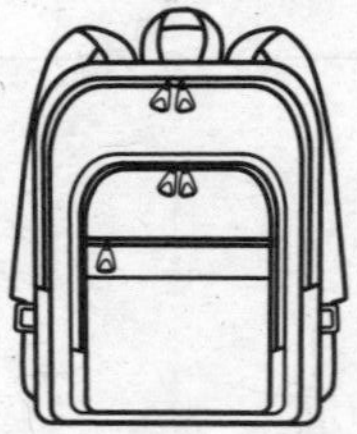

DIRECTIONS **10.** Choose all of the pictures that have lines that show how to measure length. **11.** Look at the objects. Circle the heavier object. Mark an X on the lighter object. **12.** Draw an object that is lighter than a backpack.

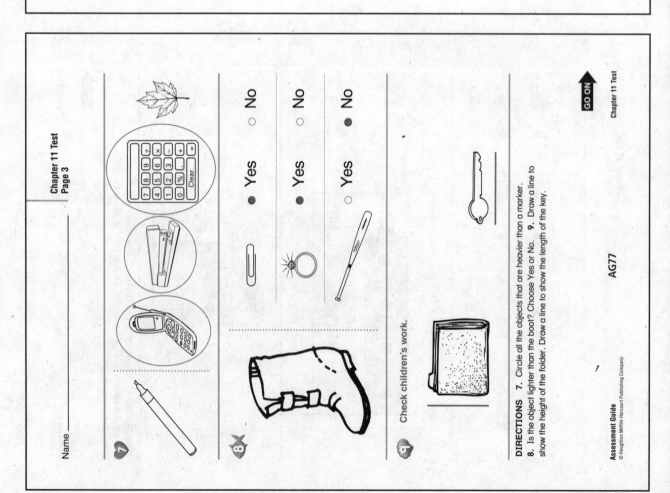

STOP

Name ____________________

Chapter 12 Test
Page 1

1

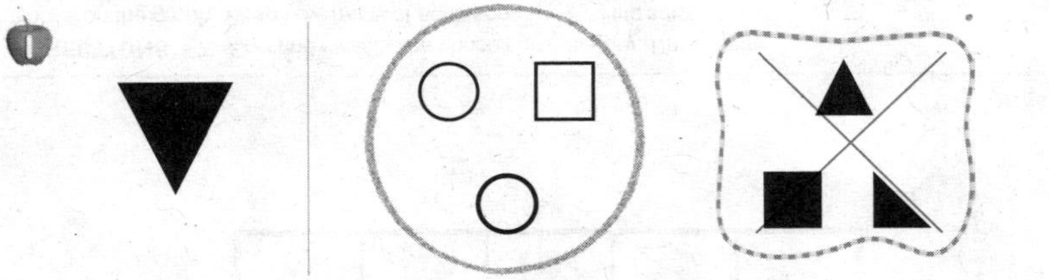

2 Check children's drawings. Possible drawing is shown.

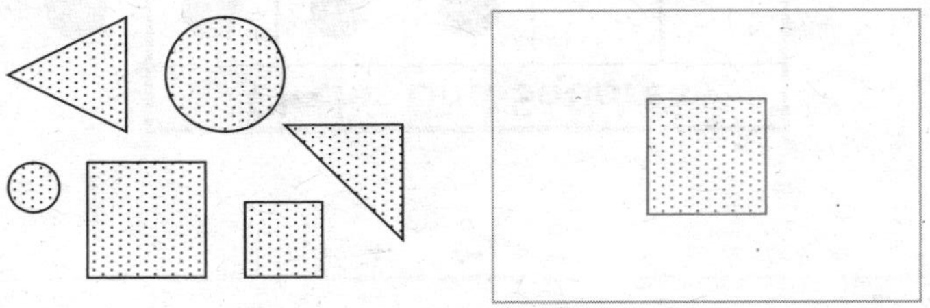

3

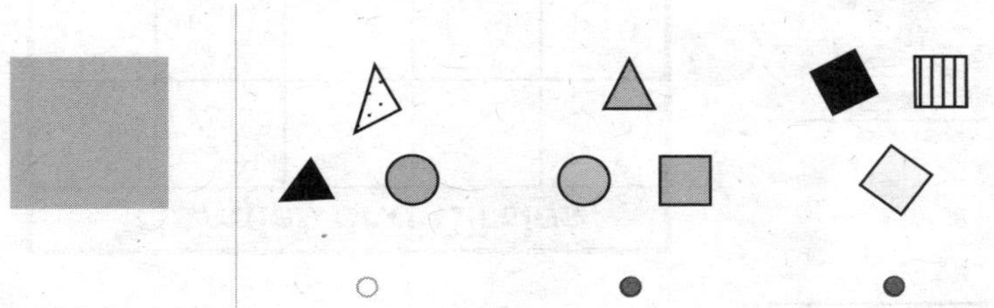

DIRECTIONS 1. Hani sorted some shapes into categories by color. Look at the shape at the beginning of the row. Mark an X on the category that shows where the shape belongs. 2. Draw and color a shape that belongs in this category. 3. Look at the shape at the beginning of the row. Mark under all of the categories where the shape can belong.

GO ON

Name ____________________

Chapter 12 Test
Page 2

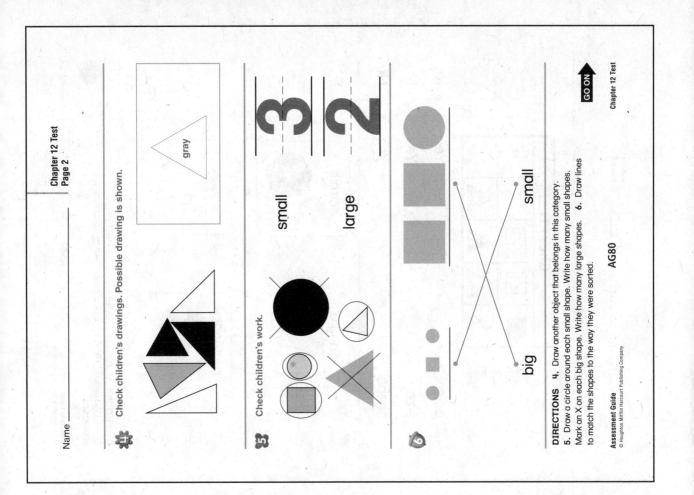

4 Check children's drawings. Possible drawing is shown.

gray

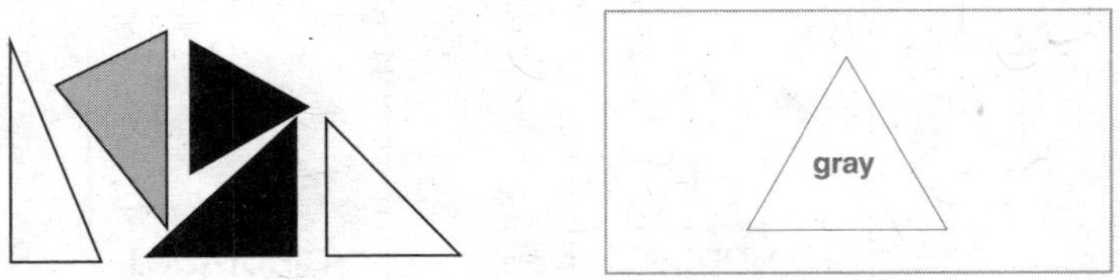

5 Check children's work.

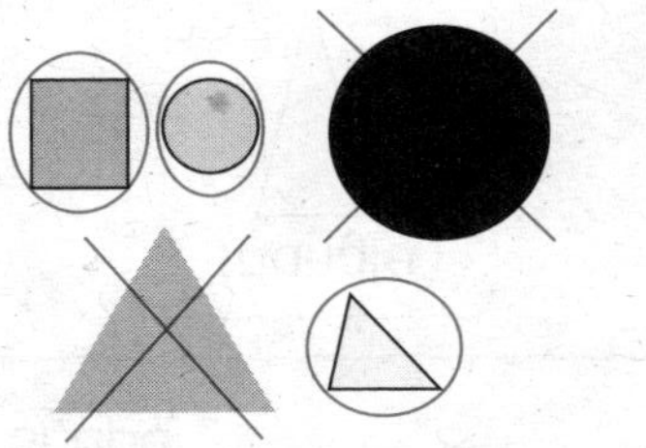

small 3

large 2

6

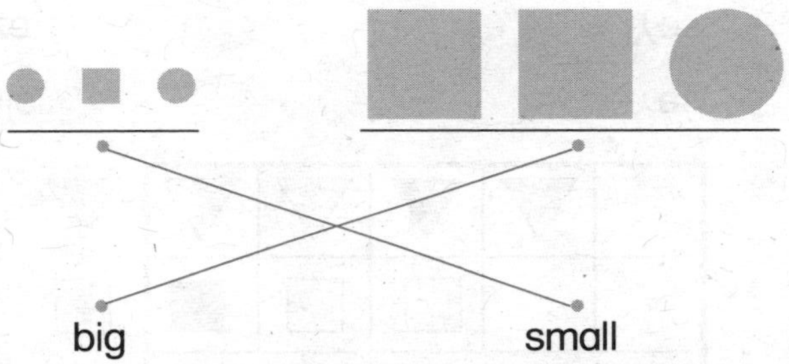

big

small

DIRECTIONS 4. Draw another object that belongs in this category. 5. Draw a circle around each small shape. Write how many small shapes. Mark an X on each big shape. Write how many large shapes. 6. Draw lines to match the shapes to the way they were sorted.

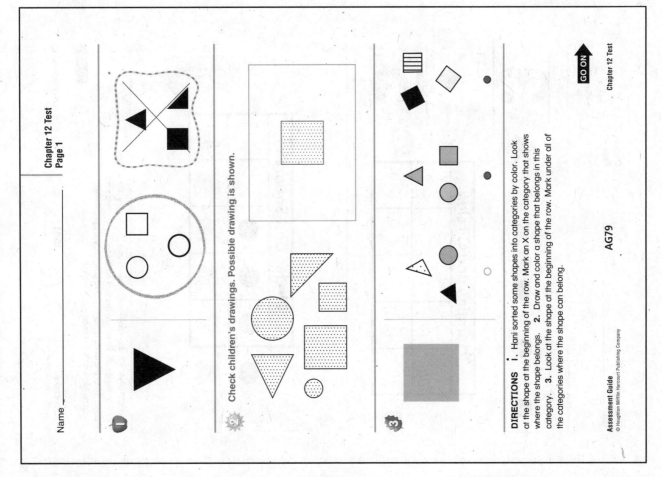

GO ON

7 Check children's work.

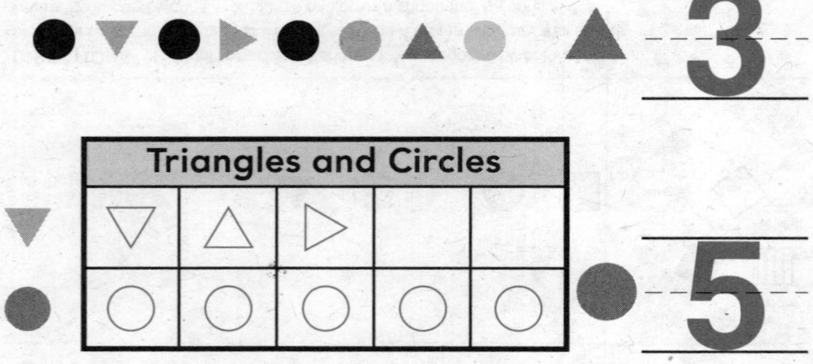

3

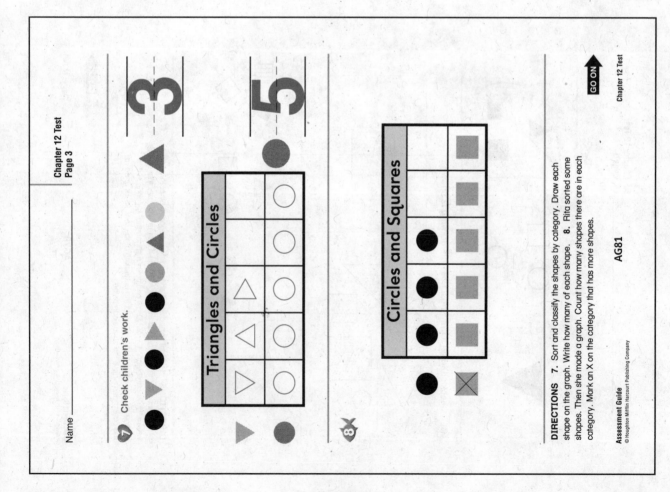

Triangles and Circles				

5

8

Circles and Squares					

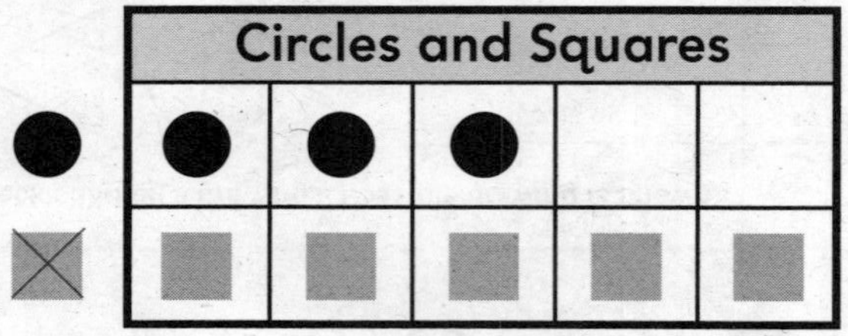

DIRECTIONS 7. Sort and classify the shapes by category. Draw each shape on the graph. Write how many of each shape. 8. Rita sorted some shapes. Then she made a graph. Count how many shapes there are in each category. Mark an X on the category that has more shapes.

GO ON

9

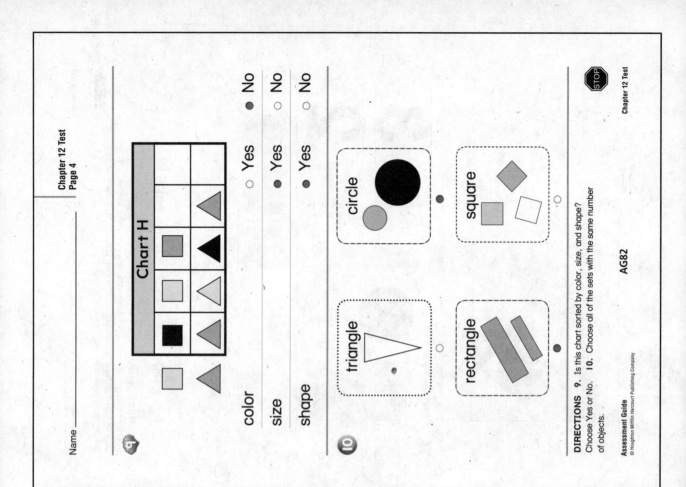

Chart H				

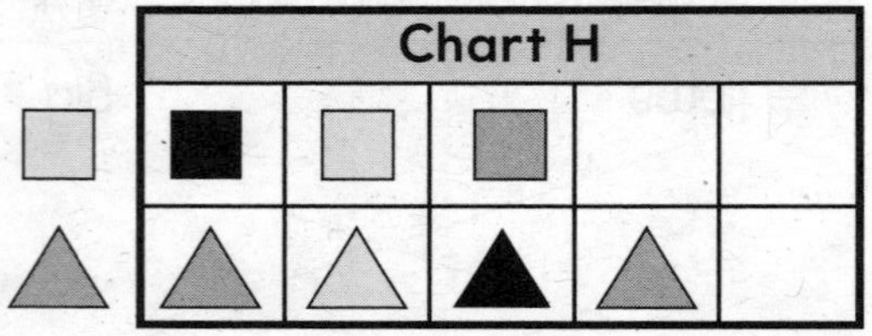

color ○ Yes ● No

size ● Yes ○ No

shape ● Yes ○ No

10

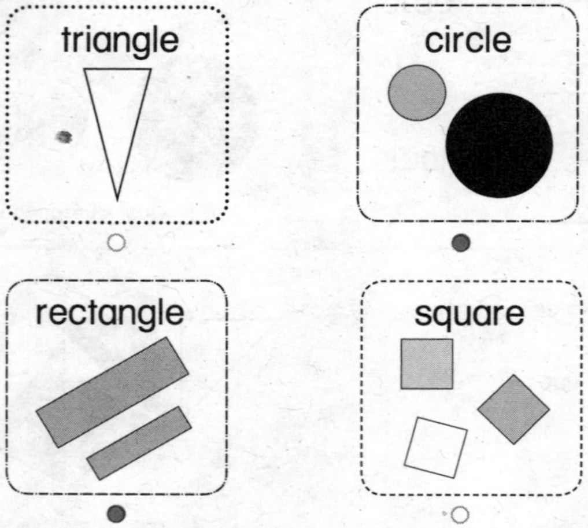

triangle ○

circle ●

rectangle ●

square ○

DIRECTIONS 9. Is this chart sorted by color, size, and shape? Choose Yes or No. 10. Choose all of the sets with the same number of objects.

STOP

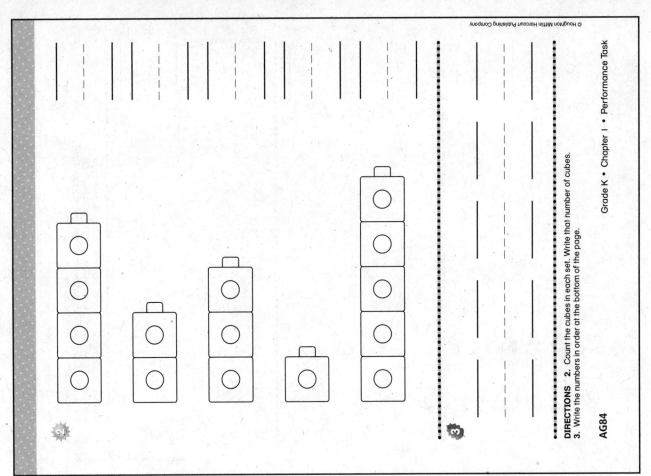

Name ____________________

Count on It

1

3

1

5

0

4

2

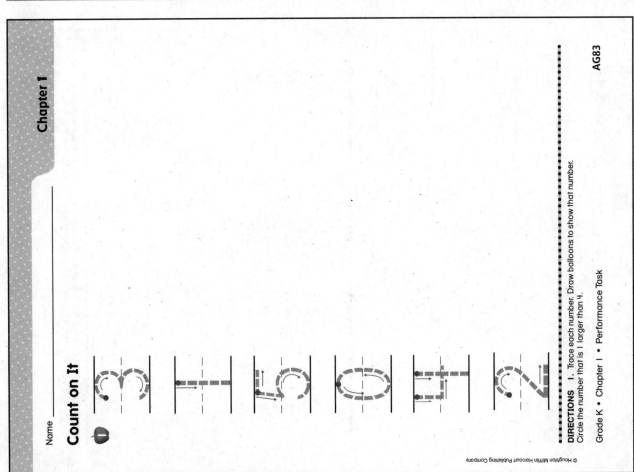

DIRECTIONS 1. Trace each number. Draw balloons to show that number. Circle the number that is 1 larger than 4.

2

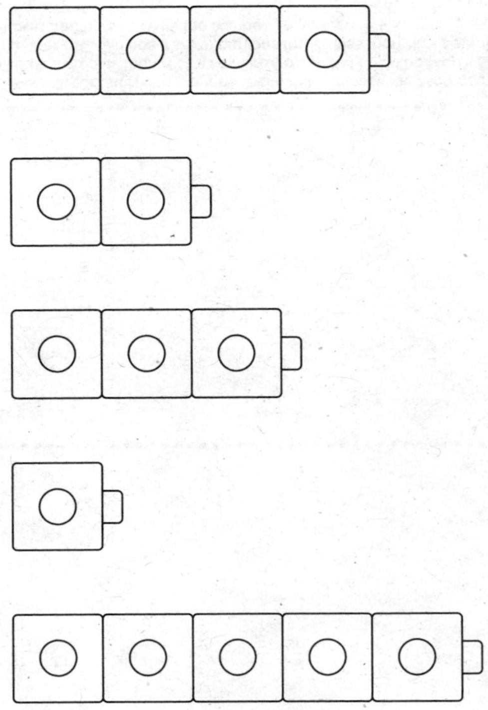

3

DIRECTIONS 2. Count the cubes in each set. Write that number of cubes.
3. Write the numbers in order at the bottom of the page.

Name ______________

Draw the Set

1

2

DIRECTIONS 1. Make a set of 2, 3, or 4 connecting cubes. Draw your set. Write the number of objects. 2. Draw another set of objects with the same number. Write the number of objects.

3 Nick

4 Matt

5 Jin

DIRECTIONS 3. Count Nick's crayons. Write the number. 4. Matt has a set of crayons that is greater than Nick's set. Draw a set that could be Matt's set. Write the number. 5. Jin has a set of crayons that is less than Nick's set. Draw a set that could be Jin's set. Write the number.

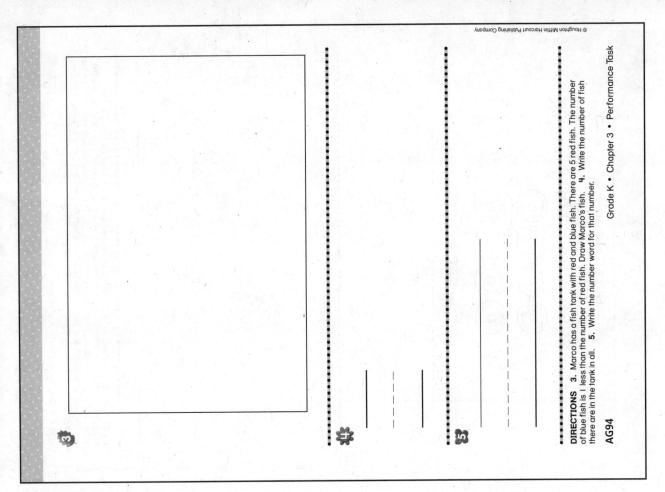

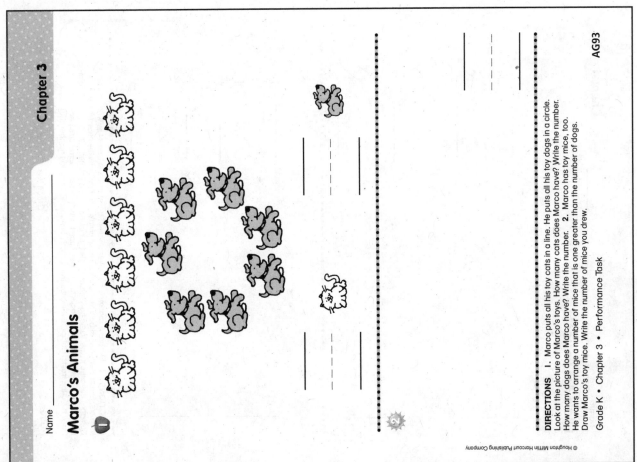

Name ______________________

Marco's Animals

1

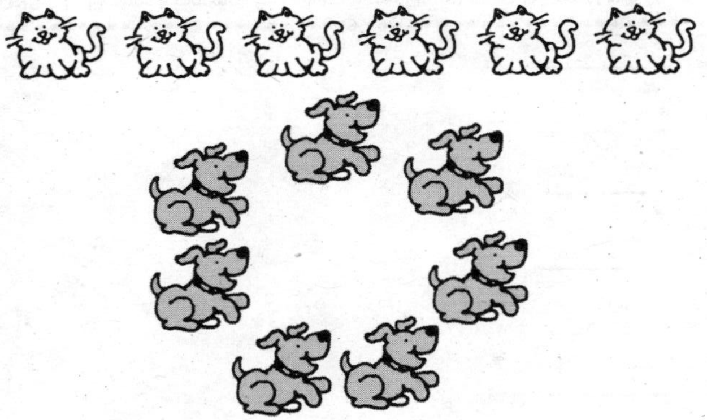

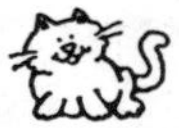

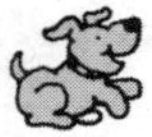

2

DIRECTIONS **1.** Marco puts all his toy cats in a line. He puts all his toy dogs in a circle. Look at the picture of Marco's toys. How many cats does Marco have? Write the number. How many dogs does Marco have? Write the number. **2.** Marco has toy mice, too. He wants to arrange a number of mice that is one greater than the number of dogs. Draw Marco's toy mice. Write the number of mice you drew.

3

4

5

DIRECTIONS **3.** Marco has a fish tank with red and blue fish. There are 5 red fish. The number of blue fish is 1 less than the number of red fish. Draw Marco's fish. **4.** Write the number of fish there are in the tank in all. **5.** Write the number word for that number.

Name ______

Ella's Art Projects

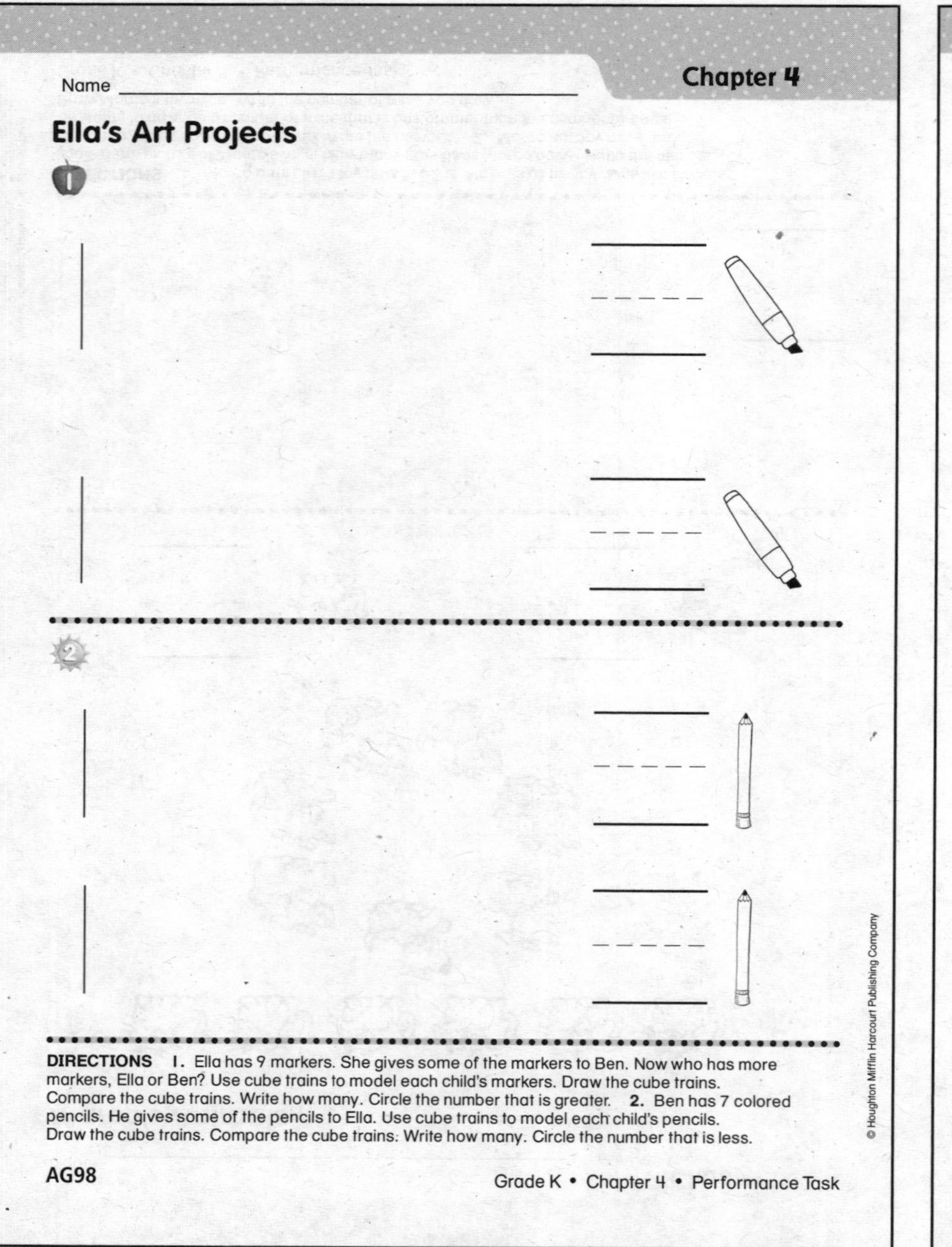

DIRECTIONS 1. Ella has 9 markers. She gives some of the markers to Ben. Now who has more markers, Ella or Ben? Use cube trains to model each child's markers. Draw the cube trains. Compare the cube trains. Write how many. Circle the number that is greater. 2. Ben has 7 colored pencils. He gives some of the pencils to Ella. Use cube trains to model each child's pencils. Draw the cube trains. Compare the cube trains. Write how many. Circle the number that is less.

Ella's Collage

DIRECTIONS 3. Ella makes a collage out of buttons and paperclips. Look at the picture of Ella's collage. How many buttons did Ella use? Write the number. How many paper clips did Ella use? Write the number. Compare the numbers. Circle the greater number. 4. Think of a number less than 10. Draw that many buttons. Draw a number of paper clips that is 1 less than the number of buttons. Write the number of buttons and paper clips you drew. Compare the numbers. Circle the greater number.

Chapter 5

Name ______________________

Bees and Flowers

1

9 = ___ + ___

2

DIRECTIONS 1. Use counters to find a number pair for 9. Write the number pair to complete the addition sentence. 2. Now use that number pair to draw or write an addition story about 9 bees.

3

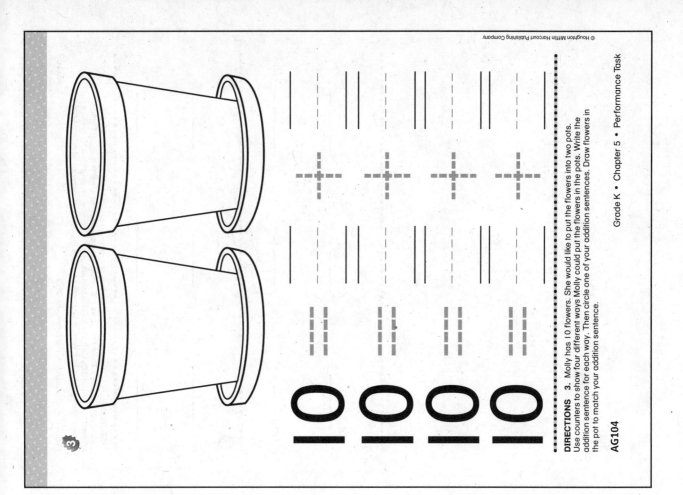

10 = ___ + ___

10 = ___ + ___

10 = ___ + ___

10 = ___ + ___

DIRECTIONS 3. Molly has 10 flowers. She would like to put the flowers into two pots. Use counters to show four different ways Molly could put the flowers in the pots. Write the addition sentence for each way. Then circle one of your addition sentences. Draw flowers in the pot to match your addition sentence.

Name ______________ Chapter 6

Sharing Stickers

1

2

___ + ___ = ___

3

___ − ___ = ___

DIRECTIONS **1.** Ana has 6 star stickers. Someone gives her 4 heart stickers. Put counters in the ten frame to show how many stickers Ana has in all. Draw the counters. **2.** Write the number sentence that tells about the stickers. **3.** Ana gives the 4 heart stickers to Paul. Cross out on your drawing to show the stickers Ana gives away. Write the number sentence that tells how many stickers Ana has left.

4

5

___ + ___ = ___

6

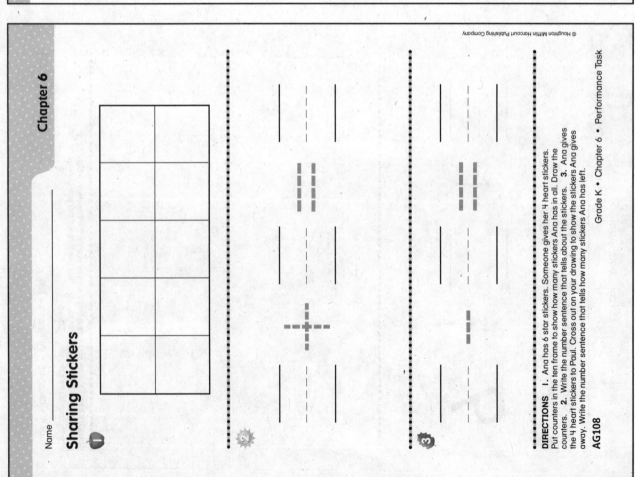

___ − ___ = ___

DIRECTIONS **4.** Dylan has 9 stickers. Some are red and some are blue. Use cubes to show Dylan's stickers. Draw the cubes. **5.** Write a number sentence that tells about Dylan's stickers. **6.** What if Dylan gives his blue stickers away? Cross out on your drawing to show the stickers Dylan gives away. Write the number sentence that tells how many stickers Dylan has left.

Name ________________

Buttons and Flowers

1

______

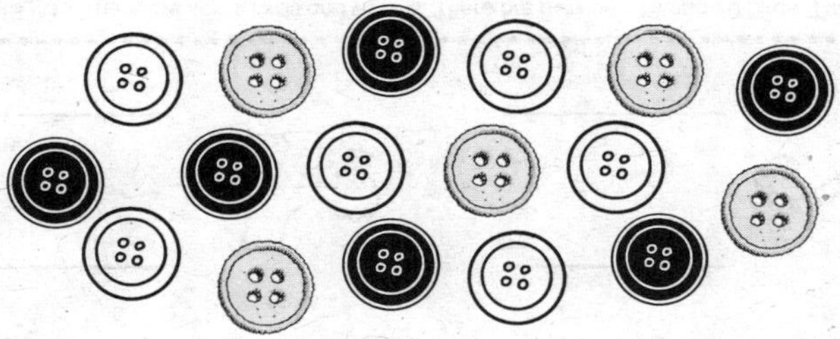

2

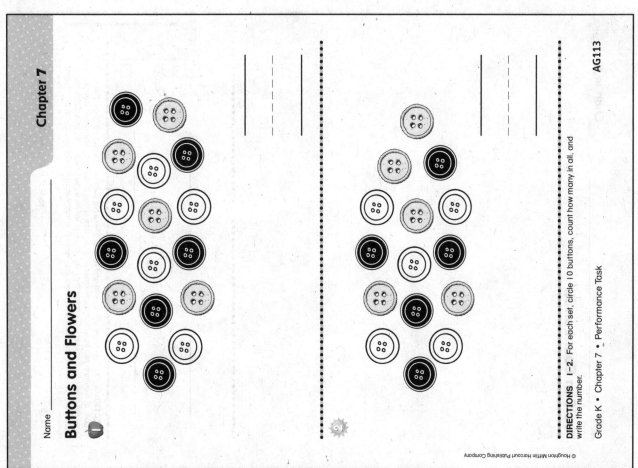

______

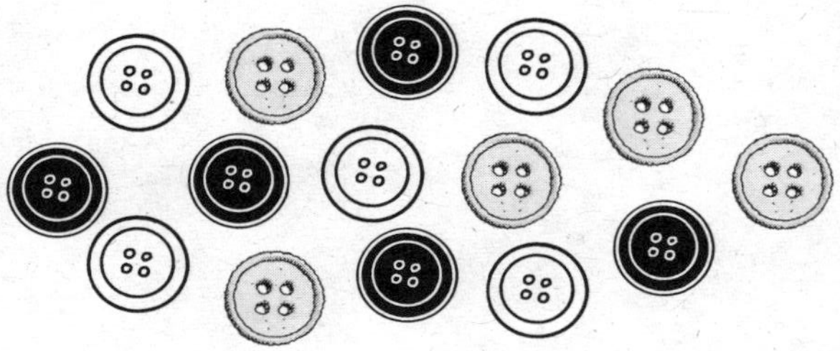

DIRECTIONS 1–2. For each set, circle 10 buttons, count how many in all, and write the number.

3

______

4

5

10 + ______ = ______

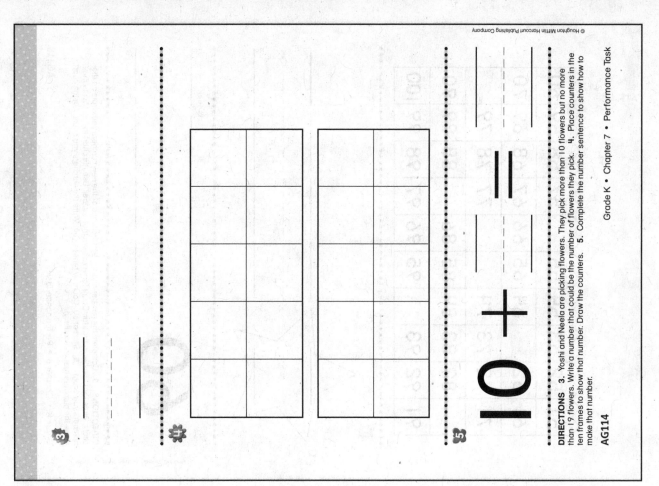

DIRECTIONS 3. Yoshi and Neela are picking flowers. They pick more than 10 flowers but no more than 19 flowers. Write a number that could be the number of flowers they pick. 4. Place counters in the ten frames to show that number. Draw the counters. 5. Complete the number sentence to show how to make that number.

Name ____________________

You Can Count on It!

1

2

DIRECTIONS 1. There are some birds and worms. There are between 15 and 20 birds. The number of worms is two less than the number of birds. Use cubes to model the birds and worms. Draw the cubes for both sets. Compare the sets. Show or tell how you compared them. Circle the larger set. 2. Write how many birds there are. Write how many worms there are. Circle the greater number.

3

51	52	53	54	55		57	58	59	60
61	62		64	65	66	67	68	69	70
71	72	73	74			77	78	79	
	82	83	84	85	86		88	89	90
91	92	93		95	96	97	98	99	100

4

5

60

DIRECTIONS 3. Complete the number chart. 4. Circle one of the new numbers you wrote on the chart. Write that number in the star. Count forward from that number. Use the chart to help. Write the numbers you count. 5. Start at 60. Count by tens to 100. Write the numbers you count. On the chart, circle the numbers that you counted.

Name ____________________ CRITICAL AREA Number and Operations

How Many Marbles?

1

____

2

____ − ____ = ____

DIRECTIONS 1. Draw 8 marbles. Write the number of marbles you drew. 2. Cross out 3 or 4 marbles. Write an equation to show how many marbles are left.

3

10 = ____ + ____

4

10 = ____ + ____

DIRECTIONS Use counters. 3. Bo has 7 blue marbles. Then he gets some red marbles. Now he has 10 marbles in all. Draw Bo's marbles. Write an equation to tell about Bo's marbles. 4. Mia has 10 marbles. Four of her marbles are yellow and the rest are green. Draw Mia's marbles. Write an equation to tell about Mia's marbles.

Name ____________

5

6

7

10 + ___ = ___

DIRECTIONS 5. Rory has 16, 17, or 18 marbles. Write a number that could be Rory's marbles. 6. Place counters in the ten frames to show that number. Draw the counters. 7. Complete the equation to show how to make that number.

8

9

DIRECTIONS 8. There are 6 bags of marbles on the table. Each bag has 10 marbles. Draw the bags of marbles. Count by tens to show how many marbles in all. Write the number. 9. Sam has 14 marbles. Liam has 2 more marbles than Sam. Draw both sets of marbles. Circle the set that has a greater number of marbles.

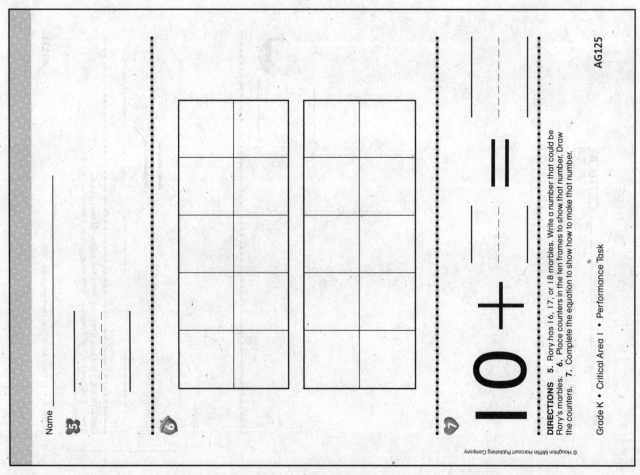

Name ______

Shape Pictures

1

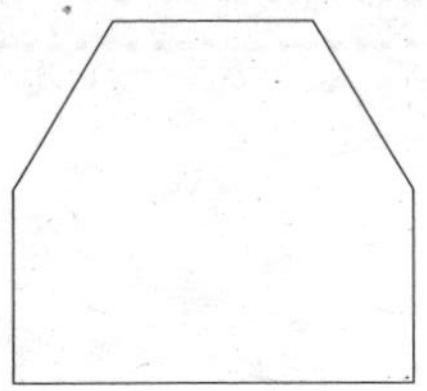

2

3

4

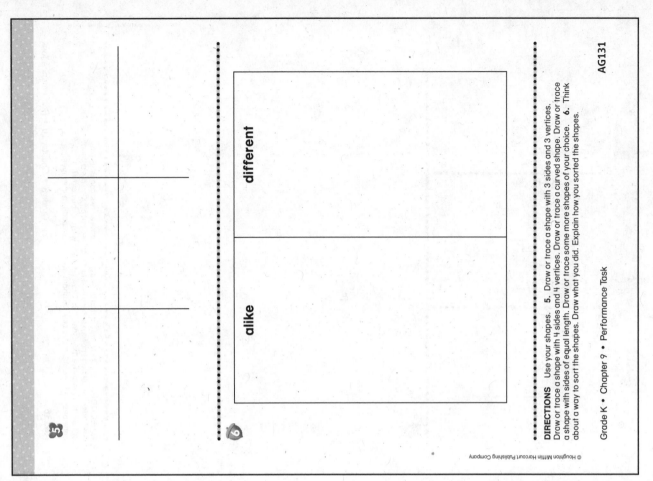

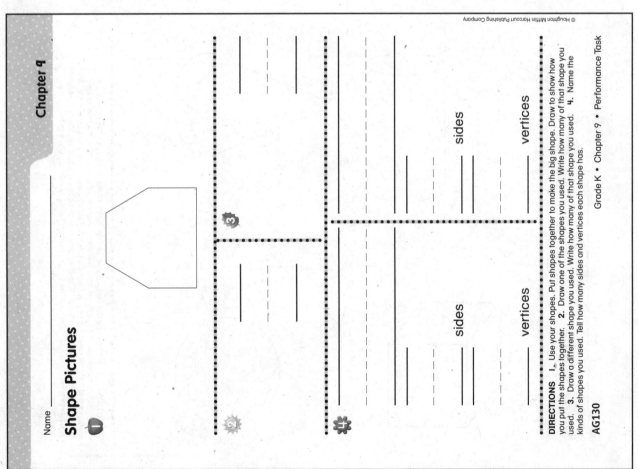

___ sides

___ vertices

___ sides

___ vertices

DIRECTIONS 1. Use your shapes. Put shapes together to make the big shape. Draw to show how you put the shapes together. 2. Draw one of the shapes you used. Write how many of that shape you used. 3. Draw a different shape you used. Write how many of that shape you used. 4. Name the kinds of shapes you used. Tell how many sides and vertices each shape has.

5

6

alike	different

DIRECTIONS Use your shapes. 5. Draw or trace a shape with 3 sides and 3 vertices. Draw or trace a shape with 4 sides and 4 vertices. Draw or trace a curved shape. Draw or trace a shape with sides of equal length. Draw or trace some more shapes of your choice. 6. Think about a way to sort the shapes. Draw what you did. Explain how you sorted the shapes.

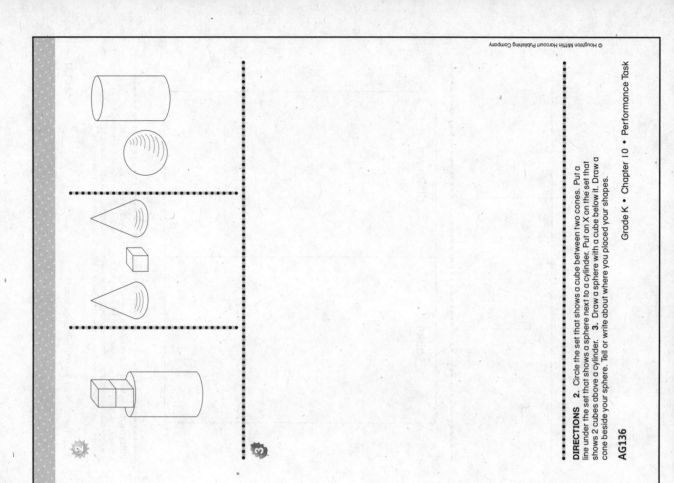

Name ______________________

Shape Safari

1

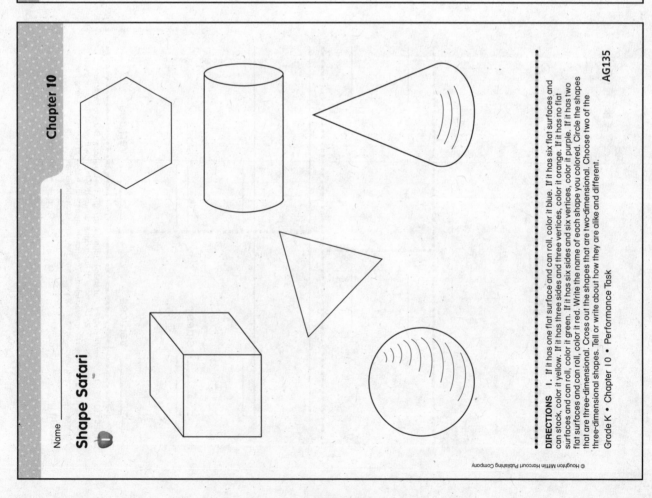

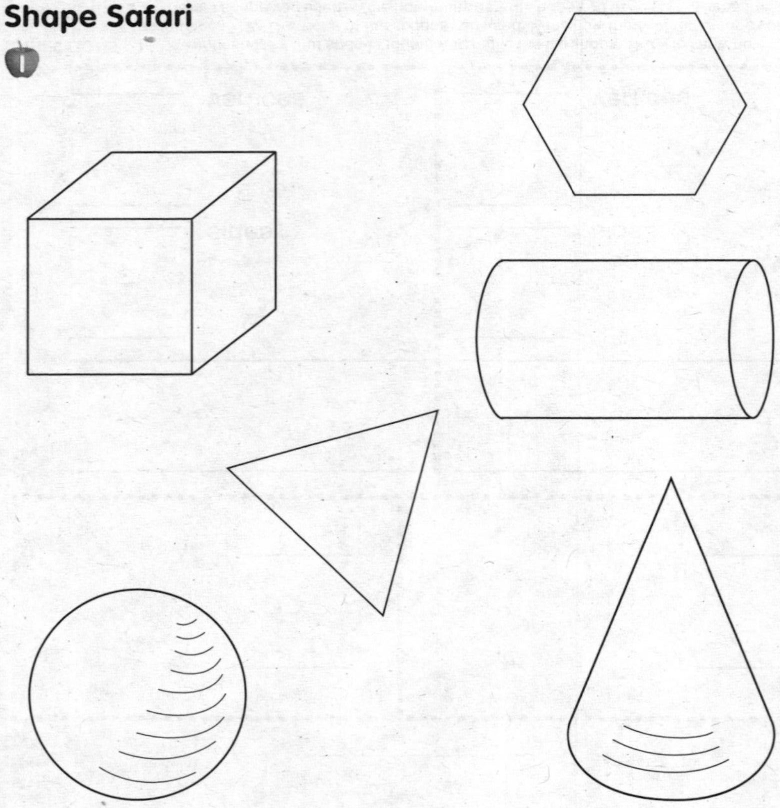

DIRECTIONS 1. If it has one flat surface and can roll, color it blue. If it has six flat surfaces and can stack, color it yellow. If it has three sides and three vertices, color it orange. If it has no flat surfaces and can roll, color it green. If it has six sides and six vertices, color it purple. If it has two flat surfaces and can roll, color it red. Write the name of each shape you colored. Circle the shapes that are three-dimensional. Cross out the shapes that are two-dimensional. Choose two of the three-dimensional shapes. Tell or write about how they are alike and different.

2

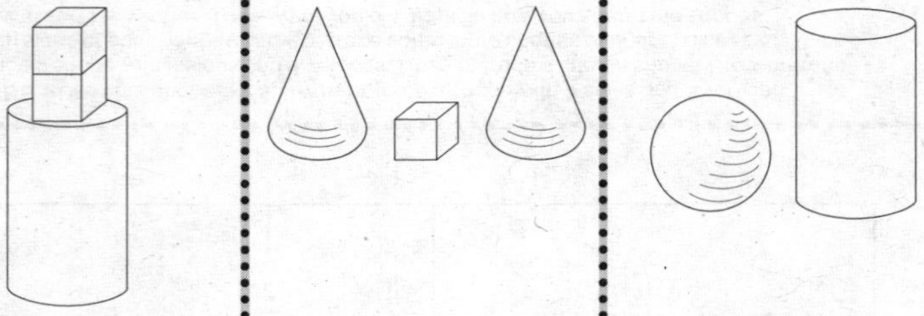

3

DIRECTIONS 2. Circle the set that shows a cube between two cones. Put a line under the set that shows a sphere next to a cylinder. Put an X on the set that shows 2 cubes above a cylinder. 3. Draw a sphere with a cube below it. Draw a cone beside your sphere. Tell or write about where you placed your shapes.

Name ____________________

CRITICAL AREA Geometry and Positions

Shapes, Shapes, Shapes!

1

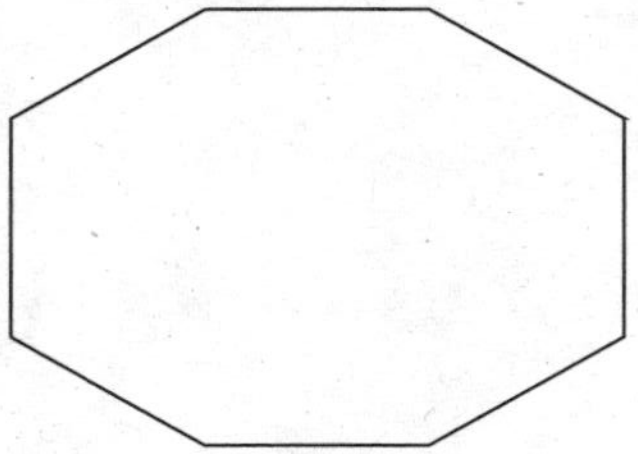

2

3

DIRECTIONS 1. Use triangles and squares to create the big shape. Draw the shapes you used. 2. How many triangles did you draw? Write the number. 3. How many squares did you draw? Write the number.

4

DIRECTIONS Use your shapes. 4. Trace the rectangle. Color it green. Above the green shape, draw a shape with no sides and no vertices. Color this shape yellow. Under the green shape, draw a shape that has 3 sides and 3 vertices. Color this shape blue. Next to the blue shape, draw a shape that has 6 sides and 6 vertices. Color this shape red. Put an X on any shape that has more than 3 sides.

5

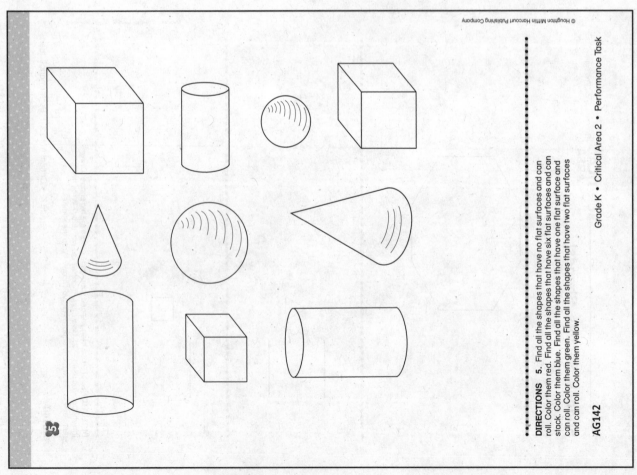

DIRECTIONS **5.** Find all the shapes that have no flat surfaces and can roll. Color them red. Find all the shapes that have six flat surfaces and can stack. Color them blue. Find all the shapes that have one flat surface and can roll. Color them green. Find all the shapes that have two flat surfaces and can roll. Color them yellow.

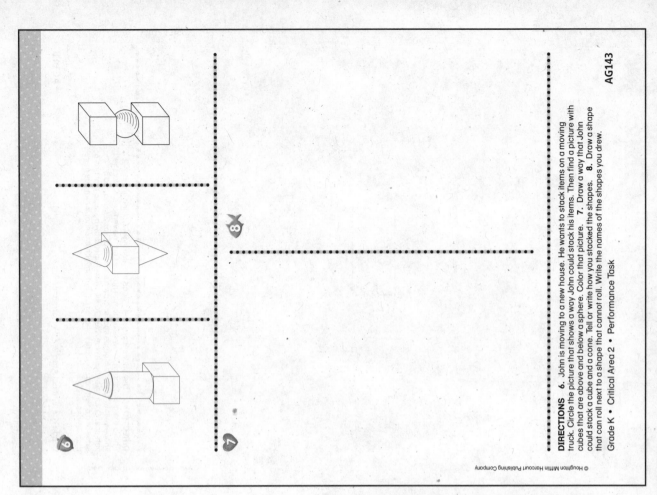

6

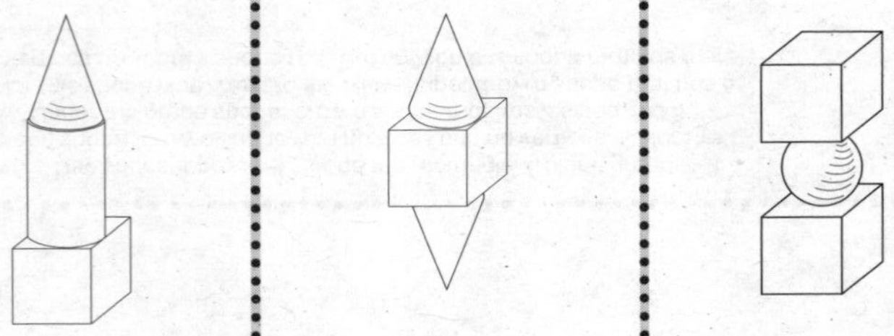

7

8

DIRECTIONS **6.** John is moving to a new house. He wants to stack items on a moving truck. Circle the picture that shows a way John could stack his items. Then find a picture with cubes that are above and below a sphere. Color that picture. **7.** Draw a way that John could stack a cube and a cone. Tell or write how you stacked the shapes. **8.** Draw a shape that can roll next to a shape that cannot roll. Write the names of the shapes you drew.

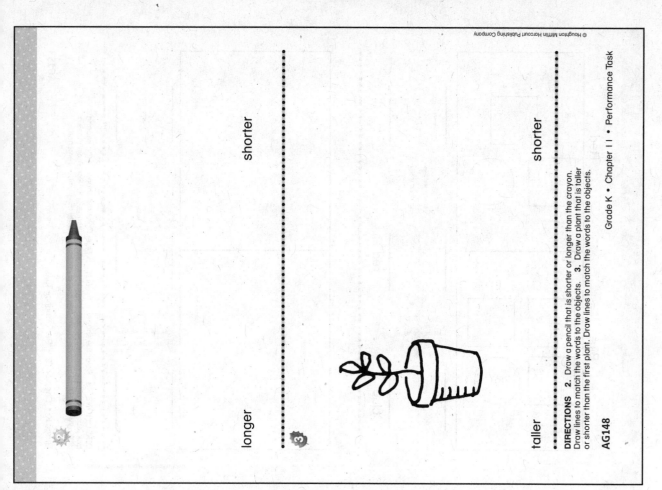

Name ______________________

Weight, Length, and Height

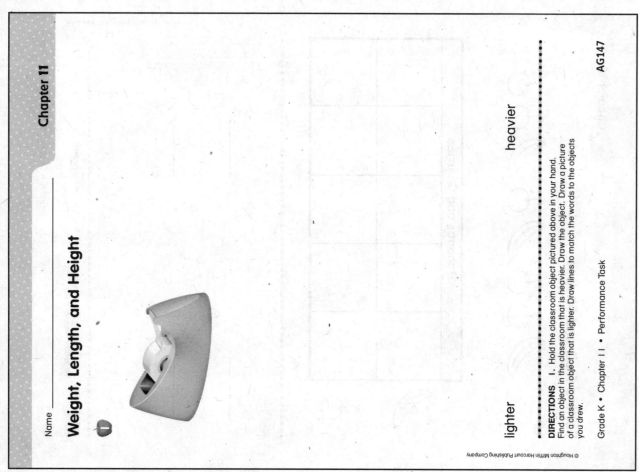

1

lighter heavier

DIRECTIONS 1. Hold the classroom object pictured above in your hand. Find an object in the classroom that is heavier. Draw the object. Draw a picture of a classroom object that is lighter. Draw lines to match the words to the objects you drew.

2

longer shorter

3

taller shorter

DIRECTIONS 2. Draw a pencil that is shorter or longer than the crayon. Draw lines to match the words to the objects. 3. Draw a plant that is taller or shorter than the first plant. Draw lines to match the words to the objects.

Sorting Fruit and Shapes

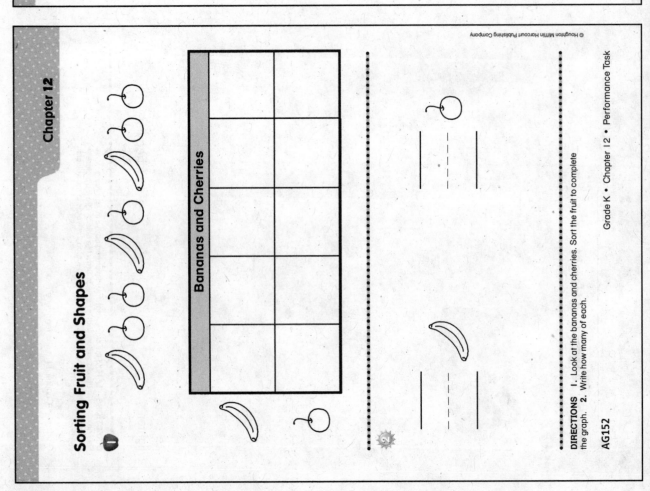

1

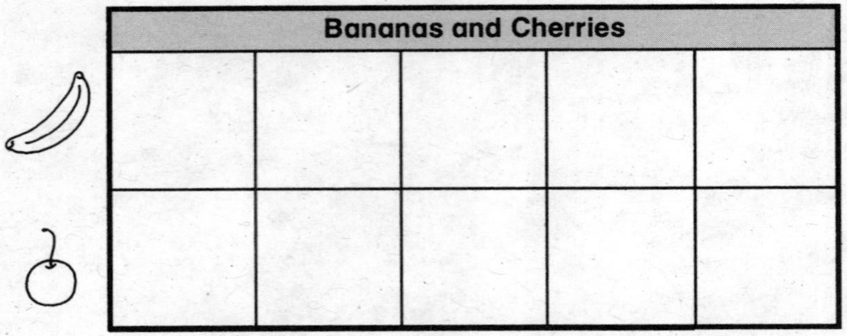

Bananas and Cherries				

2

DIRECTIONS 1. Look at the bananas and cherries. Sort the fruit to complete the graph. 2. Write how many of each.

3

Blue Red

+ =

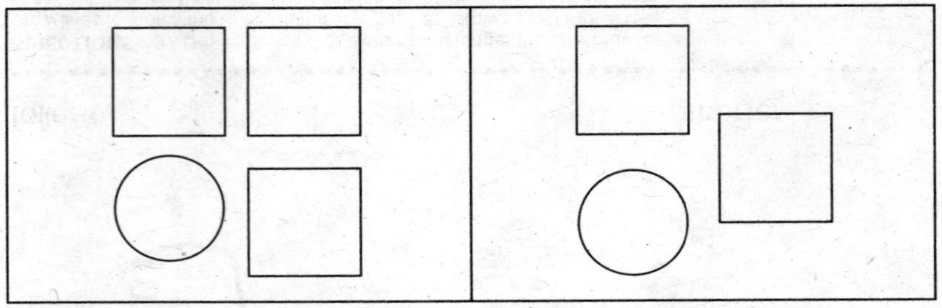

blue red

4

+ =

DIRECTIONS 3. Color the shapes in the first box blue. Color the shapes in the second box red. How are the shapes sorted? Write the number sentence. 4. Sort the shapes a different way. Draw and color them into the empty boxes. Write the number sentence.

Name ____________________ CRITICAL AREA Measurement and Data

Comparing and Sorting

Felipe's Marbles

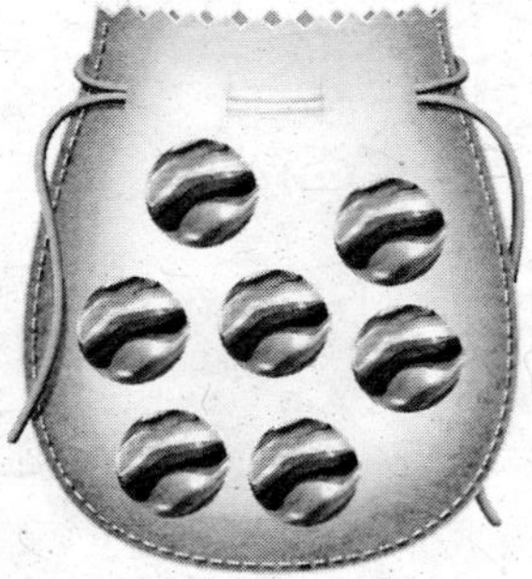

1 lighter

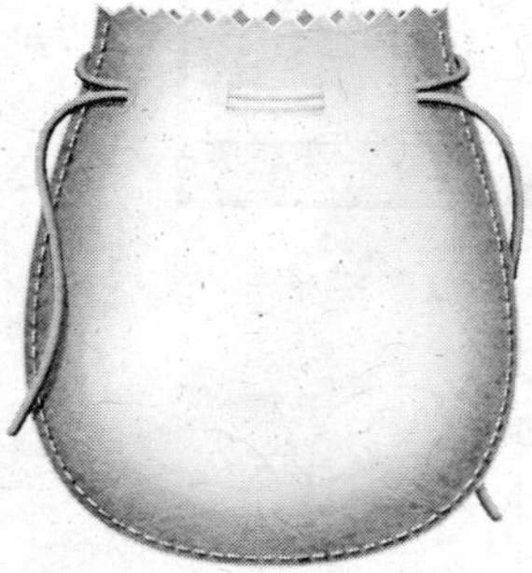

2 heavier

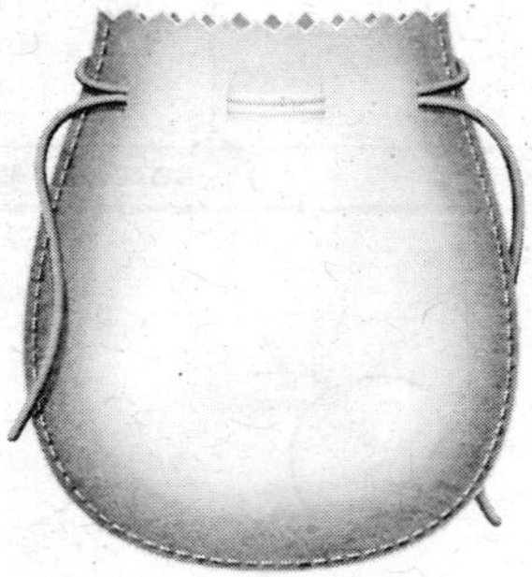

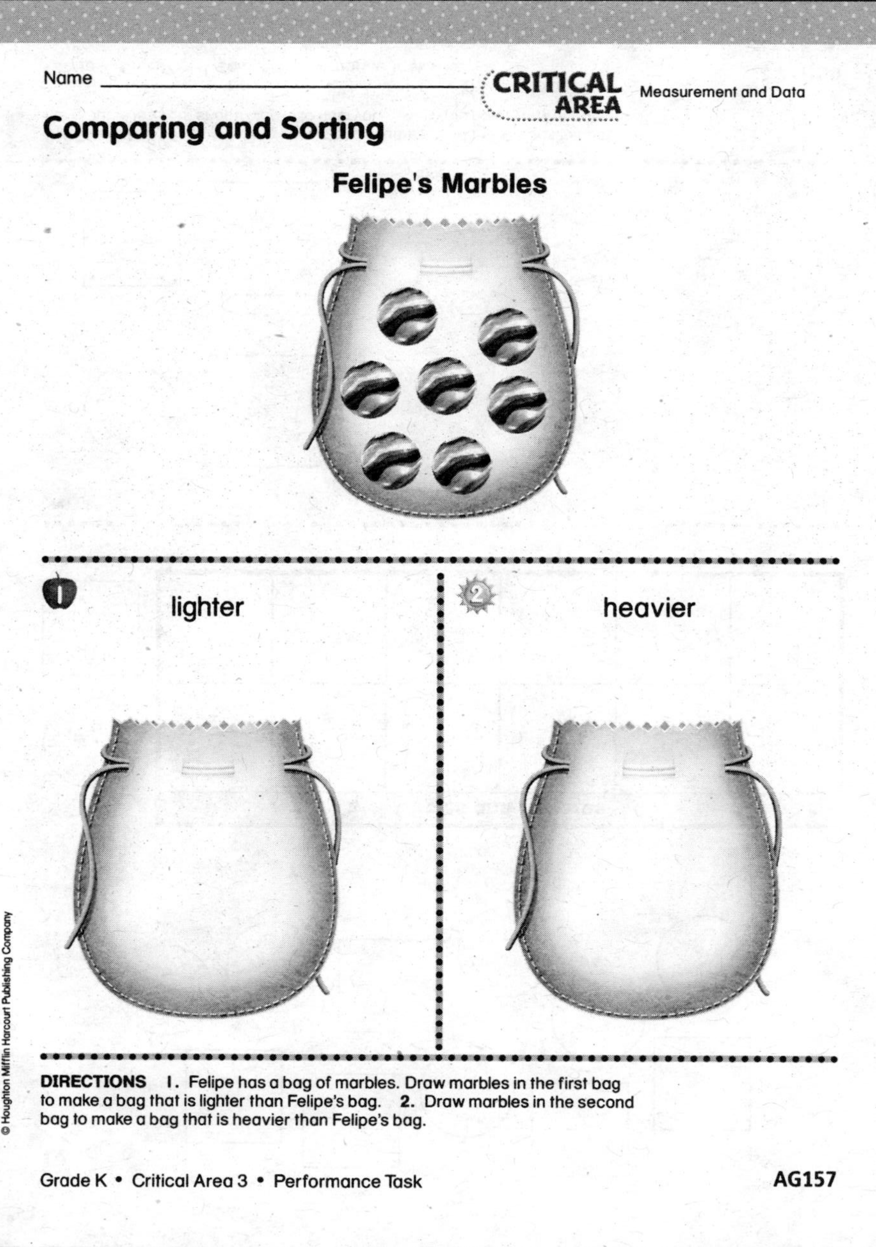

DIRECTIONS 1. Felipe has a bag of marbles. Draw marbles in the first bag to make a bag that is lighter than Felipe's bag. 2. Draw marbles in the second bag to make a bag that is heavier than Felipe's bag.

3

4

DIRECTIONS 3. Draw two worms. Make one longer than the other. Circle the worm that is shorter. 4. Draw two trees. Make one tree shorter than the other. Circle the tree that is taller.

5

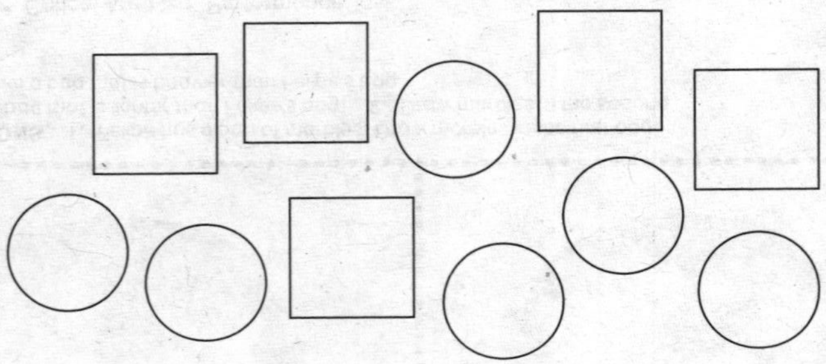

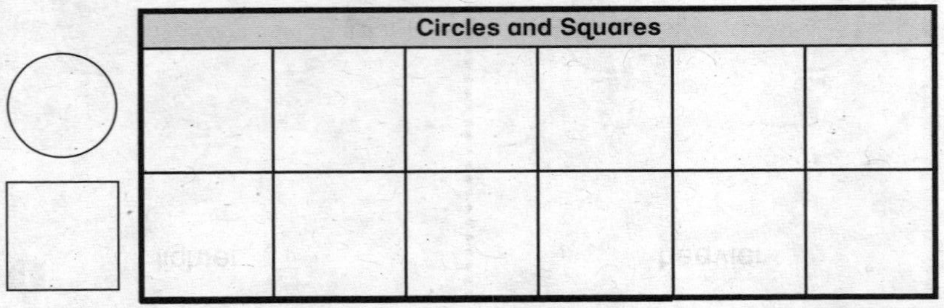

Circles and Squares					

6

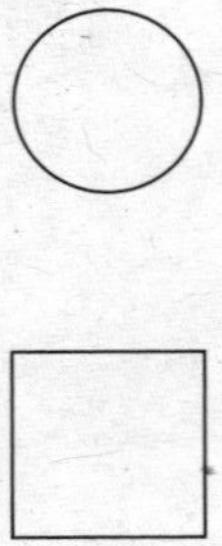

DIRECTIONS 5. Look at the circles and squares. Sort the shapes to complete the graph. Use your shape blocks to help you. 6. Write how many of each.

7

Red Blue

8

Red Blue

9

DIRECTIONS 7. Draw 1, 2, or 3 red shapes in the first box. Write the number of red shapes you drew. Draw 4, 5, or 6 blue shapes in the second box. Write the number of blue shapes you drew. 8. Write the number sentence for the number of shapes in all. 9. Write the number sentence a different way.

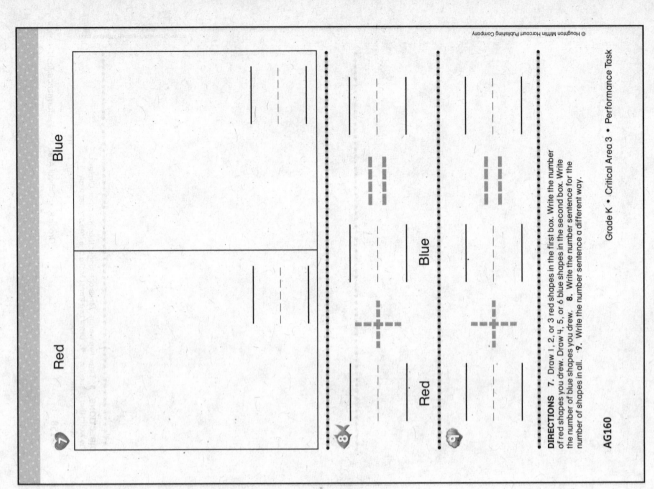

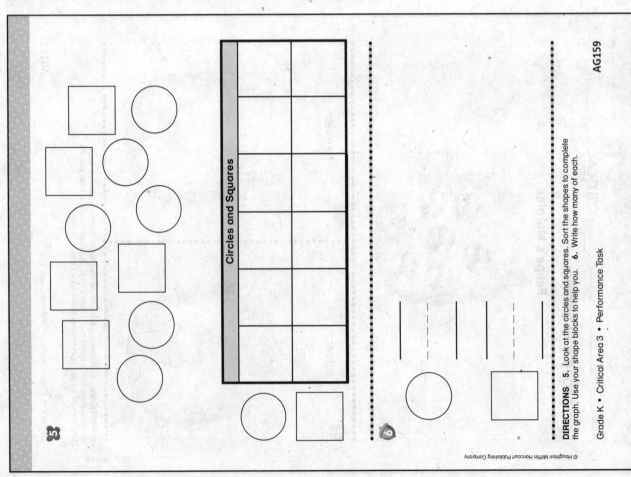

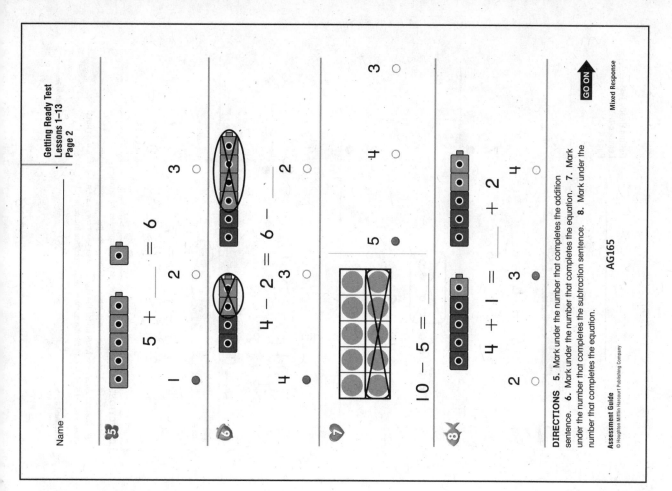

Name ____________

Getting Ready Test
Lessons 1–13
Page 1

Directions/Questions are at bottom of page to be read by teacher.

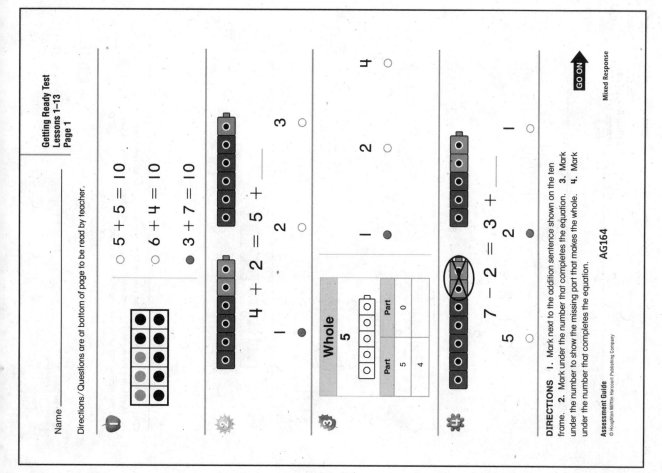

1

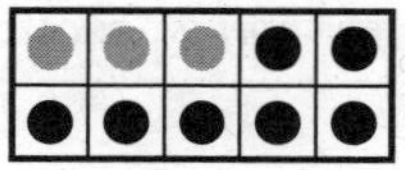

○ $5 + 5 = 10$

○ $6 + 4 = 10$

● $3 + 7 = 10$

2

$4 + 2 = 5 + \_\_$

1	2	3
●	○	○

3

Whole	
5	
Part	**Part**
5	0
4	

1	2	4
●	○	○

4

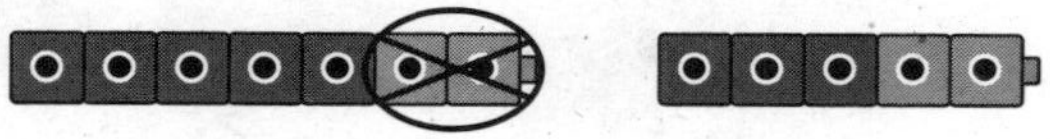

$7 - 2 = 3 + \_\_$

5	2	1
○	●	○

DIRECTIONS 1. Mark next to the addition sentence shown on the ten frame. 2. Mark under the number that completes the equation. 3. Mark under the number to show the missing part that makes the whole. 4. Mark under the number that completes the equation.

GO ON

Name ____________

Getting Ready Test
Lessons 1–13
Page 2

5

$5 + \_\_ = 6$

1	2	3
●	○	○

6

$4 - 2 = 6 - \_\_$

4	3	2
●	○	○

7

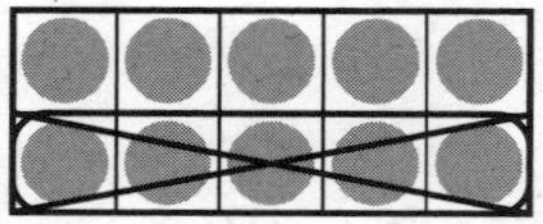

$10 - 5 = \_\_$

5	4	3
●	○	○

8

$4 + 1 = \_\_ + 2$

2	3	4
○	●	○

DIRECTIONS 5. Mark under the number that completes the addition sentence. 6. Mark under the number that completes the equation. 7. Mark under the number that completes the subtraction sentence. 8. Mark under the number that completes the equation.

GO ON

Name ____________

9

2 + 2 = ___

2	4	5
○	●	○

10

Whole	
3	
Part	Part
3	0
2	1
1	

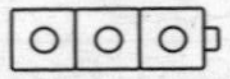

0	1	2
○	○	●

11

4 + ___ = 8

3	4	5
○	●	○

DIRECTIONS 9. Mark under the number that completes the addition sentence. 10. Mark under the number to show the missing part that makes the whole. 11. Mark under the number that completes the addition sentence.

GO ON

Name ____________

12

6 + 1 = ___

5	6	7
○	○	●

13

4 − 2 = ___

4	3	2
○	○	●

14

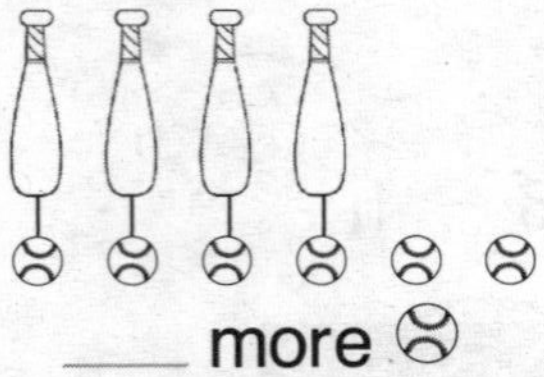

___ more

1	2	3
○	●	○

15

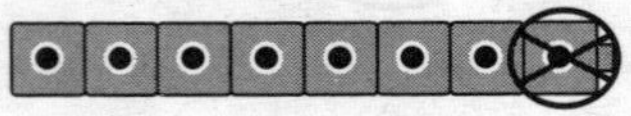

8 − ___ = 7

2	1	0
○	●	○

DIRECTIONS 12. Mark under the number that completes the addition sentence. 13. Mark under the number that completes the subtraction sentence. 14. Compare the sets. Mark under the number that tells how many more balls than bats there are. 15. Mark under the number that completes the subtraction sentence.

STOP

Name ______________________

Directions/Questions are at bottom of page to be read by teacher.

1. 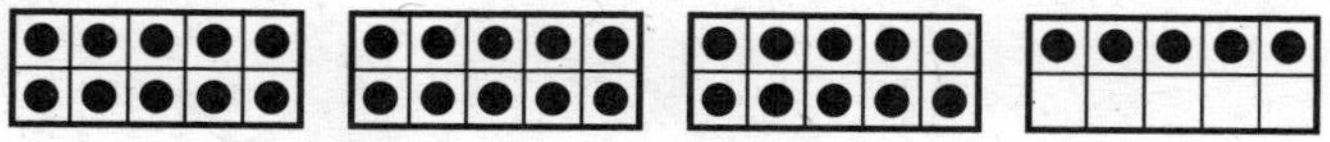
25 ○ 34 ○ 35 ●

2. 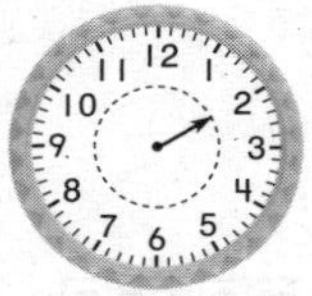
1 o'clock ○ 2 o'clock ● 3 o'clock ○

3. 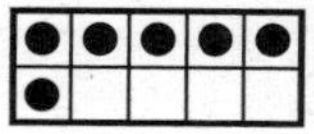
5 ones ○ 6 ones ● 7 ones ○

4.
3:00

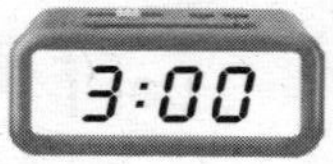

1 o'clock ○ 3 o'clock ● 5 o'clock ○

DIRECTIONS 1. How many counters are there? Mark under the number. 2. About what time does the clock show? Mark under the time. 3. How many ones are there? Mark under the number. 4. What time does the clock show? Mark under the time.

GO ON

Name ______________________

5. 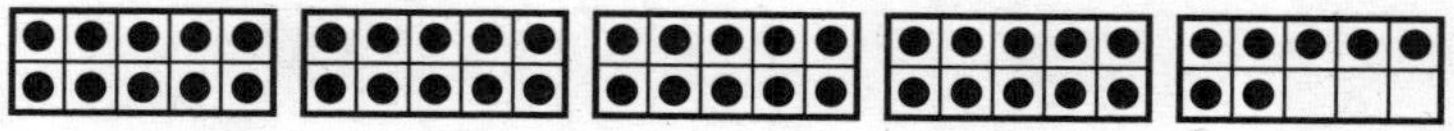
48 ○ 47 ● 46 ○

6. 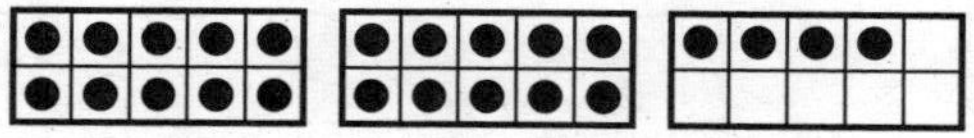
24 ● 25 ○ 34 ○

7. 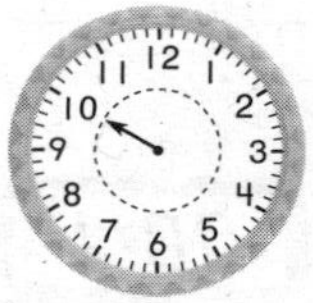
8 o'clock ○ 10 o'clock ● 12 o'clock ○

8.
1:00

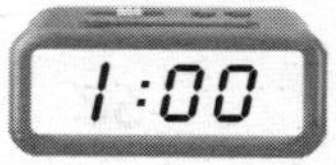

1 o'clock ● 3 o'clock ○ 11 o'clock ○

DIRECTIONS 5. How many counters are there? Mark under the number. 6. How many counters are there? Mark under the number. 7. About what time does the clock show? Mark under the time. 8. What time does the clock show? Mark under the time.

GO ON

Name ______________________

Getting Ready Test
Lessons 14–20
Page 3

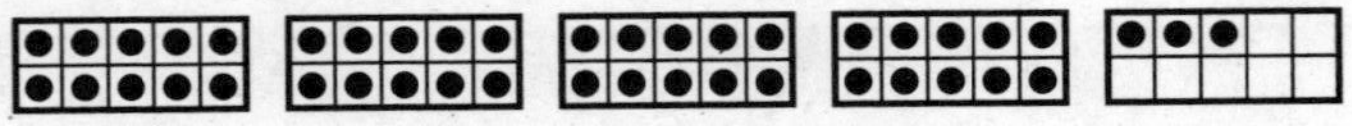

9.

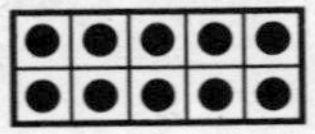

1 ten	2 tens	10 tens
●	○	○

10.

37	38	39
○	○	●

11.

45	43	33
○	●	○

12.

8	9	12
○	●	○

DIRECTIONS **9.** How many tens are shown? Mark under the answer. **10.** How many counters are shown? Mark under the number. **11.** How many counters are there? Mark under the number. **12.** What number is missing on the clock? Mark under the number.

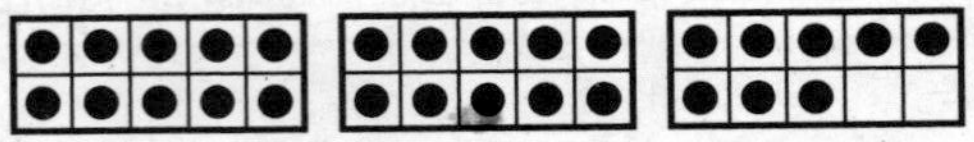

GO ON

Name ______________________

Getting Ready Test
Lessons 14–20
Page 4

13.

29	28	27
○	●	○

14. 7:00

5 o'clock	7 o'clock	9 o'clock
○	●	○

15.

6 o'clock	10 o'clock	12 o'clock
●	○	○

16.

10	11	12
○	●	○

DIRECTIONS **13.** How many counters are there? Mark under the number. **14.** What time does the clock show? Mark under the time. **15.** About what time does the clock show? Mark under the time. **16.** What number is missing on the clock? Mark under the number.

STOP

Child's Name ______________________ Date __________

Prerequisite Skills Inventory

Item	Common Error	Intervene With
1	May miscount the blocks	Activity 5
2	May not understand ordinal numbers	Activity 4
3	May not understand the value of 2	Activity 5
4	May not know the sequence of numbers to 5	Activity 5
5	May not understand the value of 1	Activity 5
6	May miscount items	Activity 5
7	May not understand how to compare groups of objects	Activity 6
8	May not understand the concept of *more*	Activity 6
9	May not understand the concept of *less*	Activity 6
10	May not understand the concept of *same*	Activity 6
11	May not understand the concept of *down*	Activity 10
12	May not understand the concept of *last*	Activity 4
13	May not understand the concept of *small*	Activity 3
14	May not understand the concept of *over*	Activity 7
15	May not understand the concept of *alike*	Activities 1, 2
16	May not understand the concept of *different*	Activities 1, 2
17	May not understand which direction is *right*	Activity 9

Child's Name ____________________ Date ____________

Prerequisite Skills Inventory

Item	Common Error	Intervene With
18	May not understand which direction is *left*	Activity 9
19	May not understand the concept of *middle*	Activity 9
20	May not understand the concept of on *top*	Activity 8
21	May not understand the concept of *under*	Activity 7
22	May not understand which direction *up* refers to	Activity 10
23	May not understand the concept of *big*	Activity 3
24	May not identify an object that does not belong in a group	Activity 2

Child's Name ______________________ Date ____________

Beginning-of-Year/Middle-of-Year/End-of-Year Test

Item	Lesson	Standard	Content Focus	Intervene With	Personal Math Trainer
1	3.3	K.CC.5	Model and count 7.	**R**—3.3	K.CC.5
2	3.8	K.CC.3	Count and write 9.	**R**—3.8	K.CC.3
3	6.6	K.OA.2	Write more subtraction sentences.	**R**—6.6	K.OA.2
4	6.7	K.OA.2	Use addition and subtraction.	**R**—6.7	K.OA.2
5	8.3	K.CC.2	Count and order to 20.	**R**—8.3	K.CC.2
6	8.6	K.CC.1	Count to 100 by ones.	**R**—8.6	K.CC.1
7	8.8	K.CC.1	Count by tens.	**R**—8.8	K.CC.1
8	5.1	K.OA.1	Add to.	**R**—5.1	K.OA.1
9	5.7	K.OA.1	Write more addition sentences.	**R**—5.7	K.OA.1
10	5.10	K.OA.3	Find number pairs for 8.	**R**—5.10	K.OA.3

Key: R—Reteach Book

Child's Name ______________________ Date ____________

Beginning-of-Year/Middle-of-Year/End-of-Year Test

Item	Lesson	Standard	Content Focus	Intervene With	Personal Math Trainer
11	10.1	K.OA.3	Identify three-dimensional shapes.	**R**—10.1	K.OA.3
12	10.4	K.G.2	Identify, name, and describe cylinders.	**R**—10.4	K.G.2
13	10.8	K.G.1	Compare above and below.	**R**—10.8	K.G.1
14	1.3	K.CC.4a	Model and count 3 and 4.	**R**—1.3	K.CC.4a
15	1.6	K.CC.4b	Count and write 5.	**R**—1.6	K.CC.4b
16	1.10	K.CC.3	Identify and write 0.	**R**—1.10	K.CC.3
17	4.3	K.OA.4	Find ways to make 10.	**R**—4.3	K.OA.4
18	4.4	K.CC.2	Count and order to 10.	**R**—4.4	K.CC.2
19	4.7	K.CC.7	Compare two numbers.	**R**—4.7	K.CC.7
20	12.4	K.MD.3	Make a concrete graph.	**R**—12.4	K.MD.3
21	12.2	K.MD.3	Classify and count by shape.	**R**—12.2	K.MD.3
22	12.3	K.MD.3	Classify and count by size.	**R**—12.3	K.MD.3

Key: R—Reteach Book

Child's Name ______________________ Date ______________

Beginning-of-Year/Middle-of-Year/End-of-Year Test

Item	Lesson	Standard	Content Focus	Intervene With	Personal Math Trainer
23	7.5	K.NBT.1	Model, count, and write 15.	**R**—7.5	K.NBT.1
24	7.9	K.NBT.1	Model and count 18 and 19.	**R**—7.9	K.NBT.1
25	9.4	K.G.4	Describe squares.	**R**—9.4	K.G.4
26	9.9	K.G.2	Identify and name hexagons.	**R**—9.9	K.G.2
27	9.11	K.G.4	Compare two-dimensional shapes.	**R**—9.11	K.G.4
28	2.4	K.CC.6	Compare by matching sets to 5.	**R**—2.4	K.CC.6
29	2.5	K.CC.6	Compare by counting sets to 5.	**R**—2.5	K.CC.6
30	11.1	K.MD.2	Compare lengths.	**R**—11.1	K.MD.2
31	11.2	K.MD.2	Compare heights.	**R**—11.2	K.MD.2
32	11.4	K.MD.2	Compare weights.	**R**—11.4	K.MD.2

Key: R—Reteach Book

Child's Name ______________________ Date ______________

Chapter 1 Test

Item	Lesson	Standard	Content Focus	Intervene With	Personal Math Trainer
1	1.1	K.CC.4a	Model and count 1 and 2.	**R**—1.1	K.CC.4a
2	1.5	K.CC.4a	Model and count 5.	**R**—1.5	K.CC.4a
3	1.10	K.CC.3	Use words and numbers to identify and write 0.	**R**—1.10	K.CC.3
4	1.2	K.CC.3	Use words and numbers to count and write 1 and 2.	**R**—1.2	K.CC.3
5	1.4	K.CC.3	Use words and numbers to count and write 3 and 4.	**R**—1.4	K.CC.3
6	1.3	K.CC.4a	Model and count 3 and 4.	**R**—1.3	K.CC.4a
7	1.2, 1.4, 1.6	K.CC.3	Use words and numbers to count and write 5.	**R**—1.2, 1.4, 1.6	K.CC.3
8,9	1.8	K.CC.4c	Count and order to 5.	**R**—1.8	K.CC.4c
10–12	1.9	K.CC.3	Model and record numbers to solve a real-world problem.	**R**—1.9	K.CC.3
13	1.7	K.CC.4b	Use two sets of objects to show 5 in more than one way.	**R**—1.7	K.CC.4b
14	1.8	K.CC.4c	Draw and record to identify a successive number.	**R**—1.8	K.CC.4c

Key: R—Reteach Book

Child's Name ______________________ Date ______________

Chapter 2 Test

Item	Lesson	Standard	Content Focus	Intervene With	Personal Math Trainer
1, 3	2.1	K.CC.6	Use matching and counting to compare sets with the same number of objects.	**R**—2.1	K.CC.6
2, 4	2.2	K.CC.6	Use matching and counting to identify the set that has a greater number of objects.	**R**—2.2	K.CC.6
5, 6	2.3	K.CC.6	Use matching and counting to identify the set that has a lesser number of objects.	**R**—2.3	K.CC.6
7, 8, 10	2.4, 2.5	K.CC.6	Make a model to solve problems using a matching strategy.	**R**—2.4, 2.5	K.CC.6
9	2.5	K.CC.6	Use counting to compare sets of objects to 5.	**R**—2.5	K.CC.6

Key: R—Reteach Book

Child's Name ____________________ Date ____________

Chapter 3 Test

Item	Lesson	Standard	Content Focus	Intervene With	Personal Math Trainer
1	3.1	K.CC.5	Model and count 6.	**R**—3.1	K.CC.5
3	3.2	K.CC.3	Count and write 6.	**R**—3.2	K.CC.3
2, 4	3.3	K.CC.5	Model and count 7.	**R**—3.3	K.CC.5
5	3.1, 3.3, 3.5	K.CC.5	Represent numbers 6 to 9.	**R**—3.4	K.CC.5
6	3.6	K.CC.3	Count and write 8.	**R**—3.6	K.CC.3
7, 12	3.8	K.CC.3	Count and write 9.	**R**—3.8	K.CC.3
8	3.7	K.CC.5	Model and count 9.	**R**—3.7	K.CC.5
9, 11	3.9	K.CC.6	Solve problems for numbers to 9 by drawing a picture.	**R**—3.9	K.CC.6
10	3.9	K.CC.7	Count and choose numbers greater than 6.	**R**—3.9	K.CC.7

Key: R—Reteach Book

Child's Name ________________ Date ________________

Chapter 4 Test

Item	Lesson	Standard	Content Focus	Intervene With	Personal Math Trainer
1, 12	4.1	K.CC.5	Model and count 10 with objects.	**R**—4.1	K.CC.5
2, 3, 10	4.2	K.CC.3	Represent objects with a number name or a written numeral.	**R**—4.2	K.CC.3
4, 5	4.3	K.OA.4	Make 10 using objects and drawings.	**R**—4.3	K.OA.4
6	4.4	K.CC.2	Count and order to 10.	**R**—4.4	K.CC.2
7	4.5	K.CC.6	Compare by matching sets to 10.	**R**—4.5	K.CC.6
10, 11	4.6	K.CC.6	Compare by counting sets to 10.	**R**—4.6	K.CC.6
9	4.7	K.CC.7	Compare two numbers between 1 and 10.	**R**—4.7	K.CC.7

Key: R—Reteach Book

Child's Name ______________________ Date ____________

Chapter 5 Test

Item	Lesson	Standard	Content Focus	Intervene With	Personal Math Trainer
1	5.1	K.OA.1	Show addition as adding to.	**R**—5.1	K.OA.1
2	5.2	K.OA.1	Show addition as putting together.	**R**—5.2	K.OA.1
3	5.3	K.OA.1	Act out addition problems.	**R**—5.3	K.OA.1
4	5.4	K.OA.5	Model and draw addition problems.	**R**—5.4	K.OA.5
5	5.5	K.OA.4	Write addition sentences for 10.	**R**—5.5	K.OA.4
6	5.6	K.OA.5	Complete addition sentences.	**R**—5.6	K.OA.5
7	5.7	K.OA.2	Complete addition sentences.	**R**—5.7	K.OA.2
8	5.8	K.OA.3	Write number pairs for sums to 5.	**R**—5.8	K.OA.3
9	5.9, 5.10	K.OA.3	Identify number pairs for sums to 8.	**R**—5.9, 5.10	K.OA.3
10	5.10	K.OA.3	Identify number pairs for sums to 8.	**R**—5.10	K.OA.3
11	5.11	K.OA.3	Write addition sentences for number pairs for sums to 9.	**R**—5.11	K.OA.3
12	5.12	K.OA.3	Write addition sentences for number pairs for sums to 10.	**R**—5.12	K.OA.3

Key: R—Reteach Book

Child's Name ______________________ Date ______________

Chapter 6 Test

Item	Lesson	Standard	Content Focus	Intervene With	Personal Math Trainer
1	6.1	K.OA.1	Subtract by taking from.	**R**—6.1	K.OA.1
2	6.2	K.OA.1	Subtract by taking apart.	**R**—6.2	K.OA.1
3	6.3	K.OA.1	Act out subtraction problems.	**R**—6.3	K.OA.1
4, 9, 10	6.5	K.OA.5	Complete subtraction sentences.	**R**—6.5	K.OA.5
5, 11, 12	6.6	K.OA.2	Complete subtraction sentences with start number unknown.	**R**—6.6	K.OA.2
6, 7	6.7	K.OA.2	Solve problems using addition and subtraction.	**R**—6.7	K.OA.2
8	6.4	K.OA.5	Model subtraction problems.	**R**—6.4	K.OA.5

Key: R—Reteach Book

Child's Name ________________________ Date ______________

Chapter 7 Test

Item	Lesson	Standard	Content Focus	Intervene With	Personal Math Trainer
1	7.1	K.NBT.1	Count and write 11 and 12.	**R**—7.1	K.NBT.1
2	7.3	K.NBT.1	Count and write 13 and 14.	**R**—7.3	K.NBT.1
3, 11	7.2	K.NBT.1	Identify ways to show 11 and 12.	**R**—7.2	K.NBT.1
4, 14	7.4	K.NBT.1	Count and write 13 and 14.	**R**—7.4	K.NBT.1
5	7.5	K.NBT.1	Model, count, and write 15.	**R**—7.5	K.NBT.1
6, 13	7.6	K.CC.3	Count and write 15.	**R**—7.6	K.CC.3
7	7.7	K.NBT.1	Model and count 16 and 17.	**R**—7.7	K.NBT.1
8	7.8	K.NBT.1	Count and write 16 and 17.	**R**—7.8	K.NBT.1
9	7.9	K.NBT.1	Model and count 18 and 19.	**R**—7.9	K.NBT.1
10, 12	7.10	K.NBT.1	Count and write 18 and 19.	**R**—7.10	K.NBT.1

Key: R—Reteach Book

Child's Name ______________________ Date ______________

Chapter 8 Test

Item	Lesson	Standard	Content Focus	Intervene With	Personal Math Trainer
1	8.1	K.CC.5	Model and count up to 20.	**R**—8.1	K.CC.5
2	8.2	K.CC.3	Count and write 20.	**R**—8.2	K.CC.3
3, 10, 12	8.3	K.CC.2	Count and order numbers to 20.	**R**—8.3	K.CC.2
4, 9	8.4	K.CC.6	Count and compare numbers to 20.	**R**—8.4	K.CC.6
5	8.5	K.CC.1	Count to 50 by ones.	**R**—8.5	K.CC.1
6	8.6	K.CC.1	Count to 100 by ones.	**R**—8.6	K.CC.1
7	8.7	K.CC.1	Count to 100 by tens.	**R**—8.7	K.CC.1
8, 11	8.8	K.CC.1	Count by tens.	**R**—8.8	K.CC.1

Key: R—Reteach Book

Child's Name ______________________ Date ______________

Chapter 9 Test

Item	Lesson	Standard	Content Focus	Intervene With	Math Gym
1	9.1	K.G.2	Identify and name circles.	**R**—9.1	K.G.2
2	9.2	K.G.4	Describe circles.	**R**—9.2	K.G.4
3	9.3	K.G.2	Identify and name squares.	**R**—9.3	K.G.2
4	9.4	K.G.4	Describe squares.	**R**—9.4	K.G.4
5	9.5	K.G.2	Identify and name triangles.	**R**—9.5	K.G.2
6	9.6	K.G.4	Describe triangles.	**R**—9.6	K.G.4
7	9.7	K.G.2	Identify and name rectangles.	**R**—9.7	K.G.2
8	9.8	K.G.4	Describe rectangles.	**R**—9.8	K.G.4
9	9.9	K.G.2	Identify and name hexagons.	**R**—9.9	K.G.2
10	9.10, 9.11	K.G.4	Identify attributes of shapes.	**R**—9.10, 9.11	K.G.4
11	9.11	K.G.4	Compare two-dimensional shapes.	**R**—9.11	K.G.4
12	9.12	K.G.6	Identify shapes that compose a larger shape.	**R**—9.12	K.G.6

Key: R—Reteach Book

Child's Name ______________________ Date ____________

Chapter 10 Test

Item	Lesson	Standard	Content Focus	Intervene With	Math Gym
1	10.1	K.G.4	Identify shapes that stack, roll, or slide.	**R**—10.1	K.G.4
2	10.2	K.G.2	Identify, name, and describe spheres.	**R**—10.2	K.G.2
3	10.3	K.G.2	Identify, name, and describe cubes.	**R**—10.3	K.G.2
4	10.4	K.G.2	Identify, name, and describe cylinders.	**R**—10.4	K.G.2
5	10.5	K.G.2	Identify, name, and describe cones.	**R**—10.5	K.G.2
6	10.6	K.G.3	Identify two- and three-dimensional shapes.	**R**—10.6	K.G.3
7	10.7	K.G.5	Model shapes by drawing.	**R**—10.7	K.G.5
8, 12	10.8	K.G.1	Use the terms *above* and *below* to describe position.	**R**—10.8	K.G.1
9, 11	10.9	K.G.1	Use the terms *beside* and *next to* to describe position.	**R**—10.9	K.G.1
10	10.10	K.G.1	Use the terms *in front of* and *behind* to describe position.	**R**—10.10	K.G.1

Key: R—Reteach Book

Child's Name _______________ Date _______________

Chapter 11 Test

Item	Lesson	Standard	Content Focus	Intervene With	Personal Math Trainer
1, 2	11.1	K.MD.2	Compare lengths.	**R**—11.1	K.MD.2
3, 4	11.2	K.MD.2	Compare heights.	**R**—11.2	K.MD.2
5, 6	11.3	K.MD.2	Draw to compare lengths or heights.	**R**—11.3	K.MD.2
7, 8, 11, 12	11.4	K.MD.2	Compare weights.	**R**—11.4	K.MD.2
9, 10	11.5	K.MD.1	Identify ways to measure objects.	**R**—11.5	K.MD.1

Key: R—Reteach Book

Child's Name ______________________________ Date ______________

Chapter 12 Test

Item	Lesson	Standard	Content Focus	Intervene With	Personal Math Trainer
1, 2	12.1	K.MD.3	Classify and sort by color.	**R**—12.1	K.MD.3
3, 4, 10	12.2	K.MD.3	Classify by category, such as shape and number.	**R**—12.2	K.MD.3
5, 6	12.3	K.MD.3	Classify by size and sort or count.	**R**—12.3	K.MD.3
7	12.4	K.MD.3	Make a graph.	**R**—12.4	K.MD.3
8, 9	12.5	K.MD.3	Read a graph.	**R**—12.5	K.MD.3

Key: R—Reteach Book

Child's Name ________________________________ Date ____________

Getting Ready Test • Lessons 1–13

Item	Lesson	Content Focus	Reteach
1	3	Add to 10 on a ten frame.	**R**—p. GRR3
2, 8	6	Identify addition sentences to 5.	**R**—p. GRR6
3	4	Identify number pairs for 4.	**R**—p. GRR4
4	12	Understand how addition and subtraction equations are related.	**R**—p. GRR12
5, 12	1	Count forward 1.	**R**—p. GRR1
6	11	Identify equivalent subtraction sentences.	**R**—p. GRR11
7	9	Subtract within 10.	**R**—p. GRR9
9	2	Count forward 2.	**R**—p. GRR2
10	10	Understand how number pairs make a number.	**R**—p. GRR10
11	5	Identify equal sets.	**R**—p. GRR5
13	8	Subtract by 2.	**R**—p. GRR8
14	13	Compare sets using the word fewer.	**R**—p. GRR13
15	7	Subtract by 1.	**R**—p. GRR7

Key: R—Online Reteach Book

Child's Name ______________________________ Date ______________

Getting Ready Test • Lessons 14–20

Item	Lesson	Content Focus	Reteach
1, 10	16	Count from 30 to 40.	**R**—p. GRR16
2, 7, 15	19	Identify the hour hand of an analog clock.	**R**—p. GRR19
3, 9	14	Count by ones.	**R**—p. GRR14
4, 8, 14	20	Read to hours on a digital clock.	**R**—p. GRR20
5, 11	17	Count from 40 to 50.	**R**—p. GRR17
6, 13	15	Count from 20 to 30.	**R**—p. GRR15
12, 16	18	Read an analog clock to the hour.	**R**—p. GRR18

Key: R—Online Reteach Book

Correlations

	Standard	Test and Item Number
	Know number names and count sequences.	
K.CC.1	1. Count to 100 by ones and by tens.	Chapter 8 Test: 5–8, 11 Chapter 8 Performance Assessment: 3–5 Critical Area 1 Performance Assessment: 5, 6 Beginning/Middle/End of Year Test: 6, 7
K.CC.2	2. Count forward beginning from a given number within the known sequence (instead of having to begin at 1).	Chapter 4 Test: 6 Chapter 8 Test: 3, 10, 12 Chapter 8 Performance Assessment: 3–5 Beginning/Middle/End of Year Test: 5, 18
K.CC.3	3. Write numbers from 0 to 20. Represent a number of objects with a written numeral 0–20 (with 0 representing a count of no objects).	Chapter 1 Test: 3–5, 7, 10–12 Chapter 3 Test: 3, 5, 6, 8, 12 Chapter 4 Test: 2, 3 Chapter 7 Test: 6, 13 Chapter 8 Test: 2 Chapter 1 Performance Assessment: 1–3 Chapter 2 Performance Assessment: 1, 2 Chapter 4 Performance Assessment: 1–4 Chapter 7 Performance Assessment: 1–3, 5 Chapter 8 Performance Assessment: 2–5 Beginning/Middle/End of Year Test: 16

	Standard	Test and Item Number
	Count to tell the number of objects	
K.CC.4	1. Understand the relationship between numbers and quantities; connect counting to cardinality.	
K.CC.4a	2. When counting objects, say the number in the standard order, pairing each object with one and only one number name and each number name with one and only one object.	Chapter 1 Test: 1, 2, 6 Chapter 1 Performance Assessment: 2, 3 Beginning/Middle/End of Year Test: 14
K.CC.4b	3. Understand that the last number name said tells the number of objects counted. The number of objects is the same regardless of their arrangement or the order in which they were counted.	Chapter 1 Test: 13 Chapter 1 Performance Assessment: 2 Beginning/Middle/End of Year Test: 15
K.CC.4c	4. Understand that each successive number name refers to a quantity that is one larger.	Chapter 1 Test: 8, 9, 14 Chapter 1 Performance Assessment: 2, 3
K.CC.5	5. Count to answer "how many?" questions about as many as 20 things arranged in a line, a rectangular array, or a circle, or as many as 10 things in a scattered configuration; given a number from 1–20, count out that many objects.	Chapter 3 Test: 1, 2, 4, 7 Chapter 4 Test: 1, 11, 12 Chapter 8 Test: 1 Chapter 3 Performance Assessment: 1, 2, 4 Chapter 4 Performance Assessment: 1–4 Beginning/Middle/End of Year Test: 1
K.CC.6	6. Identify whether the number of objects in one group is greater than, less than, or equal to the number of objects in another group, e.g., by using matching and counting strategies.	Chapter 2 Test: 1–10 Chapter 3 Test: 9, 11 Chapter 4 Test: 7, 8 Chapter 8 Test: 4, 9 Chapter 12 Test: 8 Chapter 2 Performance Assessment: 1–5 Chapter 3 Performance Assessment: 2–3 Chapter 4 Performance Assessment: 1–4 Chapter 8 Performance Assessment: 1, 2 Critical Area 1 Performance Assessment: 9 Beginning/Middle/End of Year Test: 28, 29
K.CC.7	7. Compare two numbers between 1 and 10 presented as written numerals.	Chapter 3 Test: 10 Chapter 4 Test: 9

	Standard	Test and Item Number
	Understand addition as putting together and adding to, and understand subtraction as taking apart and taking from.	
K.OA.1	1. Represent addition and subtraction with objects, fingers, mental images, drawings, sounds (e.g., claps), acting out situations, verbal explanations, expressions, or equations.	Chapter 5 Test: 1–3 Chapter 6 Test: 1, 2 Chapter 5 Performance Assessment: 1–3 Chapter 6 Performance Assessment: 1–6 Beginning/Middle/End of Year Test: 8, 9
K.OA.2	2. Solve addition and subtraction word problems, and add and subtract within 10, e.g., by using objects or drawings to represent the problem.	Chapter 5 Test: 7 Chapter 6 Test: 5–7, 11, 12 Chapter 5 Performance Assessment: 1–3 Chapter 6 Performance Assessment: 1–6 Critical Area 1 Performance Assessment: 2–4, 7 Beginning/Middle/End of Year Test: 3–5
K.OA.3	3. Decompose numbers less than or equal to 10 into pairs in more than one way, e.g., by using objects or drawings, and record each decomposition by a drawing or equation (e.g., $5 = 2 + 3$ and $5 = 4 + 1$).	Chapter 5 Test: 8–12 Chapter 5 Performance Assessment: 1–3 Critical Area 1 Performance Assessment: 1–4 Beginning/Middle/End of Year Test: 10, 11
K.OA.4	4. For any number from 1 to 9, find the number that makes 10 when added to the given number, e.g., by using objects or drawings, and record the answer with a drawing or equation.	Chapter 4 Test: 4, 5 Chapter 5 Test: 5
K.OA.5	5. Fluently add and subtract within 5.	Chapter 5 Test: 4, 6 Chapter 6 Test: 3, 4, 8–10, 13 Chapter 6 Performance Assessment: 1–6

	Standard	Test and Item Number
	Work with numbers 11–19 to gain foundations for place value.	
K.NBT.1	1. Compose and decompose numbers from 11 to 19 into ten ones and some further ones, e.g., by using objects or drawings, and record each composition or decomposition by a drawing or equation (e.g., 18 = 10 + 8); understand that these numbers are composed of ten ones and one, two, three, four, five, six, seven, eight, or nine ones.	Chapter 7 Test: 1–5, 7–12, 14 Chapter 7 Performance Assessment: 1–5 Critical Area 1 Performance Assessment: 5–9 Beginning/Middle/End of Year Test: 23, 24
	Describe and compare measurable attributes.	
K.MD.1	1. Describe measurable attributes of objects, such as length or weight. Describe several measurable attributes of a single object.	Chapter 11 Test: 9, 10 Chapter 11 Performance Assessment: 1–3 Critical Area 3 Performance Assessment: 1–4
K.MD.2	2. Directly compare two objects with a measurable attribute in common, to see which object has "more of"/"less of" the attribute, and describe the difference. *For example, directly compare the heights of two children and describe one child as taller/shorter.*	Chapter 11 Test: 1–8, 11, 12 Chapter 11 Performance Assessment: 1–3 Critical Area 3 Performance Assessment: 1–4 Beginning/Middle/End of Year Test: 30–32
	Classify objects and count the number of objects in each category.	
K.MD.3	3. Classify objects into given categories; count the numbers of objects in each category and sort the categories by count.	Chapter 12 Test: 1–7, 9–10 Chapter 11 Performance Assessment: 1–4 Critical Area 3 Performance Assessment: 5–9 Beginning/Middle/End of Year Test: 20–22

	Standard	Test and Item Number
	Identify and describe shapes (squares, circles, triangles, rectangles, hexagons, cubes, cones, cylinders, and spheres).	
K.G.1	1. Describe objects in the environment using names of shapes, and describe the relative positions of these objects using terms such as *above, below, beside, in front of, behind,* and *next to.*	Chapter 10 Test: 8–12 Chapter 10 Performance Assessment: 2, 3 Critical Area 2 Performance Assessment: 4, 6 Beginning/Middle/End of Year Test: 13
K.G.2	2. Correctly name shapes regardless of their orientations or overall size.	Chapter 9 Test: 1, 3, 5, 7, 9 Chapter 10 Test: 2–5 Chapter 9 Performance Assessment: 4 Chapter 10 Performance Assessment: 1 Critical Area 2 Performance Assessment: 5 Beginning/Middle/End of Year Test: 12
K.G.3	3. Identify shapes as two-dimensional (lying in a plane, "flat") or three-dimensional ("solid").	Chapter 10 Test: 6 Chapter 10 Performance Assessment: 1

	Standard	Test and Item Number
	Analyze, compare, create, and compose shapes.	
K.G.4	4. Analyze and compare two- and three-dimensional shapes, in different sizes and orientations, using informal language to describe their similarities, differences, parts (e.g., number of sides and vertices/"corners") and other attributes (e.g., having sides of equal length).	Chapter 9 Test: 2, 4, 6, 8, 10, 11 Chapter 10 Test: 1 Chapter 9 Performance Assessment: 1–6 Chapter 10 Performance Assessment: 1 Beginning/Middle/End of Year Test: 27
K.G.5	5. Model shapes in the world by building shapes from components (e.g., sticks and clay balls) and drawing shapes.	Chapter 10 Test: 7
K.G.6	6. Compose simple shapes to form larger shapes. *For example, "Can you join these two triangles with full sides touching to make a rectangle?"*	Chapter 9 Test: 12 Chapter 9 Performance Assessment: 1–6 Critical Area 2 Performance Assessment: 1–3

Getting Ready Correlations

	Lesson Objectives	Test/Item Numbers
1	Count forward 1.	Getting Ready • Lessons 1–13; 5, 12
2	Count forward 2.	Getting Ready • Lessons 1–13; 9
3	Add to 10 on a ten frame.	Getting Ready • Lessons 1–13; 1
4	Identify number pairs for 4.	Getting Ready • Lessons 1–13; 3
5	Identify equal sets.	Getting Ready • Lessons 1–13; 11
6	Identify addition sentences to 5.	Getting Ready • Lessons 1–13; 2, 8
7	Subtract by 1.	Getting Ready • Lessons 1–13; 15
8	Subtract by 2.	Getting Ready • Lessons 1–13; 13
9	Subtract within 10.	Getting Ready • Lessons 1–13; 7
10	Understand how number pairs make a number.	Getting Ready • Lessons 1–13; 10
11	Identify equivalent subtraction sentences.	Getting Ready • Lessons 1–13; 6
12	Understand how addition and subtraction equations are related.	Getting Ready • Lessons 1–13; 4
13	Compare sets using the word *fewer*.	Getting Ready • Lessons 1–13; 14
14	Count by ones.	Getting Ready • Lessons 14–20; 3, 9
15	Count from 20 to 30.	Getting Ready • Lessons 14–20; 6, 13
16	Count from 30 to 40.	Getting Ready • Lessons 14–20; 1, 10
17	Count from 40 to 50.	Getting Ready • Lessons 14–20; 5, 11
18	Read an analog clock to the hour.	Getting Ready • Lessons 14–20; 12, 16
19	Identify the hour hand of an analog clock.	Getting Ready • Lessons 14–20; 2, 7, 15
20	Read to hours on a digital clock.	Getting Ready • Lessons 14–20; 4, 8, 14